THE CHARLTON
STANDARD CATALOGUE

ROYAL WORCESTER
FIGURINES

THIRD EDITION

By
John Edwards

W. K. Cross
Publisher

Palm Harbor, Florida ✚ Toronto, Ontario

Library and Archives Canada Cataloguing in Publication

Royal Worcester figurines : a Charlton standard catalogue

Biennial
3rd ed -
Continues: Charlton standard catalogue of Royal Worcester figurines, ISSN
1203-469X
ISSN 1713-692X
ISBN 0-88968-271-2 (3rd edition)

1. Royal Worcester figurines—Catalogs. 2. Pottery
British—Catalogs

NK4660.C49   738.8'2'029442
C2004-9061626-7

The Charlton Press

VISIT OUR WEB SITE
www.charltonpress.com

EDITORIAL TEAM

Editor	Susan Cross
Graphic Technician	Davina Rowan

ACKNOWLEDGEMENTS

The Charlton Press wishes to thank those who have helped and assisted with the third edition of *Royal Worcester Figurines, a Charlton Standard Catalogue*.

Special Thanks

Our thanks to the staff of Royal Worcester who have helped with additional technical information: **Elizabeth Greenshields**, **Helen Fisher**, **Teresa Hammill** and **Roger Hindley**. A special thanks to **Wendy Cook**, curator of the Museum of Worcester Porcelain in Worcester, for keeping us on the straight and narrow. Also we wish to thank the staff of **Compton Woodhouse Ltd.** for furnishing information on their yearly issues.

Contributors to the Third Edition

The publisher would also like to thank **Elizabeth Mitchell**, of Huddersfield, England for the new information she supplied that was incorporated into this edition.

A SPECIAL NOTE TO COLLECTORS

We welcome and appreciate any comments or suggestions in regard to *The Charlton Standard Catalogue of Royal Worcester Figurines*. If you would like to participate in pricing or supply previously unavailable data or information, please contact Susan Cross at (416) 488-1418, or e-mail us at chpress@charltonpress.com.

Printed in Canada
in the Province of Ontario

Editorial Office:

The Charlton Press

P.O. Box 820, Station Willowdale B
North York, Ontario M2K 2R1
Telephone: (416) 488-1418 Fax: (416) 488-4656
Telephone: (800) 442-6042 Fax: (800) 442-1542
url: www.charltonpress.com; e-mail: chpress@charltonpress.com

HOW TO USE THIS CATALOGUE

THE PURPOSE

The third edition of this price guide covers the complete range of figurines produced by Royal Worcester between the years 1900 and 2004.

This publication has been designed to serve two specific purposes. First, to furnish the collector with accurate and detailed listings that provide the essential information needed to build a rewarding collection. Second, to provide collectors and dealers with an indication of current market prices for any individual figure in the Royal Worcester line during this period.

While all care has been exercised in compiling this information it is inevitable that some will be missed. If you have any information on missing figurines and would like to share with us, please use our e-mail address or our mailing address listed on page III.

PRICING AND THE INTERNET

Over the past thirty years we have gathered pricing information from auctions, dealer submissions, direct mail catalogues and newsletters, all contributed prices on one of two levels, wholesale or retail. We, at the Charlton Press, consider auctions basically a dealer affair, while price lists, naturally retail. To equate both prices, we needed to adjust the auction results upward by a margin of 30% to 40%, allowing for dealer markups, before comparing and then looking for a consensus on a retail price.

The marketplace has changed dramatically over the last few years. The Internet and on-line auctions are growing at such a rate that all other pricing sources we have used are being completely overwhelmed by the sheer weight of the items being offered online.

At a moment in time on November 01, 2004 under the Royal Worcester category on e-Bay over 2,100 individual items were posted for sale. Assuming this is an average day, then for the week 14,700 items are offered and for a year nearly 766,500 will be offered for sale. The "Economist" project the on-line auctions now have over 100,000,000 registered users.

The impact the Internet will have on collectables has yet to be appreciated by collectors and dealers alike. All the old avenues such as fairs, shows, dealer stores, retail outlets, direct mail houses and auction rooms are being forced to change due to the extreme pressure of this new marketing force. Margins have come under pressure, wholesale and retail prices are starting to blend, and competition for the Collectors' budget will intensify. However, through it all one point remains, a price guide is just that, a guide, and the final say is still between the buyer and the seller.

TABLE OF CONTENTS

How to Use This Price Guide   iv

Introduction
    A History of Royal Worcester   vi
    How to Collect Royal Worcester Animals   vii
    Care and Repair   vii
    A Guide to Backstamps and Dating   viii
    Royal Worcester Collectors Society   x
    Royal Worcester Markets   x

Further Reading   xii

Royal Worcester Figurines
    1900 to the present   1
    Animal Brooches, Menu Holders, Equine Studies   269
    Candle Snuffers   281
    P Series   277

Index   292

Advertisments   304

INTRODUCTION

A HISTORY OF ROYAL WORCESTER

Porcelain, once an exorbitant luxury item exclusive to China, began production in Germany in 1711 (Meissen) and in the early eighteenth century in Italy and France (notably Sevres). Fifty years later it was manufactured in England, with factories developing in Shropshire, Derby, Plymouth, Bow, Lowestoft, Chelsea and Bristol, along with smaller operations scattered about Wales. The Worcester Tonquin Manufacture was formed in June 1751 by Dr. John Wall and fourteen other local businessmen, and is the oldest continually existing porcelain manufacturer in Britain. The newly formed company leased their first premises, Warmstry House, on the Severn in Worcester, and began making teapots and tableware.

Together with William Davis, an apothecary, Dr. Wall appears to have developed a soft-paste method using Cornish soapstone already in use at Benjamin Lund's factory at Bristol. Unlike its contemporaries, this formula made porcelain that would not crack when brought into contact with boiling water (the ingredients have remained largely unchanged over the past 250 years). The Worcester factories, along with similar operations in Caughley, Shropshire (called "Salop ware") and Liverpool, quickly surpassed the other outfits in sales of tea and dinner services.

While the Bow, Chelsea and Derby operations produce a number of figurines at that time based on Continental models, the Worcester Porcelain Company concentrated on quality table ware. However, they and the Bristol plant (which merged with Worcester in 1752) did make a handful of unsophisticated figurines in their early years such as a white glazed Chinese man circa 1750. One early porcelain figure, "Cupid at Vulcan's Forge," was made at the Worcester factory in the 1760s. It is thought to be modelled by John Toulouse, who also produced some of the figurines made in the Worcester factory of Robert Chamberlain.

Dr. Wall retired in 1774 and died in 1776. William Davis was head of the factory until his death in 1783, whereupon the firm was purchased by the company's London agent, Thomas Flight. In 1789, following a visit to the factory by King George III and Queen Charlotte, the King granted the factory a Royal Warrant, hence the term "Royal Worcester." A London showroom was also opened at His Majesty's suggestion. The factory has continued to enjoy Royal Warrants until this day. Flight, together with his sons John and Joseph and various other family members, ran the Worcester factory until the 1840s, with the involvement of the Barr family, selling mostly tableware. At this time they merged with Chamberlain's factory. The operations were then moved from Warmstry house to Diglis, the site of Chamberlain's works, where the present factory stands. In 1851 the company was purchased by W. H. Kerr and R. W. Binns. The two men introduced Parian (a semi-matte material high in feldspar, first used by the Copeland factory in the 1840s, to the Worcester factory. This material was more lasting and easily coloured or gilded than earlier formulas, making it more suitable for the detailed modelling with which the name Worcester is now synonymous. This lead to an unpredented expansion in both the production of and demand for figurines, especially after the company issued stock and started trading as Worcester Royal Porcelain Company Ltd. in 1862.

The company also started hiring trained sculptors such as W. B. Kirk, E. J. Jones, and Charles Toft rather than factory workers to do their modelling. In the 1870s James Hadley produced the greatest number and variety of Worcester models, including a number or Oriental subjects, Middle Eastern figures and the Countries of the World series. Hadley left Worcester in 1876, and in 1896 he formed his own business with his sons. Two years after his death in 1903, his business was acquired by the Worcester Royal Porcelain Company, who had also bought their last major competitor in the city, the Grainger factory, in 1889.

At this time Royal Worcester won an important battle in the courts; another Worcester firm, Locke & Co., were using the word Worcester on their pieces. The judge ruled that "Worcester" would only be used to describe products manufactured by the Worcester Royal Porcelain Company. But the Company was entering a period of crisis. From 1900 to the First World War, Worcester produced a few animal figures, often modelled by the Evans family after Japanese Netsuke and Meissen style birds. During the War, the Worcester factory produced delicate porcelain figures in a style reminiscent of German crinolines, in a patriotic attempt to substitute British for German crafts. Though Frederick M. Gertner appears to have worked on these figurines, his best and most typical work was in the highly accurate Historical and Regimental series, which was also introduced at this time. A number of birds and small nude figures of boys and girls also appeared at this time in Crownware. Crownware (a high-fired earthenware) was much cheaper to produce than Parian, which was phased out over this period. This proved, however, to be an unsuccessful move for the Worcester factory. Worcester tried to branch out by producing powder bowls, ashtrays and various jugs including Tobies, traditionally made by Staffordshire potters. Nothing, however, could prevent the factory from closing its doors when it went into receivership on July 24, 1930.

Two weeks later the factory reopened under the direction of Joseph Grimson, who wisely discontinued Crownware production. The next few years found the Worcester factory producing many new figures. Grimson and C. W. Dyson Perrins, who bought the factory, were responsible for hiring new modellers, often on a freelance basis. From then on the company saw a period to rival their heyday of the 1700s, except during the blitz and immediately after the Second World War, when production ceased almost completely. Eileen Soper's Wartime series of 1941, Dorothy Doughty's American Birds, Doris Linder's Sporting Dogs and Zoo Babies were just a few of the series produced around this time.

Some of Worcester's most successful modellers over the next decades were Stella Crofts, Dorothy and Freda Doughty, Doris Linder, Gwendolen Parnell, Agnes Pinder-Davis, husband and wife Ronald and Ruth Van Ruyckevelt, Eva Soper and Pheobe Stabler. Each modeller's individual taste was allowed to shine through, with extremely satisfying results. While Dorothy Doughty preferred modelling flora and fauna, such as her well-known Birds series, Freda enjoyed lifelike figurines of children, such as the Nursery Rhyme, Months of the Year and Children of the Nations series. Eva Soper is known for her work on the English Birds series, while Doris Lindner worked primarily on animal models such as the Equestrian series, as well as Royal portraits. Gwendolen Parnell (who painted before modelling ceramics) is probably best known for her Cries of London series, though she also, like Agnes Pinder-Davis, did Chinoiseries. The Van Ruyckevelts were responsible for the tremendously popular Victorian Ladies series and the Nursing Sisters series, while Ronald also created fish, flowers and birds.

Royal Worcester has continued to expand in terms of technology and scope. Although soapstone from Cornwall in combination with the harder China Clay is the historically distinctive ingredient in Worcester ceramics, nowadays the factory makes both hard-paste ceramics with China clay, feldspar and quartz, and bone china. Bone china gets it name because it contains 50% ash from cattle bones, giving it the characteristic whiteness and translucency. Royal Worcester continues to sell dinnerware as well as figurines. In recent years the factory, under the direction of John Morris, has continued to issue quality figurines such as the ever-popular women in nineteenth and early twentieth century costume series, and series of children. Among the more prominent modellers and designers in the past years have been Kenneth and Timothy Potts, Elizabeth Greenshields (the present Design Manager), Maureen Halson and Richard Moore. Royal Worcester also produces figurines in conjunction with organizations like the RSPCA and UNICEF, and now accepts commissions by other firms, such as Compton & Woodhouse Ltd.

HOW TO COLLECT

A collection may begin from a variety of sources. A chance gift, a souvenir picked up on holiday, or an appreciation of Royal Worcester craftsmanship can initiate a lifetime of extremely satisfying collecting. It is not unusual for very large collections to be created in a comparatively short time as one's enthusiasm rises.

For those aspiring to form a complete collection, it is advisable to keep up with all the current introductions, as they can become very elusive once discontinued. Those searching for that special piece sometimes face stiff competition, not to mention sky-high prices. Fortunately, today's collectors have a number of options when developing their collections. Auction houses and antique fairs are both excellent sources for collectors. Estate auctions are another area to explore, as are specialist dealers. The Internet can be an invaluable tool for purchasing items, as well as gathering information on a specific piece.

As accumulating every Royal Worcester figurine produced is a rather daunting task, it is wise to decide at the beginning exactly what type of collection you wish to develop. Collections are often based around one of four general criteria: series, subject, size or artist.

Collecting by Series

Collecting by series offers the collector a general theme upon which to build a grand display of figures. *American* or *British Birds, Children of the World, Days of the Week, Dogs (small or large), Equestrian, Months of the Year, Prized Cattle, Sporting* or *Tropical Fish, Woodland Animals on Bronze* or *Zoo Babies* will all produce collections to be proud of. More elusive series such as the *Netsuke Animals, Military Commanders* or *The Cries of London* will test the mettle and pocketbook of any series collector.

Collecting by Subject

Scanning through the following pages, you will find many and varied subjects around which to build a collection. An animal collection of bird models, for example, could include figures from the *American Birds, Birds of Prey on Bronze, British Birds, English Birds on Bronze, Nature Studies, North American Birds* and *Sporting Birds* series. A figurine collection of historical figures, for example, could include figurines from the *Historical Military Figures, Military Commanders* and *Queen's Regnant* series.

Collecting by Size

In today's modern world with limited space, size can be an extremely important issue. The splendour of a collection of *Military Commanders* can easily be lost if one does not have adequate space in which to display their pieces. Figurines come in all sizes, so it is easy to select complimentary pieces in a size range that will result in a handsome display.

Collecting by Artist

The work of a specific modeller such as James Alder, Stella Crofts, Dorothy or Freda Doughty, David Fryer, Frederick M. Gertner, Doris Lindner, Kenneth Potts, Raoh Schorr, Eva Soper, Ronald Van Ruyckevelt, Bernard Winskill or Elizabeth Greenshields may interest a collector.

CARE AND REPAIR

A Royal Worcester figure collection can be enjoyed indefinately as long as care is taken when handling and cleaning. When dusting, in situ, a soft cosmetic brush or photographic lens brush is useful for getting into tight corners. When necessary, glazed figures should be washed in lukewarm water, using a mild liquid detergent, then rinsed thoroughly and dried naturally or buffed gently with a soft cloth. It is important that water does not get inside the figure, so the hole in the bottom should be blocked up beforehand, perhaps with a cork or a rubber bung. Care should be taken not to knock figures against the tap or against each other as this may cause chips or imperceptible cracks in the glaze which could open up at a later date.

If the worst does happen, a professional restorer should be consulted as they can work "miracles" with damaged figures. Whether it be a small chip or a shattered body, pieces can be mended so that the repair is invisible to all but the most experienced eye. It follows that when buying figures on the secondary market, it is advisable to check for restorations. The head and any projecting pieces are the most vulnerable parts, so look at these areas carefully in a good light. Repaired cracks can be sometimes detected by looking inside the figure through the hole in the bottom. There are special ultraviolet lamps which highlight some types of restoration but these are not widely used, except by professionals. Restored figures should be priced less than perfect examples, according to the amount of damage and the quality of the repair. Always enquire about the condition of a piece when buying, as a reputable dealer will stand by any guarantees they give regarding restorations.

INSURING YOUR COLLECTABLES

As with any other valuables, making certain your collectables are protected is a very important concern. It is paramount that you display or store any porcelain items in a secure place, preferably one safely away from traffic in your home.

Your collectables are most often covered under your basic homeowner's policy. There are generally three kinds of such policies; standard, broad and comprehensive. Each has its own specific deductible and terms.

Under a general policy, your collectables are considered contents and are covered for all of the perils listed under the contractual terms of your policy (fire, theft, water damage and so on.)

However, since collectables are extremely delicate, breakage is treated diferently by most insurance companies. There is usually an extra premium attached to insure collectables against accidental breakage by or carelessness of the owner. This is sometimes referred to as a fine arts rider.

You are advised to contact your insurance professional to get all the answers.

In order to help protect your collection, it is critical that you take inventory of your collectables and have colour photographs taken of all your pieces. This is the surest method of establishing clearly, for the police and your insurance company, the items lost or destroyed. It is also the easiest way to establish their replacement value in the event of a tragedy.

A GUIDE TO BACKSTAMPS AND DATING

In general, mainly puce marks were used between 1900 and 1940, and from 1941 to the present black backstamps have been used exclusively. Green marks were used for the *Boer War Soldiers* series and the *First World War Soldiers*. Blue marks were used for a few series only, and red marks are known to exist.

The basic marking system, for Royal Worcester, including the crest of four linked W's surmounted by a crown, originated in 1862. From 1891, the words ROYAL WORCESTER ENGLAND appear ringed around the crest.

For every subsequent year through 1903 a dot is added near the crown, to the left side in even years, to the right in odd years. In 1904 dots are placed beneath the crest as well, one for each year until 1915.

In 1916 a star is used to replace all the dots that had accumulated, a single dot being added for each year thereafter until 1927.

The Puce Marks 1925-1940

1928	Small square
1929	Diamond
1930	Three horizontal lines
1931	OO (two circles)
1932	OOO (three circles)
1933 to	Three circles and one dot
1939	Then a dot for each year

The Black Marks 1938 to date

B-1	1938	Three circles and 6 dots
	1939	Three circles and 7 dots
	1940	Three circles and 8 dots
		A blue wavy line was sometimes added for 1938, 1939 and 1940
B-2	1941	Three circles and 9 dots
	1942	Three circles and 10 dots
	1943	The black mark with no date code
	1944	Bone China in large letters
	1945 to	The black mark with no date code
	1948	Bone China in small letters

B-3	1949	Black mark with V

B-4	1950	Black mark with W

	1951 to	Black mark with W and one
	1955	dot added for each year
B-5		Black mark with R inside a circle

	1956	R and 6 dots
	1957	R and 7 dots
	1958	R and 8 dots
B-6		

	1956	Black mark which may or
	to	may not have dots added
	1972	for years

Backstamps Continued

B-10   1990 to date   Black mark with R inside a circle (Reverting back to the R inside modeller and copyright date

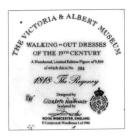

"The Princess of Tara"

B-7   1973 to 1987   black or blue mark with R inside a circle. No Dating

B-8   1988   Black mark with M inside a diamond (M replaces the R)

B-9   1989   Black mark with N inside a diamond (N replaces the M)

Commissioned figurines golden black mark with edition information

ROYAL WORCESTER

In the United Kingdom

Royal Worcester
Severn Street, Worcester
Worcestershire WR1 2NE
Tel.: +44 (1905) 23221
Fax: +44 (1905) 23601

In the United States

The Royal China and Porcelain
Companies Inc.
1265 Glen Avenue
Moorsetown, NJ 08057-0912
Tel.: (800) 257-7189

In Canada

Northdale Trading Ltd.
55-D East Beaver Creek Road
Richmond Hill
Ontario L4B 1E8
Tel.: (905) 731-9535

WEBSITE AND E-MAIL ADDRESS

www.royalworcester.com
rwgeneral@royal-worcester.co.uk

WHERE TO BUY

Discontinued Royal Worcester figurines can be found in antique shops, markets, auctions, shows and fairs. Specialist dealers in Royal Worcester figures attend many of these venues and events below. For Auction happenings it is necessary to subscribe to the catalogues provided by those Auction Houses that hold 20th Century Auctions.

ROYAL WORCESTER MARKETS

LAND AUCTIONS

AUSTRALIA

Goodman's
7 Anderson Street,
Double Bay, Sydney, 2028, N.S.W. Australia
Tel.: +61 (0) 2 9327 7311; Fax: +61 (0) 2 9327 2917
Enquiries: Suzanne Brett
www.goodmans.com.au
E-mail: info@goodmans.com.au

Sotheby's
118-122 Queen Street, Woollahra,
Sydney, 2025, N.S.W., Australia
Tel.: +61 (0) 2 9362 1000; Fax: +61 (0) 2 9362 1100
www.sothebys.com

CANADA

Empire Auctions
Montreal
5500 Paré Street, Montreal, Quebec H4P 2M1
Tel.: (514) 737-6586; Fax: (514) 342-1352
Enquiries: Isadoe Rubinfeld
E-mail: montreal@empireauctions.com

Ottawa
1380 Cyrville Road, Gloucester, On
Tel.: (613) 748-5343; Fax: (613) 748-0354
Enquiries: Elliot Melamed
E-mail: ottawa@empireauctions.com

Toronto
165 Tycos Drive
Toronto, On, M6B 1W6
Tel.: (416) 784-4261; Fax: (416) 784-4262
Enquiries: Michael Rogozinsky
www.empireauctions.com
E-mail: toronto@empireauctions.com

Maynard's Industries Ltd.
415 West 2nd Avenue, Vancouver, BC, V5Y 1E3
Tel.: (604) 876-1311; Fax: (604) 876-1323
www.maynards.com
E-mail: antiques@maynards.com

Ritchie's
Montreal
1980 Rue Sherbrooke
Suite 100, Montreal
Tel.: (514) 934-1864; Fax. (514) 934-1860

Toronto
288 King Street East, Toronto, On, M5A 1K4
Tel.: (416) 364-1864; Fax: (416) 364-0704
Enquiries: Caroline Kaiser
www.ritchies.com
E-mail: auction@ritchies.com

Waddington's
Brighton
101 Applewood Dr.,
Brighton, Ontario, K0K 1H0
Tel.: (613) 475-6223
Fax: (613) 475-6224
Enquiries: David Simmons
www.waddingtonsauctions.ca/brighton

Toronto
111 Bathurst Street, Toronto, On, M5V 2R1
Tel.: (416) 504-9100
Fax: (416) 504-0033
Enquiries: Bill Kime
www.waddingtonsauctions.com
E-mail: info@waddingtonsauctions.com

LAND AND VIRTUAL AUCTIONS

LAND AUCTIONS

UNITED KINGDOM

Bonhams

Bond Street:
101 New Bond Street, London, WI5 1SR, England

Chelsea:
65-69 Lots Road, Chelsea, London, SW10 0RN, Eng.

Knightsbridge:
Montpelier Street, Knightsbridge, London, SW7 1HH
Enquiries: Tel.: +44 (0) 20 7393 3900
www.bonhams.com
E-mail: info@bonhams.com

Christie's

London
8 King Street, London, SW1 England
Tel.: +44 (0) 207-839-9060; Fax: +44 (0) 207-839-1611

South Kensington
85 Old Brompton Road, London, SW7 3LD, England
Tel.: +44 (0) 20 7581 7611; Fax: +44 (0) 20 7321 3321
Enquires: Tel.: +44 (0) 20 7321 3237
www.christies.com; E-mail: info@christies.com

Potteries Specialist Auctions
271 Waterloo Road, Cobridge, Stoke-on-Trent
Staffordshire, ST6 3HR, England
Tel.: +44 (0) 1782 286622
Fax: +44 (0) 1782 201518
Enquiries: Stella Ashbrooke
www.potteriesauctions.com
E-mail: enquiries@potteriesauctions.com

Sotheby's

London
34-35 New Bond Street, London, W1A 2AA, England
Tel.: +44 (0) 20 7293 5000; Fax: +44 (0) 20 7293 5989

Olympia
Hammersmith Road, London WI4 8UX, England
Tel.: +44 (0) 20 7293 5555
Fax: +44 (0) 20 7293 6939

Sussex
Summers Place, Billingshurst, Sussex,
RH14 9AF, England
Tel.: +44 (0) 1403 833500
Fax: +44 (0) 1403 833699
www.sothebys.com:
E-mail: info@sothebys.com

Louis Taylor
Britannia House,
10 Town Road, Hanley
Stoke-on-Trent, Staffordshire, England
Tel.: +44 (0) 1782 214111; Fax: +44 (0) 1782 215283
Enquiries: Clive Hillier

Thomson Roddick & Medcalf
60 Whitesands
Dumfries, DG1 2RS
Scotland
Tel.: +44 (0) 1387 279879; Fax: +44 (0) 1387 266236
Enquiries: C. R. Graham-Campbell

Peter Wilson Auctioneers
Victoria Gallery, Market Street
Nantwich, Cheshire, CW5 5DG, England
Tel.: +44 (0) 1270 610508; Fax: +44 (0) 1270 610508
Enquiries: Peter Wilson

UNITED STATES

Christie's East
219 East 67th Street, New York, NY 10021
Tel.: +1 212 606 0400
Enquiries: Timothy Luke
www.christies.com

William Doyle Galleries
175 East 87th Street, New York, N.Y. 10128
Tel.: +1 212 427 2730
Fax: +1 212 369 0892

Sotheby's Arcade Auctions
1334 York Avenue, New York, N.Y. 10021
Tel.: +1 212 606 7000
Enquiries: Andrew Cheney
www.sothebys.com

VIRTUAL AUCTIONS

Amazon.com ® Auctions
Main site: www.amazon.com
Plus 4 International sites.

AOL.com Auctions ®
Main site: www.aol.com
Links to - E-bay.com
U-bid.com.

E-BAY ® The World's On-line Market Place ™
Main site: www.ebay.com
Plus 20 International sites.

YAHOO! Auctions ®
Main site: www.yahoo.com
Plus 15 International auction sites.

FAIRS, MARKETS AND SHOWS

AUSTRALIA

Royal Doulton and Antique Collectable Fair
Marina Hall, Civic Centre
Hurstville, Sydney

UNITED KINGDOM

20th Century Fairs

266 Glossop Road, Sheffield S10 2HS, England
Usually in May or June.
For information on times and dates:
Tel.: +44 (0) 114 275-0333; Fax: +44 (0) 114 275 4443

DMG Antiques Fairs Ltd.

Newark, the largest in the UK with usually six fairs
annually. For information on times and dates for this
and many other fairs contact:
DMG
Newark, P.O.Box 100, Newark,
Nottinghamshire, NG2 1DJ
Tel.: +44 (0) 1636 702326; Fax: +44 (0) 1636 707923
www.antiquesdirectory.co.uk

U.K. Fairs

Doulton and Beswick Fair for Collectors
River Park Leisure Centre, Winchester
Usually held in October. For information on times
and dates contact:
Enquiries U.K. Fairs; Tel.: +44 (0) 20 8500 3505
www.portia.co.uk
E-mail: ukfairs@portia.co.uk

LONDON MARKETS

Alfies Antique Market

13-25 Church Street, London; Tuesday - Saturday

Camden Passage Market

London; Wednesday and Saturday

New Caledonia Market

Bermondsey Square, London; Friday morning

Portobello Road Market

Portobello Road, London; Saturday

UNITED STATES

Atlantique City

Atlantic City Convention Centre
One Miss America Way
Atlantic City, NJ 08401
Tel.: (609) 449-2000; Fax: (609) 449-2090
info@accenter.com

International Gift and Collectible Expo

Donald E. Stephens Convention Centre,
Rosemont, Illinois

For information on the above two shows contact:
Krause Publications

700 East State Street, Iola, WI, 54990-0001
Tel.: (877) 746-9757; Fax: (715) 445-4389
www.collectibleshow.com
E-mail: iceshow@krause.com

FURTHER READING

The Collectors Handbook of Marks and Monograms on Pottery and Porcelain,
    by William Chaffers (revised by Referick Litchfield)
The Country Life Collector's Pocket Book of China, by G. Bernard Hughes
Encyclopaedia of British Pottery and Porcelain Marks, by Geoffrey A. Godden
English Ceramics: The Frances & Emory Cocke Collection, by Donald C. Peirce
English Pottery and Porcelain, by W. B. Honey
A Guide to the Dating of Royal Worcester Porcelain Marks from 1862, by Derek Shirley
An Illustrated Encyclopaedia of British Pottery and Porcelain, by Geoffrey A. Godden
The Parian Phenomenon, by Paul Atterbury
A Picture Book of Royal Worcester Figurines, by H. E. Frost
Royal Worcester Porcelain and the Dyson Perrins Collection,
    by Harry Frost and Wendy Cook
The Sandon Guide to Royal Worcester Figurines 1900-1970,
    by David, John and Henry SandonWigornia News (periodical)

ROYAL
WORCESTER
FIGURINES
1900 to the present

RW2101
HEBE
Modeller: Unknown
Height: 29 ¼", 74.3 cm
Colour: Parian
1. Coloured
2. Shot silks
3. White glazed
Issued: 1900

	Colour	Shot Silks	White Glazed
U.S.	$3,700.	3,250.	1,850.
Can.	$4,500.	3,900.	2,200.
U.K.	£2,000.	1,750.	1,000.

RW2102
PSYCHE
Modeller: Unknown
Height: 30", 76.2 cm
Colour: Parian
1. Coloured
2. Shot silks
3. White glazed
Issued: 1900

	Colour	Shot Silks	White Glazed
U.S.	$3,700.	3,250.	1,850.
Can.	$4,500.	3,900.	2,200.
U.K.	£2,000.	1,750.	1,000.

RW2103
CUPID WITH BOW
Modeller: Unknown
Height: 19 ¾", 50.2 cm
Colour: Parian
1. Coloured
2. White glazed
Issued: 1900

U.S.	
Can.	Extremely rare
U.K.	

RW2104
CUPID WITH SHEATH
Modeller: Unknown
Height: 19 ¾", 50.2 cm
Colour: Parian
1. Coloured
2. White glazed
Issued: 1900

U.S.	
Can.	Extremely rare
U.K.	

RW2105A
FLEMISH MAN
Modeller: Unknown
Height: 12", 30.5 cm
Colour: Parian
1. Stained ivory
2. Shot silks
3. White glazed
Issued: 1900

U.S.	
Can.	Extremely rare
U.K.	

RW2105B
FLEMISH WOMAN
Modeller: Unknown
Height: 12", 30.5 cm
Colour: Parian
1. Stained Ivory
2. Shot silks
2. White glazed
Issued: 1900

U.S.	
Can.	Extremely rare
U.K.	

RW2106
SOLDIER OF THE IMPERIAL FORCES
Modeller: George Evans
Height: 7", 17.8 cm
Colour: 1. Khaki and cream; gilding
2. Shot silks
Issued: 1900
Series: Boer War Soldiers

	Khaki	Shot Silks
U.S.	$1,100.00	925.00
Can.	$1,325.00	1,100.00
U.K.	£ 600.00	500.00

RW2107
IMPERIAL YEOMAN
Modeller: George Evans
Height: 7", 17.8 cm
Colour: 1. Khaki and cream; gilding
2. Shot silks
Issued: 1900
Series: Boer War Soldiers

	Khaki	Shot Silks
U.S.	$1,100.00	925.00
Can.	$1,325.00	1,100.00
U.K.	£ 600.00	500.00

RW2108
COLONIAL TROOPER
Modeller:	George Evans
Height:	7", 17.8 cm
Colour:	1. Khaki and cream; gilding
	2. Shot silks
Issued:	1900
Series:	Boer War Soldiers

	Khaki	Shot Silks
U.S.	$1,100.00	925.00
Can.	$1,325.00	1,100.00
U.K.	£ 600.00	500.00

RW2109A
SOLDIER OF THE BLACK WATCH
First Version
Modeller:	George Evans
Height:	7 ½", 19.1cm
Colour:	1. Khaki and cream; gilding
	2. Shot silks
Issued:	1900
Series:	Boer War Soldiers

	Khaki	Shot Silks
U.S.	$1,100.00	925.00
Can.	$1,325.00	1,100.00
U.K.	£ 600.00	500.00

RW2109B
SOLDIER OF THE BLACK WATCH
Second Version
Modeller:	George Evans
Height:	7 ½", 19.1cm
Colour:	1. Khaki and cream; gilding
	2. Shot silks
Issued:	1900
Series:	Boer War Soldiers

	Khaki	Shot Silks
U.S.	$1,100.00	925.00
Can.	$1,325.00	1,100.00
U.K.	£ 600.00	500.00

RW2110
HANDY MAN
Modeller:	George Evans
Height:	7", 17.8 cm
Colour:	1. Khaki
	2. Shot silks
Issued:	1900
Series:	Boer War Soldiers

	Khaki	Shot Silks
U.S.	$1,100.00	925.00
Can.	$1,325.00	1,100.00
U.K.	£ 600.00	500.00

RW2111
GUARDSMAN
Modeller:	George Evans
Height:	7 ¾", 19.7 cm
Colour:	1. Khaki and cream; gilding
	2. Shot silks
Issued:	1900
Series:	Boer War Soldiers

	Khaki	Shot Silks
U.S.	$1,100.00	925.00
Can.	$1,325.00	1,100.00
U.K.	£ 600.00	500.00

RW2161
WANDERING MINSTREL (Male)
Modeller:	Unknown
Height:	14 ½", 36.8 cm
Colour:	Parian:
	1. Stained
	2. White glazed
Issued:	1901

U.S.	
Can.	Extremely rare
U.K.	

RW2162
WANDERING MINSTREL (Female)
Modeller:	Unknown
Height:	14 ½", 36.8 cm
Colour:	Parian:
	1. Stained
	2. White glazed
Issued:	1901

U.S.	
Can.	Extremely rare
U.K.	

RW2213
JESTER, Style One
Modeller:	Ernest Evans
Height:	7", 17.8 cm
Colour:	1. Biscuit
	2. Black and red
	3. Shot silks
	4. Stained ivory
	5. Yellow and orange
Issued:	1902
Reissued:	c.1930-by 1953

	Coloured	White
U.S.	$1,300.00	450.00
Can.	$1,550.00	550.00
U.K.	£ 700.00	250.00

RW2214
SHEPHERDESS
Style One
Modeller:	Ernest Evans
Height:	7", 17.8 cm
Colour:	1. Shot silks
	2. Stained ivory
	3. White glazed
Issued:	1902-by 1953

U.S.	
Can.	Extremely rare
U.K.	

RW2322
BEADLE (The)
Modeller:	Ernest Evans
Height:	6 ¾", 17.2 cm
Colour:	1. Acid gold
	2. Imperial blue
	3. Pale brown, pale green, red-brown and gold (shot silks)
	4. Stained ivory
	5. White glazed
Issued:	1904-by 1953

	Acid Gold	Imperial Blue	Pale Brown	Ivory	White Glazed
U.S.	Extremely rare	Extremely rare	1,300.00	Extremely rare	500.00
Can.			1,550.00		600.00
U.K.			700.00		275.00

RW2374A
ENGLISH COSTUME FIGURE
(Female)
Modeller:	George Evans
Height:	12 ½", 31.7 cm
Colour:	Unknown
Issued:	1905-by 1927

U.S.	
Can.	Extremely rare
U.K.	

RW2374B
ENGLISH COSTUME FIGURE
(Male)
Modeller:	George Evans
Height:	12 ½", 31.7 cm
Colour:	Unknown
Issued:	1905-by 1927

U.S.	
Can.	Extremely rare
U.K.	

RW2375
GREEK FIGURE WITH CAPE
(Male)
Modeller:	George Evans
Height:	6 ½", 16.5 cm
Colour:	Unknown
Issued:	1905-by 1927

U.S.	
Can.	Extremely rare
U.K.	

RW2376
GREEK FIGURE WITH CAPE
(Female)
Modeller:	George Evans
Height:	6 ½", 16.5 cm
Colour:	Unknown
Issued:	1905-by 1927

U.S.	
Can.	Extremely rare
U.K.	

RW2377
GREEK FIGURE WITH
POINTED HAT
Modeller:	George Evans
Height:	6 ¾", 17.2 cm
Colour:	Unknown
Issued:	1905-by 1927

U.S.
Can. Extremely rare
U.K.

RW2378
GREEK FIGURE HOLDING
FLOWERS (Female)
Modeller:	George Evans
Height:	6 ½", 16.5 cm
Colour:	Unknown
Issued:	1905-by 1927

U.S.
Can. Extremely rare
U.K.

RW2379
GREEK FIGURE HOLDING DOG
(Boy)
Modeller:	George Evans
Height:	6 ½", 16.5 cm
Colour:	Unknown
Issued:	1905-by 1927

U.S.
Can. Extremely rare
U.K.

RW2380
GREEK FIGURE HOLDING KITTEN
(Girl)
Modeller:	George Evans
Height:	6 ½", 16.5 cm
Colour:	Unknown
Issued:	1905-by 1927

U.S.
Can. Extremely rare
U.K.

RW2387
BABY IN DRESSING GOWN
Modeller:	George Evans
Height:	5 ½", 14 cm
Colour:	Unknown
Issued:	1905-by 1927

U.S.
Can. Extremely rare
U.K.

RW2388
WEIGHED OUT (Jockey)
Modeller:	George Evans
Height:	9", 22.9 cm
Colour:	Unknown
Issued:	1905-by 1927

U.S.
Can. Extremely rare
U.K.

RW2389A
EARLY ENGLISH GENTLEMAN
Modeller:	George Evans	
Height:	8 ¼", 21.0 cm	
Colour:	1.	Delicate shot colours
	2.	Shot silks
Issued:	1905-by 1927	

U.S.
Can. Extremely rare
U.K.

RW2389B
EARLY ENGLISH LADY
Modeller:	George Evans	
Height:	8 ¼", 21.0 cm	
Colour:	1.	Delicate shot colours
	2.	Shot silks
Issued:	1905-by 1927	

U.S.
Can. Extremely rare
U.K.

RW2391A
MUSIC
(Male) (Holding Lute)
Modeller: Unknown
Height: 15 ½", 39.4 cm
Colour: Delicate shot colours
Issued: 1905-by 1927

U.S.:
Can.: Extremely rare
U.K.

RW2391B
MUSIC
(Female) (Holding music sheet)
Modeller: Unknown
Height: 15 ½", 39.4 cm
Colour: Delicate shot colours
Issued: 1905-by 1927

U.S.
Can.: Extremely rare
U.K.

RW2393A
PIERETTE
Modeller: Ernest Evans
Height: 8", 20.3 cm
Colour: Delicate shot colours
Issued: 1905-by 1927

U.S.:
Can.: Extremely Rare
U.K.:

RW 2393B
PIERROT WITH RUFF
Modeller: Ernest Evans
Height: 8", 20.3 cm
Colour: Delicate shot colours
Issued: 1905-by 1927

U.S.:
Can.: Extremely Rare
U.K.:

Photograph not
available
at press time

RW2400
COCKEREL STRING BOX
Modeller: Unknown
Height: 7 ¼", 18.4 cm
Colour: Red comb; black breast
        feathers
Issued: 1905-1911

U.S.:
Can.: Extremely rare
U.K.:

Note: Verse on the side in red script
      "Quand Ce Coq Chantera
      Mon Amitie Finira"

RW2468
CLOWN'S HEAD
Modeller: Ernest Evans
Height: 3 ¼", 8.3 cm
Colour: Unknown
Issued: 1908-by 1927

U.S.
Can. Extremely Rare
U.K.:

RW2484
FISH ASHTRAY
Modeller: Unknown
Height: 5", 12.7 cm
Colour: 1. Blue
        2. Green
        3. Light orange
        4. White
Issued: 1909

	Coloured	White
U.S.	$275.00	175.00
Can.	$325.00	200.00
U.K.	£150.00	100.00

RW2514
BRER RABBIT FLOWER HOLDER
Modeller: Unknown
Height: 4 ¾", 12.1 cm
Colour: 1. New silks
        2. White
Issued: 1911

	Coloured	White
U.S.	$550.00	275.00
Can.	$675.00	325.00
U.K.	£300.00	150.00

RW2517
DUCK RING STAND
Modeller: Unknown
Height: 6 ½", 16.5 cm
Colour: Unknown
Issued: 1911-by 1927

U.S.: $650.00
Can.: $775.00
U.K.: £350.00

RW2523A
LADY ON ROCOCO BASE
Modeller: Unknown
Height: 7", 17.8 cm
Colour: Unknown
Issued: 1911-by 1927

U.S.:
Can.: Extremely Rare
U.K.:

RW2523B
GENTLEMAN ON ROCOCO BASE
Modeller: Unknown
Height: 7", 17.8 cm
Colour: Unknown
Issued: 1911-by 1927

U.S.:
Can.: Extremely Rare
U.K.:

RW2537
PEACOCK MENU HOLDER
Modeller: Unknown
Height: 3 ¼", 8.3 cm
Colour: Unknown
Issued: 1912

U.S.: $325.00
Can.: $400.00
U.K.: £175.00

RW2582
FRENCH SOLDIER
Modeller: Unknown
Height: 7 ½", 19.1 cm
Colour: 1. Blush ivory
2. Blue / orange
3. Shot colours
Issued: 1914-by 1927
Series: First World War Soldiers

U.S.: $1,300.00
Can.: $1,550.00
U.K.: £ 700.00

RW2588
TERRITORIAL SOLDIER
Modeller: Unknown
Height: 7 ½", 19.1 cm
Colour: 1. Blush ivory
2. Shot colours
Issued: 1914-by 1927
Series: First World War Soldiers

U.S.: $1,300.00
Can.: $1,550.00
U.K.: £ 700.00

RW2591
SOLDIER OF THE
WORCESTERSHIRE REGIMENT
Modeller: Unknown
Height: 6", 15.0 cm
Colour: 1. Blush ivory
2. Shot colours
Issued: 1917-by 1927
Series: First World War Soldiers

U.S.: $1,300.00
Can.: $1,550.00
U.K.: £ 700.00

RW2604
TORTOISE
Modeller: Unknown
Size: 1 ¼" x 4 ½",
3.2 x 11.9 cm
Colour: 1. White with tinted
head, tail and feet
2. Shot colours
Issued: 1916-c.1950s
Series: Netsuke Animals

U.S.: $1,200.00
Can.: $1,450.00
U.K.: £ 650.00

RW2605
SNAIL
Style One
Modeller: Unknown
Height: 1 ¾", 4.5 cm
Colour: 1. Blush ivory
2. Shot colours
3. Strong enamel
colours
4. White with tinted
features
Issued: 1916-c.1950s
Series: Netsuke Animals

U.S.: $500.00
Can.: $600.00
U.K.: £275.00

RW2606
CHEETAH
Style One
Modeller: Unknown
Length: 3 ¼", 8.3 cm
Colour: 1. Blush ivory
2. Cream with light
brown, pink and
grey highlights
3. Dark blue
Issued: 1916-c.1950s
Series: Netsuke Animals

U.S. $750.00
Can. $900.00
U.K. £400.00

RW2607
RABBIT
Size: 1" x 2", 2.5 x 5.0 cm
Colour: 1. Natural colours
2. Strong enamel
colours
3. White, pink eyes
4. White, tinted body
Issued: 1916-by 1960
Series: Netsuke Animals

U.S.: $275.00
Can.: $325.00
U.K.: £150.00

Note: This model was also produced
as a menu holder, with a slit
cut into the back.

RW2608
SNAKE
Modeller: Unknown
Height: 4", 10.1 cm
Colour: 1. Shot colours
2. White
Issued: 1916-c.1975
Series: Netsuke Animals

	Original	Reissued
U.S.:	$1,850.00	425.00
Can.:	$2,200.00	550.00
U.K.:	£1,000.00	250.00

RW2609
COW
Modeller: Unknown
Height: 6", 15.0 cm long
Colour: 1. Black enamel
2. Strong colours
Issued: 1916-c.1950s
Series: Netsuke Animals

U.S. $1,850.00
Can. $2,200.00
U.K. £1,000.00

RW2610
MOUSE, Style One
Modeller: Unknown
Size: 1" x 2", 2.5 x 5.0 cm
Colour: 1. Natural colours
2. Strong colours
3. White; pink eyes
4. White; tinted body
Issued: 1916-by 1960
Varieties: RW2827, RW2828
Series: Netsuke Animals

U.S. $275.00
Can. $325.00
U.K. £150.00

RW2611
FISH
Modeller: Unknown
Size: 1" x 4", 2.5 x 10.1 cm
Colour: 1. Blush ivory
2. Tinted
3. White
Issued: 1916-c.1950s
Series: Netsuke Animals

U.S. $550.00
Can. $675.00
U.K. £300.00

RW2612
APE
Modeller: Unknown
Height: 2 ¾", 7 cm
Colour: 1. Blush ivory
2. Bright enamel
colours
3. Tinted
Issued: 1916-c.1950s
Series: Netsuke Animals

U.S. $450.00
Can. $550.00
U.K. £250.00

RW2613
RAM
Modeller:	Unknown
Length:	2 ¼", 5.7 cm
Colour:	1. Bright colours
	2. Ivory
	3. White, light grey shading
Issued:	1916-c.1950s
Series:	Netsuke Animals
U.S.	$550.00
Can.	$675.00
U.K.	£300.00

RW2615
MOTHER AND TWO GIRLS
Designer:	J. Wadsworth
Modeller:	Frederick M. Gertner
Height:	5", 12.7 cm
Colour:	White; black caps; lilac bows
Issued:	1916-by 1927
U.S.	$ 825.00
Can.	$1,000.00
U.K.	£ 450.00

RW2616
TWO LADIES
Designer:	J. Wadsworth
Modeller:	Frederick M. Gertner
Height:	4", 10.1 cm
Colour:	Black capes with lilac bows; lilac mob caps with black bows; white skirts with painted flowers; black shoes
Issued:	1916-by 1927
U.S.	$ 925.00
Can.	$1,100.00
U.K.	£ 500.00

RW2617
WIND
Designer:	J. Wadsworth
Modeller:	Frederick M. Gertner
Height:	5 ¾", 14.6 cm
Colour:	1. Black cape; black skirt trimmed with blue dots; turquoise-green mob cap
	2. Green cape; white and black skirt; green mob cap
	3. White cape with black checks; black mob cap with blue bow; black skirt with white lining; white mound base
Issued:	1916-by 1927
U.S.	$500.00
Can.	$600.00
U.K.	£275.00

RW2618
BOY AND RABBIT
Modeller:	Frederick M. Gertner
Height:	3 ¼", 8.3 cm
Colour:	Unknown
Issued:	1916-by 1927
U.S.	
Can.	Extremely rare
U.K.	

RW2619
CRUCIFIX
Modeller:	Frederick M. Gertner
Height:	7 ¾" x 7 ¼", 19.7 x 18.4 cm
Colour:	White
Issued:	1916
U.S.	$550.00
Can.	$675.00
U.K.	£300.00

RW2620
CRINOLINE FIGURE WITH CAP
Designer:	J. Wadsworth
Modeller:	Frederick M. Gertner
Height:	4 ¾", 12.1 cm
Colour:	1. Purple jacket, reticule; white skirt and hat with rose design
	2. White dress edged in black; black hat and reticule
	3. White dress edged in black, lilac flowers on skirt; black hat and reticule
Issued:	1916-by 1927

U.S.	$425.00
Can.	$500.00
U.K.	£225.00

Note: Issued as a dinner bell.

RW2621
CRINOLINE FIGURE WITH BOOK
Designer:	J. Wadsworth
Modeller:	Frederick M. Gertner
Height:	4 ½", 11.5 cm
Colour:	1. Black and green dress with pink roses; black book
	2. Green overjacket, white skirt with pink and green design
	3. White dress; black collar, lacing and edging; black bow and book
Issued:	1916-by 1927

U.S.	$425.00
Can.	$500.00
U.K.	£225.00

Note: Issued as a dinner bell.

RW2622
BLACKCOCK
Modeller:	Unknown
Height:	3", 7.6 cm
Colour:	1. Black
	2. White with grey and light green highlights
Issued:	1916-c.1950s
Series:	Netsuke Animals

U.S.	$550.00
Can.	$675.00
U.K.	£350.00

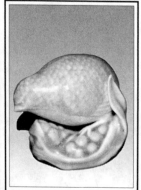

RW2623
QUAIL
Modeller:	Unknown
Height:	2", 5.1 cm
Colour:	Bright colours
Issued:	1916-c.1950s
Series:	Netsuke Animals

U.S.	$550.00
Can.	$675.00
U.K.	£300.00

RW2624
TOAD
Modeller:	Unknown
Height:	1 ¾", 4.5 cm
Colour:	1. Blush ivory
	2. Bright enamels
	3. Shot bronze (matt)
	4. White with tinted features
Issued:	1916-c.1950s
Series:	Netsuke Animals

U.S.	$550.00
Can.	$675.00
U.K.	£300.00

RW2625
THE IMMACULATE
(VIRGIN MARY)
Modeller:	Frederick M. Gertner
Height:	13 ¾", 34.9 cm
Colour:	1. Coloured
	2. Shot gold
	3. White glazed
Issued:	1916

	Coloured	White
U.S.	$750.00	375.00
Can.	$900.00	450.00
U.K.	£400.00	200.00

RW2626
ST. JOSEPH
Modeller:	Frederick M. Gertner
Height:	13 ¾", 34.9 cm
Colour:	1. Coloured
	2. Shot gold
	3. White glazed
Issued:	1916

	Coloured	White
U.S.	$750.00	375.00
Can.	$900.00	450.00
U.K.	£400.00	200.00

RW2629
OFFICER OF THE FRENCH MARINES
Modeller:	Frederick M. Gertner
Height:	10 ¾", 27.8 cm
Colour:	Blue, red, white and black
Issued:	1916-by 1930
Series:	Historical Military Figures

U.S.	$1,100.00
Can.	$1,325.00
U.K.	£ 600.00

RW2632
GENTLEMAN IN EVENING DRESS WITH CIGAR
Modeller:	Frederick M. Gertner
Height:	5", 12.7 cm
Colour:	1. Black jacket; grey trousers; green tablecloth
	2. Purple jacket; lilac trousers; yellow tablecloth
Issued:	1916-by 1920

U.S.	$750.00
Can.	$900.00
U.K.	£400.00

RW2633
GENTLEMAN WITH CLOAK AND OPERA HAT
Modeller:	Frederick M. Gertner
Height:	5", 12.7 cm
Colour:	1. Blue cape, pale blue coat, hat and trousers
	2. Lilac cape edged in black and lined in pale yellow; black coat, hat and trousers
Issued:	1916-by 1920

U.S.	$750.00
Can.	$900.00
U.K.	£400.00

RW2634
MARY, QUEEN OF SCOTS
Style One
Modeller:	Frederick M. Gertner
Height:	8", 20.3 cm
Colour:	Grey cape; pale pink and gold dress; gold headdress
Issued:	1916-by 1927
Reissued:	c.1950-1979
Series:	Historical Figures

	Original	Reissued
U.S.	$1,100.00	925.00
Can.	$1,325.00	1,100.00
U.K.	£ 6500.00	500.00

RW2635
OFFICER OF THE COLDSTREAM GUARDS 1815
First Version
Modeller:	Frederick M. Gertner
Height:	10 ½", 26.7 cm
Colour:	Red tunic; white trousers; black hat and boots; gold decoration
Issued:	1917-by 1927
Variations:	RW2676 (Second Version), RW3675 (Third Version)
Series:	Historical Military Figures

U.S.	$1,100.00
Can.	$1,325.00
U.K.	£ 600.00

RW2636
DOUBLE MOUSE
Modeller:	Unknown	
Height:	2 ½", 6.4 cm	
Colour:	1.	Shot bronze and ivory
	2.	White with tinted features
Issued:	1916	
Series:	Netsuke Animals	

U.S.	$750.00
Can.	$900.00
U.K.	£400.00

RW2637
HENRY VIII
Modeller:	Frederick M. Gertner
Height:	9", 22.9 cm
Colour:	Burgundy, yellow and black
Issued:	1916-by 1927
Reissued:	c.1950-1979
Series:	Historical Figures

	Original	Reissued
U.S.	$1,300.00	1,150.00
Can.	$1,550.00	1,325.00
U.K.	£ 700.00	600.00

RW2643
EDWARD VI
Modeller:	Frederick M. Gertner	
Height:	8 ½", 21.6 cm	
Colour:	1.	Black and gold
	2.	Light blue-grey and gold
Issued:	1.	1916-by 1927
Reissued:	2.	c.1950-1979
Series:	Historical Figures	

	Original	Reissued
U.S.	$1,100.00	925.00
Can.	$1,325.00	1,100.00
U.K.	£ 600.00	500.00

RW2645
SOLDIER OF THE FIRST WORLD WAR (Standing)
Modeller:	William Pointon
Height:	10 ¼", 26 cm
Colour:	Khaki
Issued:	1916
Series:	First World War Soldiers

U.S.	$1,150.00
Can.	$1,325.00
U.K.	£ 600.00

RW2646
SOLDIER OF THE FIRST WORLD WAR (Seated)
Modeller:	William Pointon
Height:	5 ½", 14.0 cm
Colour:	Khaki
Issued:	1916
Series:	First World War Soldiers

U.S.	$1,150.00
Can.	$1,325.00
U.K.	£ 600.00

RW2648
ELIZABETH I
Style One
Modeller:	Frederick M. Gertner
Height:	8 ¼", 21.0 cm
Colour:	Burgundy and gold dress; light blue cape
Issued:	1917-by 1927
Reissued:	c.1950-1979
Series:	Historical Figures

	Original	Reissued
U.S.	$1,300.00	925.00
Can.	$1,550.00	1,100.00
U.K.	£ 700.00	500.00

RW2649
LADY WITH MIRROR - TRUTH
Modeller:	Frederick M. Gertner
Height:	11 ½", 29.2 cm
Colour:	1. Coloured
	2. White glazed
Issued:	1916-by 1930
Series:	Female Dancing Figures

U.S.	
Can.	Extremely Rare
U.K.	

RW2650
LADY WITH MASK - FALSEHOOD
Modeller:	Frederick M. Gertner
Height:	11 ½", 29.2 cm
Colour:	1. Coloured
	2. White glazed
Issued:	1916-by 1930
Series:	Female Dancing Figures

U.S.	
Can.	Extremely Rare
U.K.	

RW2651
CHARLES I
Modeller:	Frederick M. Gertner
Height:	9 ½", 24.0 cm
Colour:	1. Dark blue jacket; dark green trousers; black hat; brown boots
	2. Mouse-grey jacket; red trousers; light blue shirt; black hat
Issued:	1917-by 1927
reissued:	c.1950-1979
Series:	Historical Figures

	Original	Reissued
U.S.	$ 925.00	750.00
Can.	$1,100.00	900.00
U.K.	£ 500.00	400.00

RW2652
ANNE BOLEYN
Modeller:	Frederick M. Gertner
Height:	8 ¼", 21 cm
Colour:	Blue dress; grey-gold robe and headdress; gold trim
Issued:	1917-by 1927
Reissued:	c.1950-1979
Series:	Historical Figures

	Original	Reissued
U.S.	$ 925.00	750.00
Can.	$1,100.00	900.00
U.K.	£ 500.00	400.00

RW2654
FEMALE DANCING FIGURE
Style One
Modeller:	Unknown
Height:	11", 27.9 cm
Colour:	Unknown
Issued:	1916
Series:	Female Dancing Figures

U.S.	
Can.	Extremely Rare
U.K.	

RW2655
FEMALE DANCING FIGURE
Style Two
Modeller:	Unknown
Height:	11", 27.9 cm
Colour:	Unknown
Issued:	1916
Series:	Female Dancing Figures

U.S.	
Can.	Extremely Rare
U.K.	

RW2657
OFFICER OF THE SEAFORTH HIGHLANDERS 1812
Modeller:	Frederick M. Gertner
Height:	11 ¾", 28.5 cm
Colour:	Red jacket with gold epaulettes; green, blue and turquoise kilt; black bearskin
Issued:	1917-by 1927
Reissued:	c.1950-1979
Varieties:	Also called "Officer of the Scots Guards" RW3677
Series:	Historical Military Figures

	Original	Reissued
U.S.	$1,100.00	875.00
Can.	$1,325.00	1,050.00
U.K.	£ 600.00	475.00

Note: This model is also known on a 'ground' base.

RW2658
OFFICER OF THE ROYAL ARTILLERY 1815
Modeller:	Frederick M. Gertner
Height:	10 ½", 29.8 cm
Colour:	Blue and red tunic; white trousers; black hat and boots; gold trim
Issued:	1917-by 1927
Reissued:	c.1950-1979
Series:	Historical Military Figures

	Original	Reissued
U.S.	$1,100.00	875.00
Can.	$1,325.00	1,050.00
U.K.	£ 600.00	475.00

RW2659
CLASSICAL LADY WITH LYRE
Modeller:	Frederick M. Gertner
Height:	14 ¼", 36.2 cm
Colour:	1. Gold, with ivory head and arms
	2. Traditional shot colours
Issued:	1916

U.S.	
Can.	Extremely Rare
U.K.	

RW2660
CLASSICAL LADY WITH TAMBOURINE
Modeller:	Frederick M. Gertner
Height:	14 ¼", 36.2 cm
Colour:	1. Gold, with ivory head and arms
	2. Traditional shot colours
Issued:	1916

U.S.	
Can.	Extremely Rare
U.K.	

RW2661
THE ADMIRAL 1780
Modeller:	Frederick M. Gertner
Height:	11 ½", 29.2 cm
Colour:	Deep blue uniform with gold trim; cream waistcoat and black base
Issued:	1917-by 1927
Reissued:	c.1950-1979
Series:	Historical Military Figures

	Original	Reissued
U.S.	$ 925.00	750.00
Can.	$1,100.00	900.00
U.K.	£ 500.00	400.00

RW2662
BULLFINCH (On stump)
Modeller: Frederick M. Gertner
Height: 6", 15.0 cm
Colour: Red-brown breast, blue-grey feathers; white stump with
             gilt flecks and painted flowers
Issued: 1. Crownware: 1917
             2. Bone china: 1918-1977
Series: Birds on Stumps

	Crownware	Bone China	
		Puce	Black
U.S. $	375.00	550.00	425.00
Can. $	450.00	675.00	500.00
U.K. £	200.00	300.00	225.00

Note: RW2662-2667 were also issued as Flower Holders / Table Decorations
with holes in the stumps.

RW2663
PARROQUET, Female (On stump), Style One
Modeller: Frederick M. Gertner
Height: 7", 17.8 cm
Colour: 1. Blue bird, black markings; white stump with gilt flecks and
                 painted flowers
             2. Green bird, black markings; white stump with gilt flecks and
                 painted flowers
             3. Yellow bird; white stump with gilt flecks and painted flowers
Issued: 1. Crownware: 1917   2. Bone china: 1918-1977
Series: Birds on Stumps

	Crownware	Bone China	
		Puce	Black
U.S.	$375.00	500.00	425.00
Can.	$450.00	600.00	500.00
U.K.	£200.00	275.00	225.00

RW2664
PARROT, Male (On stump)
Modeller: Frederick M. Gertner
Height: 5", 12.7 cm
Colour: 1. Blue bird, black markings; white stump with gilt flecks
             2   Green bird, black and yellow markings; white stump with
                 gilt flecks
             3. Yellow bird, black markings; white stump with gilt flecks
Issued: 1. Crownware: 1917: 2. Bone china: 1918-1977
Varities: Also called "Parroquet," Style Two
Series: Birds on Stumps

	Crownware	Bone China	
		Puce	Black
U.S.	$325.00	450.00	425.00
Can.	$400.00	550.00	500.00
U.K.	£175.00	250.00	225.00

RW2665
CANARY (On stump)
Modeller: Frederick M. Gertner
Height: 6 ¼", 15.9 cm
Colour: Bright yellow bird; white stump with gilt flecks and painted
             flowers
Issued: 1. Crownware: 1917
             2. Bone china: 1918-1977
Series: Birds on Stumps

	Crownware	Bone China	
		Puce	Black
U.S.	$325.00	450.00	425.00
Can.	$400.00	550.00	500.00
U.K.	£175.00	250.00	225.00

RW2666
KINGFISHER (On stump)
Modeller: Frederick M. Gertner
Height: 5 ¾", 14.6 cm
Colour: Orangey-red breast, blue flowers; white stump with gilt flecks
            and painted flowers
Issued: 1.   Crownware: 1917
            2.   Bone china: 1918-1977
Series: Birds on Stumps

	Crownware	Bone China	
		Puce	Black
U.S.	$325.00	450.00	425.00
Can.	$400.00	550.00	500.00
U.K.	£175.00	250.00	225.00

RW2667
GOLDFINCH (On stump)
Modeller: Frederick M. Gertner
Height: 5 ¾", 14.6 cm
Colour: 1.   Crownware: Red head, yellow breast; green-brown base
            2.   Bone china: Red head, red-brown breast; white stump with
                 gilt flecks and painted flowers
Issued: 1.   Crownware: 1917
            2.   Bone china: 1918-1977
Series: Birds on Stumps

	Crownware	Bone China	
		Puce	Black
U.S.	$325.00	450.00	425.00
Can.	$400.00	550.00	500.00
U.K.	£175.00	250.00	225.00

RW2668
SIR WALTER RALEIGH
Modeller: Frederick M. Gertner
Height: 9 ¾", 24.7 cm
Colour: Cream/burgundy cape,
            light green vest,
            black knickers
Issued: 1917-1927
Reissued: c.1950-1979
Series: Historical Figures

	Original	Reissued
U.S.	$ 925.00	750.00
Can.	$1,100.00	900.00
U.K.	£ 500.00	400.00

RW2672
CHARLES II
Modeller: Frederick M. Gertner
Height: 9 ¾", 24.7 cm
Colour: 1.   Burgundy coat
            2.   Taupe coat
Issued: 1917-1927
Reissued: c.1950-1979
Series: Historical Figures

	Original	Reissued
U.S.	$ 925.00	750.00
Can.	$1,100.00	900.00
U.K.	£ 500.00	400.00

RW2673
**MAIDEN WITH BALL IN RIGHT
HAND**
Modeller: Frederick M. Gertner
Height: 12", 30.5 cm
Colour: White
Issued: 1917

U.S.
Can.   Extremely Rare
U.K.

Note: Pair with RW2674 Maiden with
        Both Hands Outstretched

RW2674
**MAIDEN WITH BOTH HANDS
OUTSTRETCHED**
Modeller: Frederick M. Gertner
Height: 12", 30.5 cm
Colour: White
Issued: 1917

U.S.
Can.   Extremely Rare
U.K.

Note: Pair with RW2673 Maiden with
        Ball in Right Hand

RW2675
OFFICER OF THE 3RD DRAGOON GUARDS 1806
Modeller:	Frederick M. Gertner
Height:	11 ½", 29.2 cm
Colour:	Red tunic; white trousers; black hat and boots; gold decoration
Issued:	1917-by 1927
Reissued:	c.1950-1979
Series:	Historical Military Figures

	Original	Reissued
U.S.	$1,100.00	875000
Can.	$1,325.00	1,050.00
U.K.	£ 600.00	475.00

RW2676
OFFICER OF THE COLDSTREAM GUARDS 1815
Second Version
Modeller:	Frederick M. Gertner
Height:	11 ½", 29.2 cm
Colour:	Red tunic; white trousers; black hat and boots; gold decoration
Issued:	1917-by 1930
Varieties:	RW2635 (First Version), RW3675 (Third Version)
Series:	Historical Military Figures

U.S.	$1,100.00
Can.	$1,325.00
U.K.	£ 600.00

RW2677
OFFICER OF THE 17TH DRAGOON GUARDS 1814
Modeller:	Frederick M. Gertner
Height:	11 ¾", 29.8 cm
Colour:	1. Navy and white uniform; black base
	2. Navy and white uniform; black base; gilt metal wire on cap
Issued:	1917-by 1930
Reissued:	c.1950-1979
Series:	Historical Military Figures

	Original	Reissued
U.S.	$1,100.00	875.00
Can.	$1,325.00	1,050.00
U.K.	£ 600.00	475.00

Note: Later models had a metal wire added to the cap.

RW2679
COLUMBINE
Style One
Modeller:	Frederick M. Gertner
Height:	9 ½", 24.0 cm
Colour:	1. Crownware: Ivory; powder blue costume and base
	2. Bone china: Pink and gold tutu, stockings and cap
Issued:	1917-by 1930

	Crownware	Bone China
U.S.	$650.00	1,000.00
Can.	$775.00	1,200.00
U.K.	£350.00	550.00

Note: Crownware figures carry a CW number.

RW2680
HARLEQUIN
Style One
Modeller: Frederick M. Gertner
Height: 9 ½", 24.0 cm
Colour: Crownware:
                   1. Ivory colourings; powder blue costume and base
                  Bone china:
                   2. Black costume, mask and cap
                   3. Gold and white
Issued: 1917-by 1930

	Crownware	Bone China
U.S.	$ 825.00	1,000.00
Can.	$1,000.00	1,200.00
U.K.	£ 450.00	550.00

RW2681
COLUMBINE
Style Two
Modeller: Frederick M. Gertner
Height: 9 ½", 24.0 cm
Colour: Crownware:
                   1. Ivory colourings; powder blue costume and base
                  Bone china:
                   2. Gold costume, stockings, cap; white and gold base
Issued: 1917

	Crownware	Bone China
U.S.	$ 825.00	1,000.00
Can.	$1,000.00	1,200.00
U.K.	£ 450.00	550.00

RW2682
PIERROT
Style One
Modeller: Frederick M. Gertner
Height: 9 ½", 24.0 cm
Colour: Crownware:
                   1. Ivory colourings; powder blue costume and base
                  Bone china:
                   2. Yellow jacket, trousers, shoes and cap; flowered shirt;
                       white, gold and black base
Issued: 1917

U.S.	
Can.	Extremely rare
U.K.	

RW2683
NUDE GIRL WITH FLOWERS
(Seated)
Modeller: Frederick M. Gertner
Height: 4 ¼", 10.8 cm
Colour: Crownware:
                   1. Light blue
                  Bone china:
                   2. Ivory finish;
                       green base
Issued: 1917

	Crownware	China
U.S.	$450.00	650.00
Can.	$550.00	775.00
U.K.	£250.00	350.00

RW2684
NUDE BOY WITH FLOWERS
(Seated)
Modeller: Frederick M. Gertner
Height: 4 ¼", 10.8 cm
Colour: Crownware:
                   1. Light blue base
                  Bone china:
                   2. Ivory finish;
                       green base
Issued: 1917

	Crownware	China
U.S.	$450.00	650.00
Can.	$550.00	775.00
U.K.	£250.00	350.00

RW2685
NUDE BOY WITH FLOWERS
(Standing)
Style One
Modeller:	Frederick M. Gertner
Height:	6 ¼", 15.9 cm
Colour:	1. Green and ivory (matt)
	2. White glazed
Issued:	1917-by 1930

	Crownware	China
U.S.	$325.00	500.00
Can.	$400.00	600.00
U.K.	£175.00	275.00

RW2686
NUDE GIRL WITH FLOWERS
(Standing)
Modeller:	Frederick M. Gertner
Height:	6", 15.0 cm
Colour:	1. Green and ivory (matt)
	2. White glazed
Issued:	1917

	Crownware	China
U.S.	$325.00	500.00
Can.	$400.00	600.00
U.K.	£175.00	275.00

RW2687
NUDE CHILD (Seated)
Modeller:	Frederick M. Gertner
Height:	5", 12.7 cm
Colour:	Crownware:
	1. Light blue
	Bone china:
	2. Green and ivory
Issued:	1917

	Crownware	China
U.S.	$325.00	500.00
Can.	$400.00	600.00
U.K.	£175.00	275.00

RW2688
NUDE FEMALE LEANING ON A PEDESTAL
Modeller:	Frederick M. Gertner
Height:	6", 15.0 cm
Colour:	Crownware:
	1. Light blue
	Bone china:
	2. Green and ivory
Issued:	1917-by 1927

	Crownware	China
U.S.	$375.00	550.00
Can.	$450.00	675.00
U.K.	£200.00	300.00

RW2689
NUDE FEMALE PUTTING SLIPPER ON FOOT
Modeller:	Frederick M. Gertner
Height:	5 ¾", 14.6 cm
Colour:	Crownware:
	1. Unknown
	Bone china:
	2. Ivory; yellow slippers, headband; matt green plinth
	3. Light blue; gold details
	4. Shagreen; gold details
Issued:	1917

	Crownware	Bone China
U.S.	$375.00	550.00
Can.	$450.00	675.00
U.K.	£200.00	300.00

RW2690
NUDE BATHER RECLINING ON PLINTH, Style One
Modeller:	Unknown
Height:	7 ½", 19.1 cm
Colour:	Crownware:
	1. Ivory and light blue
	2. Ivory and matt green
	3. Strongly coloured
	Bone china:
	4. Light blue
	5. White glazed
Issued:	1. Crownware — 1917 2. Bone China — 1918-by 1930

	Crownware	Bone China	White Glazed
U.S.	$375.00	600.00	325.00
Can.	$450.00	725.00	400.00
U.K.	£200.00	325.00	175.00

20

RW2691
FEMALE NUDE, HAND ON BREAST
Modeller:	Frederick M. Gertner
Height:	7 ½", 19.1 cm
Colour:	Crownware:
	1. Ivory and light blue
	2. Ivory and matt green
	Bone china:
	3. Light blue
	4. Shagreen
	5. White glazed
Issued:	1. Crownware — 1918 2. Bone China — 1918-by 1930

	Crownware	Bone China	White Glazed
U.S.	$450.00	600.00	275.00
Can.	$500.00	725.00	325.00
U.K.	£225.00	325.00	150.00

RW2692
FEMALE NUDE, HAND BEHIND SHOULDER
Modeller:	Frederick M. Gertner
Height:	7 ½", 19.1 cm
Colour:	Crownware:
	1. Ivory and light blue
	2. Ivory and matt green
	Bone china:
	3. Light blue
	4. Shagreen
	5. White glazed
Issued:	1. Crownware — 1918 2. Bone China — 1918-by 1930

	Crownware	Bone China	White Glazed
U.S.	$450.00	600.00	275.00
Can.	$500.00	725.00	325.00
U.K.	£225.00	325.00	150.00

RW2693
NUDE FEMALE SLIPPER IN RIGHT HAND
Modeller:	Frederick M. Gertner
Height:	5 ¾", 14.6 cm
Colour:	Crownware:
	1. Unknown
	Bone China:
	2. Ivory
	3. Light blue; gold details
	4. Shagreen; gold details
Issued:	1. Crownware — 1917
	2. Bone China —1918-by 1930

	Crownware	Bone China
U.S.	$450.00	600.00
Can.	$500.00	725.00
U.K.	£225.00	325.00

RW2694
NUDE BOY WITH FRUIT
Standing
Modeller:	Unknown
Height:	7", 17.8 cm
Colour:	Creamy glaze
Issued:	1918-by 1927

	Crownware	China
U.S.	$375.00	750.00
Can.	$450.00	900.00
U.K.	£200.00	400.00

RW2695
FLAMINGO (Neck curved)
Modeller:	Frederick M. Gertner
Height:	6", 15.0 cm (mounted
	on brass legs)
Colour:	Pink
Issued:	1918

U.S.	$135.00
Can.	$165.00
U.K.	£ 75.00

Note: This bird was intended to be mounted on brass legs.

RW2696
FLAMINGO (Neck stretched forward)
Modeller:	Frederick M. Gertner
Height:	6", 15.0 cm (mounted on brass legs)
Colour:	Pink
Issued:	1918
U.S.	$135.00
Can.	$165.00
U.K.	£ 75.00

Note: This bird was intended to be mounted on brass legs.

RW2697
NUDE BATHER RECLINING ON PLINTH
Style Two
Modeller:	Frederick M. Gertner
Height:	7 ¾", 19.7 cm
Colour:	Crownware:
	1. Ivory and light blue
	2. Ivory and matt green
	3. Red-brown hair; green, pink and beige foliage
	Bone China:
	4. Light blue
	5. White glazed
Issued:	1. Crownware — 1917 2. Bone china — 1918-by 1930

	Crownware	Bone China	White Glazed
U.S.	$425.00	600.00	225.00
Can.	$500.00	725.00	275.00
U.K.	£225.00	325.00	125.00

RW2698
NAIAD (On plinth)
Modeller:	Frederick M. Gertner
Height:	8 ½", 21.6 cm
Colour:	1. Ivory
	2. Matt green
	3. Powder blue and gold
	4. White; light blue base
	5. White; shagreen base
Issued:	1. Crownware — 1918: 2. Bone china — 1918-by 1930
Varieties:	RW3030 Naiad; RW2783 Naiad Powder Bowl (First Version); RW2820 Naiad Powder Bowl (Second Version)

	Crownware	Bone China
U.S.	$500.00	700.00
Can.	$600.00	850.00
U.K.	£275.00	375.00

RW2702
NUDE BOY WITH DOLPHIN
Modeller:	Frederick M. Gertner
Height:	5 ¾", 14.6 cm
Colour:	Crownware:
	Cream body; red hair; green dolphin
Issued:	1919-by 1927
U.S.	$ 925.00
Can.	$1,100.00
U.K.	£ 500.00

RW2703
NUDE BOY WITH SEAWEED
Modeller:	Frederick M. Gertner
Height:	7 ½", 19.1 cm
Colour:	Crownware:
	Creamy glaze
Issued:	1919-by 1927
U.S.	$750.00
Can.	$900.00
U.K.	£400.00

RW2704
NUDE BOY WITH VINES (Standing)
Modeller:	Frederick M. Gertner
Height:	8 ½", 21.6 cm
Colour:	Crownware: Unknown
Issued:	1919-by 1927
U.S.	$750.00
Can.	$900.00
U.K.	£400.00

RW2705
NUDE BOY WITH FLOWERS (Standing)
Style Two
Modeller:	Frederick M. Gertner
Height:	8 ¼", 21.0 cm
Colour:	Crownware: Unknown
Issued:	1919-by 1927
U.S.	$750.00
Can.	$900.00
U.K.	£400.00

RW2706
NUDE BOY WITH FRUIT
(Seated, facing right)
Modeller:	Frederick M. Gertner
Height:	8 ½", 21.6 cm
Colour:	Crownware: Unknown
Issued:	1919-by 1927
U.S.	$750.00
Can.	$900.00
U.K.	£400.00

RW2707
NUDE BOY WITH FRUIT
(Seated, facing left)
Modeller:	Frederick M. Gertner
Height:	8 ½", 21.6 cm
Colour:	Crownware: Unknown
Issued:	1919-by 1927
U.S.	$750.00
Can.	$900.00
U.K.	£400.00

RW2715
NUDE GIRL WITH GARLAND OF LEAVES (Seated)
Modeller:	Frederick M. Gertner
Height:	6", 15.0 cm
Colour:	Crownware: Unknown
Issued:	1919
U.S.	$750.00
Can.	$900.00
U.K.	£400.00

RW2716
NUDE GIRL WITH GARLAND OF FRUIT AND LEAVES (Seated)
Modeller:	Frederick M. Gertner
Height:	5 ¾", 14.6 cm
Colour:	Crownware: Fleshtone; red-brown hair; green leaves; black base
Issued:	1919
U.S.	$650.00
Can.	$775.00
U.K.	£350.00

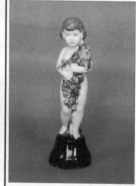

RW2717
NUDE BOY WITH ROSES (Standing)
Modeller:	Frederick M. Gertner
Height:	6 ¼", 15.9 cm
Colour:	Crownware: 1. Light blue 2. White glazed
Issued:	1919
U.S.	$750.00
Can.	$900.00
U.K.	£400.00

RW2718
NUDE GIRL WITH ROSES AND LEAVES (Standing)
Modeller:	Frederick M. Gertner
Height:	6 ¼", 15.9 cm
Colour:	Crownware: 1. Light blue 2. White; red-brown hair; green leaves; yellow roses
Issued:	1919
U.S.	$650.00
Can.	$775.00
U.K.	£350.00

RW2719
**NUDE GIRL WITH BASKET OF
ROSES (Seated)**
Modeller: Frederick M. Gertner
Height: 5 ¼", 13.3 cm
Colour: Crownware:
Unknown
Issued: 1919
U.S. $650.00
Can. $775.00
U.K. £350.00

RW2720
**NUDE GIRL WITH BOUQUET OF
ROSES (Seated)**
Modeller: Frederick M. Gertner
Height: 5 ¼", 13.3 cm
Colour: Crownware:
Unknown
Issued: 1919
U.S. $650.00
Can. $775.00
U.K. £350.00

RW2723
DRUMMER BOY
Modeller: Frederick M. Gertner,
altered from a James
Hadley model
Height: 7 ½", 19.1 cm
Colour: Bone China:
Unknown
Issued: 1919
U.S. $ 825.00
Can. $1,000.00
U.K. £ 450.00

RW2724
VIVANDIÈRE
Modeller: Frederick M. Gertner,
altered from a James
Hadley model
Height: 7 ½", 19.1 cm
Colour: Bone China:
Unknown
Issued: 1919
U.S. $ 825.00
Can. $1,000.00
U.K. £ 450.00

RW2725
KATE GREENAWAY BOY
Style One (Hands in pockets)
Modeller: James Hadley
Height: 6 ½", 16.5 cm
Colour: 1. Cream clothes edged in gilding
2. Green trousers; lilac shirt with white ruff; yellow hat;
black shoes
3. Green suit, white ruff, straw hat
Issued: 1919
U.S. $ 925.00
Can. $1,100.00
U.K. £ 500.00

Note: Model RW2725 was based on RW800 originally issued in 1880.
Also issued as sugar sifters.

RW2726
KATE GREENAWAY GIRL
Style One (Hands clasped in front)
Modeller: James Hadley
Height: 6 ½", 16.5 cm
Colour: 1. Light green dress; grey collar; brown shoes and hat
2. White dress with pink flowers and blue trim; black shoes
Issued: 1919
U.S. $ 925.00
Can. $1,100.00
U.K. £ 500.00

Note: Model RW2726 was based on RW800 originally issued in 1880.
Also issued as sugar sifters.

RW2727
KATE GREENAWAY BOY
Style Two (Left arm behind back)
Modeller: Frederick Gertner,
            altered from a James
            Hadley model
Height: 6 ¾", 17.2 cm
Colour: Unknown
Issued: 1919

U.S. $ 925.00
Can. $1,100.00
U.K.   £ 500.00

RW2728
KATE GREENAWAY GIRL
Style Two (Hands behind back)
Modeller: Frederick M. Gertner,
            altered from a James
            Hadley model
Height: 6 ¾", 17.2 cm
Colour: Pink bodice; cream
            fichu, cuffs and apron;
            grey skirt; brown hat
Issued: 1919

U.S. $ 925.00
Can. $1,100.00
U.K.   £ 500.00

RW2732
COUNTRY GIRL WITH WALKING STICK
Modeller: Frederick M. Gertner
Height: 6 ½", 16.5 cm
Colour: Unknown
Issued: 1919

U.S.
Can.   Extremely Rare
U.K.

RW2733
COUNTRY GIRL WITH GLOVES
Modeller: Frederick M. Gertner
Height: 6 ½", 16.5 cm
Colour: Unknown
Issued: 1919

U.S.
Can.   Extremely Rare
U.K.

RW2734
YOUNG HUNTSMAN WITH WHIP
Modeller: Frederick M. Gertner
Height: 7", 17.8 cm
Colour: Unknown
Issued: 1919

U.S.
Can.   Extremely Rare
U.K.

RW2735
YOUNG HUNTSMAN WITH TOP HAT
Modeller: Frederick M. Gertner
Height: 7", 17.8 cm
Colour: Unknown
Issued: 1919

U.S.
Can.   Extremely Rare
U.K.

RW2780A
TIGER (Lying, facing left)
Modeller: Frederick M. Gertner
Height: 3", 7.6 cm
Colour: 1. Golden brown with
               dark brown stripes
         2. White
Issued: 1920-by 1940

	Coloured	White
U.S.	$1,350.00	550.00
Can.	$1,800.00	675.00
U.K.	£ 725.00	300.00

RW2780B
TIGER (Lying, facing right)
Modeller: Frederick M. Gertner
Height: 3", 7.6 cm
Colour: 1. Golden brown with
               dark brown stripes
         2. White
Issued: 1920-by 1940

	Coloured	White
U.S.	$1,350.00	550.00
Can.	$1,500.00	675.00
U.K.	£ 725.00	300.00

RW2783
NAIAD POWDER BOWL, First Version
Modeller:	Frederick M. Gertner
Height:	8", 20.3 cm
Colour:	1. Light blue
	2. Matt ivory
	3. Pink
	4. Shagreen
Issued:	1920
Varieties:	RW3030 Naiad; RW2698 Naiad (on plinth); RW2820 Naiad Powder Bowl (Second Version)
Comm. by:	DuBarry et Cie.
U.S.	$ 825.00
Can.	$1,000.00
U.K.	£ 450.00

RW2798
ROSES
Modeller:	François Clemencin
Height:	10 ¼", 26.0 cm
Colour:	1. Full colours
	2. Light blue drapery
	3. Matt ivory
	4. Shot silk with gilding
Issued:	1922
U.S.	$ 925.00
Can.	$1,100.00
U.K.	£ 500.00

RW2799
GRAPES
Modeller:	François Clemencin
Height:	10 ¼", 26.0 cm
Colour:	1. Full colours
	2. Light blue drapery
	3. Matt ivory
	4. Shot silk with gilding
Issued:	1922
U.S.	$ 925.00
Can.	$1,100.00
U.K.	£ 500.00

RW2800
FEMALE NUDE WITH MIRROR
Modeller:	François Clemencin
Height:	9 ¾", 24.7 cm
Colour:	1. Full colours
	2. Light blue drapery
	3. Matt ivory
	4. Shot silk with gilding
Issued:	1922-by 1930
U.S.	$ 925.00
Can.	$1,100.00
U.K.	£ 500.00

RW2801
FEMALE NUDE WITH LEAVES
(Seated)
Modeller:	François Clemencin
Height:	7 ½", 19.1 cm
Colour:	1. Full colours
	2. Light blue drapery
	3. Matt ivory
	4. Shot silk with gilding
Issued:	1922
U.S.	$ 925.00
Can.	$1,100.00
U.K.	£ 500.00

RW2805
FEMALE NUDE (Seated, facing left)
Modeller:	Possibly François Clemencin
Height:	4 ½", 11.9 cm
Colour:	Crownware:
	1. Light blue and ivory
	2. Shot silk and ivory
	3. White glazed
Issued:	1922-by 1930

	Coloured	White
U.S.	$650.00	175.00
Can.	$775.00	200.00
U.K.	£350.00	100.00

RW2806
FEMALE NUDE
(Seated, facing right)

Modeller:	Possibly François Clemencin
Height:	4 ½", 11.9 cm
Colour:	Crownware:
	1. Light blue and ivory
	2. Shot silk and ivory
	3. White glazed
Issued:	1922

	Coloured	White
U.S.	$650.00	175.00
Can.	$775.00	200.00
U.K.	£350.00	100.00

RW2807
INFANT POWDER BOWL

Modeller:	Unknown
Height:	7" x 8", 17.8 x 20.3 cm
Colour:	Pink bowl with gold trim; cream infant
Issued:	1922
U.S.	$ 825.00
Can.	$1,00.00
U.K.	£ 450.00

RW2820
NAIAD POWDER BOWL
Second Version

Modeller:	Frederick M. Gertner
Height:	6 ½" x 6", 16.5 x 15.0 cm
Colour:	1. Light blue
	2. Matt ivory
	3. Pink
	4. Shagreen
Issued:	1922
Varieties:	RW3030 Naiad; RW2698 Naiad (on plinth); RW2783 Naiad Powder Bowl (First Version)
U.S.	$ 825.00
Can.	$1,000.00
U.K.	£ 450.00

RW2821A
KOOKABURRA

Modeller:	Frederick M. Gertner
Height:	2 ¼", 5.7 cm
Colour:	1. Yellow, white and grey
	2. White
Issued:	c. 1923-by 1927
Varieties:	Kookaburra Ashtray (Circular) RW2823
	Kookaburra Ashtray (Rectangular) RW2822
	Kookaburra Powder Bowl RW2821B
U.S.	
Can.	Very rare
U.K.	

Note: Although the Kookaburra was issued as a separate model, it was only given a model number when used as a derivative.

RW2821B
KOOKABURRA POWDER BOWL

Modeller:	Frederick M. Gertner
Size:	4 ¾" x 6", 12.1 x 15.0 cm
Colour:	Yellow, white and grey bird; powder blue and gold bowl
Issued:	1923
Varieties:	Kookaburra RW2821A
	Kookaburra Ashtray (Circular) RW2823
	Kookaburra Ashtray (Rectangular) RW2822
U.S.	$550.00
Can.	$675.00
U.K.	£300.00

RW2822
KOOKABURRA ASHTRAY (Rectangular)

Modeller:	Frederick M. Gertner
Size:	2 ¼" x 4" x 5 ½", 5.7 x 10.1 x 14.0 cm
Colour:	1. Yellow, white and grey bird; gold edged tray
	2. Yellow, white and grey bird; powder blue tray
	3. White
Issued:	1924
Varieties:	Kookaburra RW2821A
	Kookaburra Ashtray (Circular) RW2823
	Kookaburra Powder Bowl RW2821B

	Coloured	White
U.S.	$425.00	225.00
Can.	$500.00	275.00
U.K.	£225.00	125.00

RW2823
KOOKABURRA ASHTRAY (Circular)

Modeller:	Frederick M. Gertner
Height:	2 ¼", 5.7 cm
Colour:	1. Yellow, white and grey bird; black tray
	2. Yellow, white and grey bird; powder blue tray
	3. White
Issued:	1924
Varieties:	Kookaburra RW2821A
	Kookaburra Ashtray (Rectangular) RW2822
	Kookaburra Powder Bowl RW2821B

	Coloured	White
U.S.	$425.00	225.00
Can.	$500.00	275.00
U.K.	£225.00	125.00

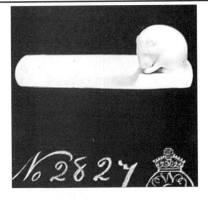

RW2827
MOUSE ASHTRAY (Right)

Modeller:	Unknown
Size:	5 ½" x 4 ¼" x 2", 14.0 x 10.8 x 5.0 cm
Colour:	1. Tinted mouse; powder blue tray
	2. White
Issued:	1924-by 1953
Varieties:	Mouse RW2610; Mouse Ashtray (Left) RW2828

	Coloured	White
U.S.	$175.00	135.00
Can.	$200.00	165.00
U.K.	£100.00	75.00

RW2828
MOUSE ASHTRAY (Left)

Modeller:	Unknown
Size:	5 ½" x 4 ¼", 14.0 x 10.8 x 5.0 cm
Colour:	1. Tinted mouse; powder blue tray
	2. White
Issued:	1924-by 1953
Varieties:	Mouse RW2610; Mouse Ashtray (Right) RW2827

	Coloured	White
U.S.	$175.00	135.00
Can.	$200.00	165.00
U.K.	£100.00	75.00

RW2842
WILFRED
Modeller: Frederick M. Gertner
Height: 4 ¾", 12.1 cm
Colour: 1. Brown and white
body; pink nose;
black base
2. White
Issued: 1927-by 1930

	Coloured	White
U.S.	$500.00	225.00
Can.	$600.00	275.00
U.K.	£275.00	125.00

RW2843
DUCK
Modeller: Frederick M. Gertner
Height: 3 ¾", 9.5 cm
Colour: 1. Yellow body;
orange feet and
beak; green base
2. White
Issued: 1927-by 1930

	Coloured	White
U.S.	$500.00	225.00
Can.	$600.00	275.00
U.K.	£275.00	125.00

RW2848
CHINESE FAMILY GROUP
Modeller: Frederick M. Gertner
Height: 5 ½", 14.0 cm
Colour: Unknown
Issued: 1928
U.S.
Can. Extremely rare
U.K.

RW2851A
ELEPHANT JUG
Modeller: Frederick M. Gertner
Height: 3 ½", 8.9 cm
Colour: 1. Grey elephant;
orange handle;
black base
2. White
Issued: 1929

	Coloured	White
U.S.	$450.00	225.00
Can.	$550.00	275.00
U.K.	£250.00	125.00

RW2851B
ELEPHANT SALT, PEPPER AND MUSTARD POTS
Modeller: Frederick M. Gertner
Height: 3 ½", 8.9 cm
Colour: 1. Mustard Pot: Unknown
2. Pepper: Black elephant; orange top and base
3. Salt: Grey elephant; orange top; black base
4. White
Issued: 1929

	Mustard	Pepper	Salt	Coloured Cruet	White Cruet
U.S.	$375.00	375.00	375.00	1,200.00	650.00
Can.	$450.00	450.00	450.00	1,450.00	775.00
U.K.	£200.00	200.00	200.00	650.00	350.00

Note: Rims are E.P.N.S.

RW2852A
COCKATOO JUG
Modeller: Frederick M. Gertner
Height: 3 ¼", 8.3 cm
Colour: 1. Coloured
2. White
Issued: 1929

	Coloured	White
U.S.	$450.00	225.00
Can.	$550.00	275.00
U.K.	£250.00	125.00

Photograph not
available
at press time

RW2852B
COCKATOO SALT AND PEPPER POTS
Modeller: Frederick M. Gertner
Height: 3 ¼", 8.3 cm
Colour: Unknown
Issued: 1929

	Salt	Pepper
U.S.		
Can.	Very rare	
U.K.		

Note: Rims are E.P.N.S.

WORCESTER CHILDREN

RW3012
Spring, Style One

RW3452
January

RW3534
Tuesday's Child (Boy)

RW3454
March

RW3011
Peter Pan

RW3149
Sister

À LA MODE

RW4150
Chic (1933)

RW4153
Promenade (1922)

RW4139
En Repose (1926)

RW4140
Soiree (1926)

THE WORLD OF THE IMPRESSIONISTS

RW4084
Camille

RW4100
La Midinette

RW4073
Jeanne

RW4072
Germaine

RW4085
Alphonsine

RW4089
Norbert

UPSTAIRS, DOWNSTAIRS COLLECTION

RW4428
Gentleman of the House

RW4415
Lady of the House

RW4385
Cook

RW4369
Parlour Maid

RW4368
Chamber Maid

RW4371
Scullery Maid

AGE OF ROMANCE

RW3546
Rachael, Style One

RW4083
Rebecca, Style Two

RW4090
Diana, Style Two

RW4079
Emily, Style Two

RW4149
Masquerade, Style Two

RW3547
Sarah, Style One

CANDLE SNUFFERS

RW4942
Toddie

RW4943
Budge

RW4941
Howard

RW4846
Mandarin

RW4753
Japanese Girl

RW4833
Emperor

RW4832
Empress

RW4902
Benjamin Bunny

RW4884
Mouse Tailor

RW4914
Hunca Munca

RW4915
Jeremy Fisher

CANDLE SNUFFERS

RW4748
Nelson Elephant

RW4766
Giles Cat

RW4763
Imari Cockerel

RW4755
Kingfisher

RW4891
Nelson Cat

RW4762
Blue Tit

RW4826
Snowy Owl

RW4764
Tawny Owl

RW4909
Little Owl

RUTH VAN RUYCKEVELT

RW3700
The Tea Party

Photograph not
available
at press time

RW2853A
PELICAN JUG
Modeller: Frederick M. Gertner
Height: 4 ¼", 10.8 cm
Colour: 1. Light grey, white
and black body;
yellow beak; green
handle
2. White
Issued: 1929-by 1940

	Coloured	White
U.S.	$450.00	175.00
Can.	$550.00	200.00
U.K.	£250.00	100.00

RW2853B
PELICAN SALT AND PEPPER POTS
Modeller: Frederick M. Gertner
Height: 4 ¼", 10.8 cm
Colour: 1. Light grey, white
and black body;
yellow beak; green
base
2. White
Issued: 1929-by 1940

	Coloured	White
U.S.	$425.00	175.00
Can.	$500.00	200.00
U.K.	£225.00	100.00

RW2854A
SQUIRREL JUG
Modeller: Frederick M. Gertner
Height: 3 ¼", 8.3 cm
Colour: 1. Brown squirrel;
green leaf spout
2. White
Issued: 1929

	Coloured	White
U.S.	$450.00	175.00
Can.	$550.00	200.00
U.K.	£250.00	100.00

RW2854B
SQUIRREL SALT AND PEPPER POTS
Modeller: Frederick M. Gertner
Height: 3 ¼", 8.3 cm
Colour: 1. Brown squirrel;
green base and lid
2. White
Issued: 1929

	Coloured	White
U.S.	$425.00	175.00
Can.	$500.00	200.00
U.K.	£225.00	100.00

RW2855A
BONZO
Modeller: Frederick M. Gertner
Height: 3", 7.6 cm
Colour: 1. Black with tinting
2. Fawn and black
3. Puce and pink
4. Tinted white with black patches; black collar; pink tongue
Issued: 1929
Varieties: Bonzo Salt and Pepper Pots RW2855B

U.S.	$750.00
Can.	$900.00
U.K.	£400.00

RW2855B
BONZO SALT AND PEPPER POTS
Modeller: Frederick M. Gertner
Height: 3 ¼", 8.3 cm
Colour: 1. Black with tinting
2. Fawn and black
3. Puce and pink
4. Tinted white with black patches; black collar; pink tongue
Issued: 1929
Varieties: Bonzo RW2855A

	Single	Pair
U.S.	$550.00	1,100.00
Can.	$675.00	1,325.00
U.K.	£300.00	600.00

Note: The top of the head of the original Bonzo figure was pierced to create
salt and pepper pots.

30

RW2858A
BRER RABBIT
Modeller: Frederick M. Gertner
Height: 3 ¼", 8.3 cm
Colour: 1. Blue coat; red waistcoat
 2. Green coat; red waistcoat
 3. Red coat; blue waistcoat
Issued: 1929-by 1940
Varieties: Brer Rabbit Salt and Pepper Pots RW2858B

U.S. $650.00
Can. $775.00
U.K. £350.00

Photograph not
available
at press time

RW2858B
BRER RABBIT SALT AND PEPPER POTS
Modeller: Frederick M. Gertner
Height: 3 ¼", 8.3 cm
Colour: Unknown
Issued: 1929
Varieties: Brer Rabbit RW2858A
U.S.
Can. Very rare
U.K. Few made

RW2865
CORA
Modeller: Doris Lindner
Height: 6", 15.0 cm
Colour: 1. Fleshtone;
 green veil and
 base; black pigeon
 2. Fleshtone:
 purple veil and
 base; silver pigeon
Issued: 1931-by 1940

U.S. $ 900.00
Can. $1,125.00
U.K. £ 450.00

Note: This model is also found
 without the pigeon.

RW2866
HARLEQUIN AND COLUMBINE BOOKEND
Modeller: Doris Lindner
Height: 8", 20.3 cm
Colour: Harlequin: Checkered costume; black mask
 Columbine: White costume
 Curtain: Red
Issued: 1931

	Single Bookend	Pair
U.S.	$ 925.00	1,850.00
Can.	$1,100.00	2,200.00
U.K.	£ 500.00	1,000.00

Note: Pair with RW2867

RW2867
PIERROT BOOKEND
Modeller: Doris Lindner
Height: 8", 20.3 cm
Colour: White costume; black buttons; red curtain
Issued: 1931

	Single Bookend	Pair
U.S.	$ 925.00	1,850.00
Can.	$1,100.00	2,200.00
U.K.	£ 500.00	1,000.00

Note: Pair with Harlequin and Columbine.

30

RW2868
HARLEQUIN
Style Two
Modeller: Doris Lindner
Height: 6 ½", 16.5 cm
Colour: 1. Orange and grey checkered trousers; red shoes; grey base
2. Orange, red, green and black checkered trousers; red shoes; black base
3. Orange, yellow, black and beige checkered trousers; white shirt; black mask and base
Issued: 1931
Derivative: Bookend

	Figure	Bookend Pair
U.S.	$ 925.00	2,000.00
Can.	$1,100.00	2,400.00
U.K.	£ 500.00	1,100.00

RW2869
PIERROT
Style Two
Modeller: Doris Lindner
Height: 6", 15.0 cm
Colour: 1. Blue-green / white
2. Green / silver
3. Grey / black
4. Red / black base
5. White / black
Issued: 1931
Derivative: Bookend, Pen and ink tray

	Figure	Bookend, Pair	Pen/Ink Tray
U.S.	$1,100.00	2,400.00	1,000.00
Can.	$1,325.00	2,900.00	1,200.00
U.K.	£ 600.00	1,300.00	550.00

RW2870
TERRIER (On plinth)
Modeller: Doris Lindner
Height: 3 ½", 8.9 cm
Colour: 1. White with red brown patches; fawn base
2. White with grey patches; green base
3. White with black and brown patches; pink and blue base
Issued: 1931-by 1940
Varieties: Terrier Powder Bowl / Bon Bon Box RW2927; Wire-Haired Terrier (Standing, head to right, without plinth) RW3026

U.S.	$450.00
Can.	$550.00
U.K.	£250.00

RW2871
SETTER (On plinth)
Modeller: Doris Lindner
Height: 3", 7.6 cm
Colour: 1. Chestnut red; fawn base
2. Chestnut red; green base
Issued: 1931-by 1953
Varieties: Setter (Without plinth) RW2952

B/S:	Puce	Black
U.S.	$375.00	325.00
Can.	$450.00	400.00
U.K.	£200.00	175.00

RW2872
HOUND ASHTRAY

Modeller:	Doris Lindner
Size:	2" x 4", 5.1 x 10.1 cm
Colour:	White with chestnut brown and black spots; cream tray
Issued:	1931-by c.1960s
Varieties:	Hound (Lying on curved base) RW2951
	Hound Tobacco Jar RW2926
Comm. by:	Betzemann

B/S:	Puce	Black
U.S.	$185.00	160.00
Can.	$200.00	185.00
U.K.	£100.00	90.00

RW2873
FOX ASHTRAY

Modeller:	Doris Lindner
Size:	2" x 4", 5.1 x 10.1 cm
Colour:	Chestnut red fox; cream tray
Issued:	1931
Varieties:	Fox (Lying on curved base) RW2950
	Fox (Lying, without base) RW3527
	Fox Tobacco Jar RW2925
Comm. by:	Betzemann

B/S:	Puce	Black
U.S.	$185.00	160.00
Can.	$200.00	185.00
U.K.	£100.00	90.00

RW2874
SLEEPING DOE

Modeller:	Eric Aumonier
Height:	4 ¾", 12.1 cm
Colour:	1. Buff and maroon
	2. Mottled grey
Issued:	1931

U.S.	$550.00
Can.	$675.00
U.K.	£300.00

RW2875
HORSEMAN BOOKEND

Modeller:	Eric Aumonier
Height:	8 ¼", 21.0 cm
Colour:	Horseman: Green trousers, hat, collar
	Horse: White; blue tassles; gold circles;
	blue, gold and black on hooves
Issued:	1931-by 1940

U.S.	$650.00
Can.	$775.00
U.K.	£350.00

Note: Available with or without the wooden fitting.

RW2876
LION BOOKEND

Modeller:	Eric Aumonier
Height:	8 ¼", 21.0 cm
Colour:	Mottled grey with green circles; blue claws
Issued:	1931-by 1940

U.S.	$650.00
Can.	$775.00
U.K.	£350.00

Note: Available with or without the wooden fitting.

RW2877A
YOUNG HORSE
Modeller:	Eric Aumonier
Height:	1. With base: 6 ¼", 15.9 cm
	2. Without base: 6", 15.0 cm
Colour:	1. Mottled grey
	2. Pinky beige
Issued:	1931-by 1940
Varieties:	Young Horse Ink Blotter RW2877B
Comm. by:	Betzemann for mounting

U.S.	$325.00
Can.	$400.00
U.K.	£175.00

Note: This model comes with and without a base.

RW2877B
YOUNG HORSE INK BLOTTER
Modeller:	Eric Aumonier
Width:	7", 17.8 cm
Colour:	White horse, mirror base, black blotter
Issued:	1931-by 1940
Varieties:	Young Horse RW2877A
Comm. by:	Betzemann for mounting

U.S.	$450.00
Can.	$550.00
U.K.	£250.00

RW2879
DREAMING
Modeller:	Phoebe Stabler
Height:	4", 10.1 cm

Colour: **Plinth:**
1. Chrome green; indigo base
2. Ivory; indigo base
3. Pink; indigo base
4. Turquoise; black base
5. Yellow; indigo base

Shallow base:
6. Pink; brown base
7. Turquoise; brown base

Issued:	1931-by 1940

U.S.	$600.00
Can.	$725.00
U.K.	£325.00

Note: This model was available with either a shallow base or tall black plinth (illustrated).

RW2880
FLOWER GIRL
Style One
Modeller:	Phoebe Stabler
Height:	8", 20.3 cm
Colour:	Yellow dress; pink and blue striped shawl
Issued:	1931-by 1940

U.S.	$ 825.00
Can.	$1,000.00
U.K.	£ 450.00

RW2881
SAUCE

Modeller:	Phoebe Stabler
Height:	Shallow base: 7 ¼", 18.4 cm
	Thick plinth: 8 ¾", 22.2 cm
Colour:	1. Emerald green dress and petticoat, blonde hair
	2. Green dress; yellow petticoat; blonde hair
	3. Mauve dress; orange petticoat; blonde hair
	4. Pink dress; white petticoat; blonde hair
	5. Sea green dress
	6. Turquoise dress; gold and orange petticoat; red-brown hair
	7. Yellow dress and petticoat; brown hair
	8. Yellow dress; pink petticoat; light brown hair
Issued:	1931-1952

U.S.	$650.00
Can.	$775.00
U.K.	£350.00

Note: The figure was available with either a flat base, as illustrated, or a tall black plinth.

RW2882
BOY ON BOAR

Modeller:	Phoebe Stabler
Height:	3 ½", 8.9 cm
Colour:	Fleshtone; blonde hair; shaded brown pig; pale green oval base
Issued:	1931-by 1940

U.S.	$1,300.00
Can.	$1,550.00
U.K.	£ 700.00

RW2883
LITTLE DANCER

Modeller:	Phoebe Stabler
Height:	3 ¼", 8.3 cm
Colour:	1. Blue
	2. Flame
	3. Light green
	4. Pink
	5. Turquoise
	6. Yellow
Issued:	1931
Varieties:	Little Dancer Powder Bowl RW2938

U.S.	$500.00
Can.	$600.00
U.K.	£275.00

RW2884
COQUETTE
Style One
Modeller: Phoebe Stabler
Height: 3 ¼", 8.3 cm
Colour: 1. Flame dress, beige hat, black base
2. Light green dress, yellow hat, black base
3. Pale blue dress, yellow hat, black or brown base
4. Pink dress, beige hat, deep black base
5. Pink dress, yellow hat, black base
6. Pink and ivory dress, black base
7. White dress and hat with lilac design, indigo base
8. Yellow dress and hat, black base
Issued: 1931

U.S. $550.00
Can. $675.00
U.K. £300.00

RW2885
THE MOTHER
Modeller: Phoebe Stabler
Height: 7 ¾", 19.7 cm
Colour: Green dress;
pinkish-ivory body;
blue stepped octagonal
base
Issued: 1931

U.S.
Can. Extremely rare
U.K.

RW2886
THE OLD GOAT WOMAN
Modeller: Phoebe Stabler
Height: 5 ¾", 14.6 cm
Colour: 1. Blue squares on dress; white apron and bonnet;
ivory shoes; yellow pot; fawn goat; green base
2. Flame and yellow dress; blue bonnet; beige
apron; brown and white goat; green base
3. Green dress and bonnet; white apron; lavender
and yellow shawl; black and white goat
4. Orange-red and mauve skirt; violet blouse;
yellow and pink apron and shoes; orange-red
and yellow bonnet and shawl; brown circular
base
5. Yellow apron with pink line; flame bonnet and
cloak; ivory pot; purple and white goat; brown
base
Issued: 1931-1938

U.S. $ 825.00
Can. $1,000.00
U.K. £ 450.00

Note: This model was also used on a lamp base.

36

RW2887
PICK A BACK
Modeller: Phoebe Stabler
Height: 8", 20.3 cm
Colour: 1. Mother: Burgundy striped jacket; green patterned skirt;
                      yellow apron
          Child: Yellow coat; light blue trousers
    2. Mother: Yellow and grey striped coat; red and blue-grey
                      shapes on dress
          Child: Yellow coat with shot shading; light blue trousers
Issued: 1931-by 1940

U.S. $1,300.00
Can. $1,550.00
U.K.   £ 700.00

RW2891
GREYHOUNDS (Four)
Modeller: Stella R. Crofts
Size: 3" x 6 ¾",
            7.6 x 17.2 cm
Colour: Brown; white with black
            patches; black; white
            with black patches;
            beige base
Issued: 1931

U.S. $650.00
Can. $775.00
U.K.   £350.00

Note: Pair with Hare RW2892.

RW2892
HARE
Modeller: Stella R. Crofts
Height: 3", 7.6 cm
Colour: Brown and white hare;
            green base
Issued: 1931

U.S. $650.00
Can. $775.00
U.K.   £350.00

Note: Pair with Greyhounds RW2891.

RW2893
PELICAN ASHTRAY
Modeller: Stella R. Crofts
Height: 3 ¾", 9.5 cm
Colour: White with grey
            highlights; yellow beak;
            blue or grey tray
Issued: 1931

U.S. $275.00
Can. $325.00
U.K.   £150.00

RW2894
BOY WITH DONKEY
Modeller: Stella R. Crofts
Height: 6", 15.0 cm
Colour: Blue clothing; brown
            hair; grey donkey
Issued: 1931-by 1940

U.S. $1,850.00
Can. $2,200.00
U.K.   £1,000.00

RW2895
GIRAFFES
Modeller: Stella R. Crofts
Height: 8", 20.3 cm
Colour: Brown and cream;
            green base
Issued: 1931

U.S. $1,300.00
Can. $1,550.00
U.K.   £ 700.00

Note: Model RW2895 was available
       by special order only.

RW2896
CALF
Modeller: Stella R. Crofts
Height: 2 ¼", 5.7 cm
Colour: Light fawn; green base
Issued: 1931-by 1940

U.S. $750.00
Can. $900.00
U.K.   £400.00

RW2897
CAT (Eating)
Modeller: Stella R. Crofts
Height: 3", 7.6 cm
Colour: 1. Black and grey;
fawn base
2. Brown; blue base
Issued: 1931-by 1940

U.S. $600.00
Can. $725.00
U.K.   £325.00

RW2898
THE HARPIST
Modeller: Ethelwyn Baker
Height: 9", 22.9 cm
Colour: 1. Cream dress, blue trim; cream and light green
harp
2. Green dress with light blue dots; orange, black
and brown harp
3. Grey dress with blue highlights; grey harp
4. Ivory dress with light blue dots; orange, black
and brown harp
5. Pale yellow dress with blue dots; yellow harp
Issued: 1931-by 1949
Series: Victorian Musicians

U.S. $1,400.00
Can. $1,675.00
U.K.   £ 750.00

RW2899
THE LUTE PLAYER
Modeller: Ethelwyn Baker
Height: 9", 22.9
Colour: 1. Claret coat; ivory trousers
2. Grey coat and trousers with blue highlights
Issued: 1931-by 1949
Series: Victorian Musicians

U.S. $1,400.00
Can. $1,675.00
U.K.   £ 750.00

Note: This model was also available mounted on a lamp base.

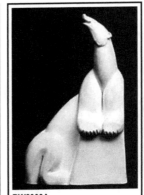

RW2900A
BARBARA (Polar Bear Bookend)
Modeller: Ethelwyn Baker
Height: 6 ½", 16.5 cm
Colour: 1. Coloured
2. White
Issued: 1931-by 1940

	Coloured	White
U.S.	$750.00	700.00
Can.	$900.00	850.00
U.K.	£400.00	375.00

Note: Pair with Sam (RW2900B).
These bookends were
available with or without the
wooden fitting.

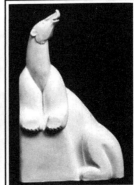

RW2900B
SAM (Polar Bear Bookend)
Modeller: Ethelwyn Baker
Height: 6 ½", 16.5 cm
Colour: 1. Coloured
2. White
Issued: 1931-by 1940

	Coloured	White
U.S.	$750.00	700.00
Can.	$900.00	850.00
U.K.	£400.00	375.00

Note: Pair with Barbara (RW2900A).
These bookends were
available with or without the
wooden fitting.

RW2901
THE FLUTE PLAYER
Modeller: Ethelwyn Baker
Height: 9", 22.9 cm
Colour: 1. Blue coat, yellow and lilac striped waistcoat, taupe trousers
        2. Brown coat, lilac waistcoat, ivory trousers
        3. Grey coat, waistcoat and trousers with blue highlights
Issued: 1931-by 1949
Series: Victorian Musicians

U.S. $1,400.00
Can. $1,675.00
U.K.   £ 750.00

Note: This model was also available mounted on a lamp base.

RW2902
THE SONG
Modeller: Ethelwyn Baker
Height: 8 ½", 21.6 cm
Colour: 1. Grey dress trimmed with blue
        2. Orange dress; turquoise underskirt
        3. Pink dress edged in yellow; flowered green underskirt
Issued: 1931-by 1949
Series: Victorian Musicians

U.S. $1,400.00
Can. $1,675.00
U.K.   £ 750.00

RW2903
BLUEBEARD
Modeller: Jessamine Bray, Sybil Williams
Height: 10 ¼", 26.0 cm
Colour: 1. Flame; green and black checkered base
        2. Green robe with leaf print; purple pantaloons; red sash;
           yellow and orange turban; brown slippers; green and
           black checkered base
Issued: 1931-by 1940

U.S. $1,575.00
Can. $1,900.00
U.K.   £ 850.00

Note: This model was also available mounted on a lamp base.

RW2904
FATIMA
Modeller: Jessamine Bray, Sybil Williams
Height: 10", 25.4 cm
Colour: 1. Light green dress; shot turquoise and pink cloak with green
           and white decoration; ivory pantaloons; green and black
           base
        2. Yellow dress; brown top; grey-blue pantaloons and cloak
        3. Yellow jacket edged in flame; pale turquoise skirt; yellow
           pantaloons; flame shoes
Issued: 1931-by 1949

U.S. $1,575.00
Can. $1,900.00
U.K.   £ 850.00

Note: This model was also available mounted on a lamp base

RW2905
NOEL

Modeller: Jessamine Bray, Sybil Williams
Height: 1. Large — 7 ¼", 18.4 cm
 2. Small — 4 ½", 11.9 cm
Colour: 1. Blue dress and cloak; ermine trim; turquoise and green bonnet; pink balloons
 2. Crimson dress and cloak; ermine trim; blue bonnet; orange and green balloons
 3. Peacock and orange dress and cloak; ermine trim; pink bonnet; orange and red balloons
 4. Pink dress; blue-green cloak with ermine trim; green bonnet
 5. Turquoise dress and cloak; ermine trim; yellow and green bonnet; yellow and purple balloons
Issued: 1931-by 1959

	Large	Small
U.S.	$550.00	225.00
Can.	$675.00	275.00
U.K.	£300.00	125.00

RW2906
JUNE
Style One

Modeller: Jessamine Bray, Sybil Williams
Height: 1. Large — 6 ¾", 17.2 cm
 2. Small — 4 ¼", 10.8 cm
Colour: 1. Blue with shot gold
 2. Deep blue dress; fawn and blue bonnet; flame and yellow flowers
 3 Chrome green dress with darker green spotted frills; mauve and turquoise bonnet; pink and blue flowers
 4. Golden orange with shot gold
 5. Green dress; golden fawn and blue bonnet; pink and yellow flowers
 6. Green with shot gold
 7. Pink dress; lilac and yellow bonnet; blue and red flowers
 8. Pink with shot gold
 9. Pink dress with white spotted frills; mauve bonnet; red and blue flowers
 10. Purple dress; orange-fawn bonnet; yellow and blue flowers
 11. Ultramarine dress; golden fawn bonnet; pink, red and yellow flowers
 12. Yellow dress; turquoise and pink bonnet; pink and blue flowers
 13. Yellowish-green dress; mauve and yellow bonnet; pink and blue flowers
 14. White dress with green and lilac design; blue and yellow bonnet; pink and blue flowers
Issued: 1931-by 1959

Description:	Large (Puce)	Large (Black)	Small (Puce)	Small (Black)
U.S.	$550.00	500.00	225.00	175.00
Can.	$675.00	600.00	275.00	200.00
U.K.	£300.00	275.00	125.00	100.00

RW2907
INDIAN CHIEF
Modeller: Frederick M. Gertner
Height: 7", 17.8 cm
Colour: Green, blue and red
blanket; grey headdress
Issued: 1931-by 1940
Series: Red Indian

U.S. $1,200.00
Can. $1,450.00
U.K. £ 650.00

RW2908
INDIAN BRAVE
Modeller: Frederick M. Gertner
Height: 7", 17.8 cm
Colour: Brown blanket with
black and red designs;
black feather
Issued: 1931-by 1940
Series: Red Indian

U.S. $1,200.00
Can. $1,450.00
U.K. £ 650.00

RW2909
**INDIAN SQUAW WITH CHILD ON
BACK**
Modeller: Frederick M. Gertner
Height: 6 ¼", 15.9 cm
Colour: Greeny-grey skirt;
red shawl; brown base
Issued: 1931-by 1940
Series: Red Indian

U.S.
Can. Extremely rare
U.K.

RW2910
**INDIAN SQUAW WITH CHILD ON
SHOULDER**
Modeller: Frederick M. Gertner
Height: 6", 15.0 cm
Colour: Green, white, red
and yellow
Issued: 1931-by 1940
Series: Red Indian

U.S. $1,200.00
Can. $1,450.00
U.K. £ 650.00

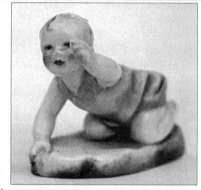

RW2911
LADY WITH FAN
Modeller: Frederick M. Gertner
Height: 7 ¼", 18.4 cm
Colour: 1. Blue, green and pink dress with floral sprigs; purple
ribbons; red fan
2. Blue dress with yellow flowered ribbons; multicoloured fan
3. Mottled blue and green dress; lilac ribbons; purple fan
4. Yellow dress with floral sprigs; pink ribbons; mauve fan
Issued: 1931-by 1940

U.S. $550.00
Can. $675.00
U.K. £300.00

RW2912
MICHAEL
Modeller: Freda Doughty
Height: 2 ½", 6.4 cm
Colour: 1. Blue suit
2. Green suit
3. Red suit
4. Yellow suit
Issued: 1931-1957
Varieties: RW2928 Michael Powder Bowl / Bon Bon Box
Series: Michael, Tommy, Mischief and Joan

B/S:	Puce	Black
U.S.	$375.00	375.00
Can.	$450.00	450.00
U.K.	£200.00	200.00

RW2913
TOMMY
Modeller: Freda Doughty
Height: 4 ¼", 10.8 cm
Colour: 1. Flame shirt; mauve shorts
             2. Mauve shirt; blue shorts
             3. Pale green shirt; white shorts
             4. Pink shirt; turquoise shorts
             5. Sea green shirt; blue shorts
             6. White shirt with blue and pink border;
                 blue shorts
             7. Yellow shirt; grey shorts
Issued: 1931-1957
Series: Michael, Tommy, Mischief and Joan

B/S:	Puce	Black
U.S.	$325.00	275.00
Can.	$400.00	325.00
U.K.	£175.00	150.00

RW2914
MISCHIEF
Modeller: Freda Doughty
Height: 3 ½", 8.9 cm
Colour: 1. Flame dress; lilac and flame flowers
             2. Green sheen dress; yellow flowers
             3. Mauve sheen dress; yellow flowers
             4. Turquoise dress; lilac and yellow flowers
             5. Yellow dress; pink flowers
             6. Yellow dress with red dots; blue and mauve
                 flowers
             7. Yellow dress with red dots; lilac flowers
Issued: 1931-1957
Series: Michael, Tommy, Mischief and Joan

B/S:	Puce	Black
U.S.	$500.00	450.00
Can.	$600.00	550.00
U.K.	£275.00	250.00

RW2915
JOAN
Modeller:	Freda Doughty
Height:	4 ¼", 10.8 cm
Colour:	1. Flame dress with spotted yellow smocking and sleeve line; yellow knickers
	2. White dress with blue dots; mauve knickers
	3. White dress with patterned yellow, red and green borders; pink knickers
	4. Yellow dress with green and purple design; purple knickers
Issued:	1931-1957
Series:	Michael, Tommy, Mischief and Joan

B/S:	Puce	Black
U.S.	$450.00	375.00
Can.	$550.00	450.00
U.K.	£250.00	200.00

RW2916
THE MONGREL PUP
Modeller:	Margaret Cane
Height:	7 ¾", 19.7 cm
Colour:	1. Blue and yellow dress
	2. Flame dress; blonde hair; brown and white puppy
	3. Turquoise dress trimmed with dots; brown hair; brown and white puppy
	4. Yellow dress; brown hair; black and white puppy
Issued:	1931-by 1959
U.S.	$1,450.00
Can.	$1,725.00
U.K.	£ 775.00

RW2917
SEA URCHIN
Modeller:	Margaret Cane
Height:	6 ¼", 15.9 cm
Colour:	Fleshtones; light brown hair; dark green and brown base
Issued:	1931-by 1948
U.S.	$ 875.00
Can.	$1,050.00
U.K.	£ 475.00

RW2918
SLEEPY BOY
Modeller:	Margaret Cane
Height:	3 ¼", 8.3 cm
Colour:	1. Blue sweater; brown shorts; fawn base
	2. Green sweater; brown shorts; indigo base
	3. Mauve sweater; brown shorts; green base
	4. Pink sweater; brown shorts; indigo base
	5. Orange-pink sweater; blue shorts; fawn base
	6. Ultramarine sweater; brown shorts; indigo base
	7. Yellow sweater; brown shorts; green base
Issued:	1931-by 1957

B/S:	Puce	Black
U.S.	$500.00	450.00
Can.	$600.00	550.00
U.K.	£275.00	250.00

RW2919
TANGLES
Modeller:	Anne Acheson
Height:	9 ½", 24 cm
Colour:	Fleshtones; yellow, pink and green ribbons and balloons
Issued:	1931-by 1940
U.S.	
Can.	Extremely rare
U.K.	

RW2920
LOUGH NEAGH MARY
Modeller:	Anne Acheson
Height:	7", 17.8 cm
Colour:	White and light blue apron; black dress; brown head shawl; straw basket; green base
Issued:	1931-by 1940
U.S.	$700.00
Can.	$850.00
U.K.	£375.00

RW2921
DUBLIN FLOWER GIRL
Modeller:	Anne Acheson
Height:	6 ¼", 15.9 cm
Colour:	Black dress; white apron; yellowish-lilac shawl; yellow and blue flowers; pale lilac base
Issued:	1931-by 1940
U.S.	$800.00
Can.	$950.00
U.K.	£425.00

RW2922
DUTCH GIRL
Modeller:	Frederick M. Gertner
Height:	5 ¼", 13.3 cm
Colour:	1. Flame skirt; mauve top
	2. Turquoise skirt; blue top
	3. White skirt with blue stripes; white apron with checkered edge; black bodice; white hat and sleeves
Issued:	1931-by 1957

B/S:	Puce	Black
U.S.	$450.00	425.00
Can.	$550.00	500.00
U.K.	£250.00	225.00

RW2923
DUTCH BOY
Modeller:	Frederick M. Gertner
Height:	5 ¼", 13.3 cm
Colour:	1. Blue trousers; green jacket
	2. Brown trousers; flame jacket
	3. Flame trousers; purple jacket
Issued:	1931-by 1957

B/S:	Puce	Black
U.S.	$450.00	425.00
Can.	$550.00	500.00
U.K.	£250.00	225.00

RW2924
THE FORTUNE TELLER
Modeller:	Freda Doughty
Height:	5 ¾", 14.6 cm
Colour:	1. Green dress; grey patterned shawl
	2. Lilac and red dress; green shawl
	3. Purple and orange dress; orangey-red shawl
Issued:	1931-by 1957
Varieties:	Also called "Mother Machree"

B/S:	Puce	Black
U.S.	$700.00	650.00
Can.	$850.00	775.00
U.K.	£375.00	350.00

RW2925
FOX TOBACCO JAR

Modeller:	Doris Lindner
Height:	5 ¾",14.6 cm
Colour:	Coloured fox; cream jar with small or large hunting scene in print and enamel
Issued:	1931
Varieties:	Fox (Lying on curved base) RW2950
	Fox (Lying, without base) RW3527
	Fox Ashtray RW2873
Comm. by:	Betzemann
U.S.	$500.00
Can.	$600.00
U.K.	£275.00

Note: Moulds for jar only destroyed 1953.

RW2926
HOUND TOBACCO JAR

Modeller:	Doris Lindner
Height:	5 ¼", 13.3 cm
Colour:	Coloured hound; cream jar with large or small hunting scene in print and enamel
Issued:	1931
Varieties:	Hound (Lying on curved base) RW2951
	Hound Ashtray RW2872
Comm. by:	Betzemann
U.S.	$500.00
Can.	$600.00
U.K.	£275.00

Note: Moulds for jar only destroyed 1953.

RW2927
TERRIER POWDER BOWL / BON BON BOX

Modeller:	Doris Lindner
Height:	6", 15.0 cm
Colour:	Grey crackle bowl and tinted dog
Issued:	1931
Varieties:	Terrier (On plinth) RW2870; Wire-Haired Terrier (Standing, head to right, without plinth) RW3026
U.S	$500.00
Can.	$600.00
U.K.	£275.00

RW2928
MICHAEL POWDER BOWL / BON BON BOX

Modeller:	Freda Doughty
Height:	5 ¾", 14.6cm
Colour:	Boy: See RW2912 for possible colourways of Michael's suit
	Bowl: Grey bowl with blue, yellow and green design
Issued:	1931
Varieties:	RW2912 Michael
U.S.	$ 825.00
Can.	$1,000.00
U.K.	£ 450.00

RW2930
BETTY

Model 2930 was issued in seven different colourways, with each of the colourway models being given individual names.

Modeller: Anne Acheson
Height: 3 ½", 8.9 cm
Colour: See below
Issued: 1931-by 1957

Betty	Pale blue dress with gilt lustre; blue shoes; grey kitten; pale green base
Buttercup	Yellow dress and shoes
Lavender	Mauve dress and shoes; grey kitten; green base
Lily	Sea-green dress with gilt lustre; sea-green shoes; grey kitten; yellow-green base
Marigold	Flame dress and shoes; grey kitten; yellow and green base
Pansy	Shaded blue dress; blue shoes; black kitten; green base
Rose, Style One	Rose-pink dress and shoes; grey kitten; green base

B/S:	Puce	Black
U.S.	$650.00	550.00
Can.	$775.00	675.00
U.K.	£350.00	300.00

RW2931
BULL TERRIER "BILL"

Modeller: Doris Lindner
Height: 1. Large: 8", 20.3 cm
 2. Small: 4 ½", 11.90 cm
Colour: 1. Large: White dog, green base
 2. Small: White dog, yellow base
Issued: 1931-by 1957

B/S:	Large (Puce)	Large (Black)	Small (Puce)	Small (Black)
U.S.	$750.00	700.00	550.00	500.00
Can.	$900.00	850.00	675.00	600.00
U.K.	£400.00	375.00	300.00	275.00

Note: These models are also known without the base.

RW2932
SEALYHAM TERRIER "THOMAS" (On plinth)

Modeller: Doris Lindner
Height: 4 ½", 11.9 cm
Colour: White with reddish-brown accents
Issued: 1931-by 1940
Varieties: Sealyham Terrier (Without plinth) RW2934
 Sealyham Terrier on Cigar Tray RW2935

U.S.	$450.00
Can.	$550.00
U.K.	£250.00

RW2934
SEALYHAM TERRIER (Without plinth)
Modeller:	Doris Lindner
Height:	4", 10.1 cm
Colour:	White with reddish-brown accents
Issued:	1931-by 1940
Varieties:	Sealyham Terrier "Thomas" (On plinth) RW2932
	Sealyham Terrier on Cigar Tray RW2935

U.S.	$550.00
Can.	$675.00
U.K.	£300.00

RW2935
SEALYHAM TERRIER ON CIGAR TRAY
Modeller:	Doris Lindner
Height:	4 ½", 11.9 cm
Colour:	White with reddish-brown accents
Issued:	1931-by 1940
Varieties:	Sealyham Terrier "Thomas" (On plinth) RW2932
	Sealyham Terrier (Without plinth) RW2934

U.S.	$500.00
Can.	$600.00
U.K.	£275.00

RW2936
ARGENTINA
Modeller:	Anne Acheson
Height:	8", 20.3 cm
Colour:	1. Flame and yellow dress; patterned blue shawl with black fringe
	2. Green dress; red patterned shawl with red fringe
	3. Green and black dress; patterned red shawl with red fringe
	4 Green skirt with red flowers; blue bodice; patterned flame shawl with flame fringe
	5. Orange skirt; patterned blue shawl with blue fringe
	6. Pink skirt; white patterned shawl with yellow fringe
	7. White dress; white shawl with pink, blue and yellow flowers and a yellow fringe
Issued:	1931-by 1949
Varieties:	Also called "Spanish Lady"

U.S.	$ 925.00
Can.	$1,100.00
U.K.	£ 500.00

RW2937
GIRL AND RABBIT
Modeller:	Unknown
Height:	4 ½", 11.9 cm
Colour:	Unknown
Issued:	1932

U.S.	
Can.	Extremely rare
U.K.	

Note: This model was also available on a lamp base.

RW2938
LITTLE DANCER POWDER BOWL
Modeller: Phoebe Stabler
Height: 5 ½", 14.0 cm
Colour: Woman: See RW2883 for possible colourways of dress
Bowl: Grey bowl with blue, yellow and green design
Issued: 1932-by 1940
Varieties: RW2883 Little Dancer

U.S. $ 825.00
Can. $1,000.00
U.K. £ 450.00

RW2941
PEKINESE (Standing)
Modeller: Doris Lindner
Height: 2", 5.0 cm
Colour: 1. Reddish-brown
2. White
Issued: 1932-by 1957
Series: Small Dogs

	Red-brown	White
U.S.	$275.00	225.00
Can.	$325.00	275.00
U.K.	£150.00	125.00

RW2942
AIREDALE TERRIER / WIRE-HAIRED TERRIER (Seated)
Modeller: Doris Lindner
Height: 2 ½", 6.4 cm
Colour: **Airedale Terrier:** 1. Brown with darker brown markings
Wire-haired Terrier: 2. White with brown markings
3. White
Issued: 1932-by 1957
Series: Small Dogs

	Brown/Brown	White/Brown	White
U.S.	$275.00	275.00	135.00
Can.	$325.00	325.00	165.00
U.K.	£150.00	150.00	75.00

Note: Model RW2942 could be painted as either a Wire-haired Terrier or as an Airedale Terrier.

RW2943
DANDIE DINMONT TERRIER
Modeller: Doris Lindner
Height: 2", 5.0 cm
Colour: 1. Grey
2. Light brown and cream
3. White
Issued: 1932-by 1957
Series: Small Dogs

	Grey	Brown	White
U.S.	$275.00	225.00	135.00
Can.	$325.00	275.00	165.00
U.K.	£150.00	150.00	75.00

RW2944
COCKER SPANIEL, Style One (No space between front legs) / ENGLISH SPRINGER SPANIEL (Standing)

Modeller:	Doris Lindner	
Height:	2 ¼", 5.7 cm	
Colour:	**Cocker Spaniel:**	**English Springer Spaniel:**
	1. Black	3. White with black markings
	2. Red	4. White with liver markings
		5. White
Issued:	1932	
Series:	Small Dogs	

	Cocker Spaniel	English Springer	White
U.S.	$275.00	275.00	135.00
Can.	$325.00	325.00	165.00
U.K.	£150.00	150.00	75.00

RW2945
ENGLISH BULLDOG

Modeller:	Doris Lindner
Height:	2 ½", 6.4 cm
Colour:	1. Brindle
	2. White with black markings
	3. White with reddish-brown markings
	4. White
Issued:	1932
Series:	Small Dogs

	Coloured	White
U.S.	$275.00	135.00
Can.	$325.00	165.00
U.K.	£150.00	75.00

RW2946
ABERDEEN TOY TERRIER / SCOTTISH TERRIER (Standing)

Modeller:	Doris Lindner
Height:	2 ¼", 5.7 cm
Colour:	1. Black
	2. White
Issued:	1932
Series:	Small Dogs

	Black	White
U.S.	$275.00	135.00
Can.	$325.00	165.00
U.K.	£150.00	75.00

Note: Model RW2946 could be painted as either an Aberdeen Toy Terrier or as a Scottish Terrier.

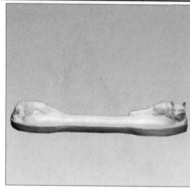

RW2947
FOX AND HOUND PEN TRAY

Modeller:	Doris Lindner
Height:	Unknown
Colour:	Cream tray; reddish-brown fox; white hound with brown and black markings
Issued:	1932
Comm. by:	Betzemann for mounting

U.S.	$450.00
Can.	$550.00
U.K.	£250.00

Note: Models used on this pen tray are Fox (lying on curved base) RW2950 and Hound (lying on curved base) RW2951.

RW2949
THE DANCERS
First Version
Modeller: Doris Lindner
Height: 9 ¾", 24.7 cm
Colour: 1. Blue-grey suit; red dress
             2. Dark grey suit; pale grey dress
             3. Steel grey suit; orange dress
Issued: 1932-by 1940
Varieties: RW4836

U.S. $1,850.00
Can. $2,250.00
U.K.   £1,000.00

RW2950
FOX (Lying, on curved base)
Modeller: Doris Lindner
Height: 2", 5.0 cm
Colour: Chestnut red fox; cream base
Issued: 1932
Varieties: Fox (Lying, without base) RW3527
             Fox Ashtray RW2873
             Fox Tobacco Jar RW2925
Comm. by: Betzemann for mounting

U.S. $275.00
Can. $325.00
U.K.   £150.00

Note: Model RW2950 was also used to make the Fox and Hound Pen Tray
RW2947.

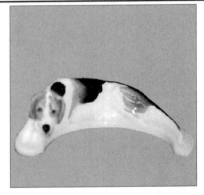

RW2951
HOUND (Lying, on curved base)
Modeller: Doris Lindner
Height: 2", 5.0 cm
Colour: White with chestnut brown and black markings; cream base
Issued: 1932
Varieties: Hound Ashtray RW2872; Hound Tobacco Jar RW2926
Comm. by: Betzemann for mounting

U.S. $275.00
Can. $325.00
U.K.   £150.00

Note: Sold through Aspreys and Thomas Goode, London, England.
Model RW2951 was also used to make the Fox and Hound Pen Tray
RW2947.

RW2952
SETTER (Without plinth)
Modeller: Doris Lindner
Height: 2 ½", 6.4 cm
Colour: Chestnut-red
Issued: 1932
Varieties: Setter (On plinth)
             RW2871

U.S. $450.00
Can. $550.00
U.K.   £250.00

RW2993
FOX (Seated)
Modeller: Doris Lindner
Height: 7", 17.8 cm
Colour: Red-brown, white
             and dark brown
Issued: 1932-1974

B/S:	Puce	Black
U.S.	$600.00	550.00
Can.	$725.00	675.00
U.K.	£325.00	300.00

Note: Also mounted as bookend by
Betzemann.

RW2994
HOUND (Seated)
Modeller: Doris Lindner
Height: 6 ¾", 17.2 cm
Colour: White with brown
            markings
Issued: 1932-1974

B/S:	Puce	Black
U.S.	$550.00	500.00
Can.	$675.00	600.00
U.K.	£300.00	275.00

Note: Also mounted as bookend by
        Betzemann.

RW2997
FOX (Lying, on straight base)
Modeller: Doris Lindner
Length: 4 ½", 11.9 cm
Colour: Reddish-brown
Issued: 1932
Varieties: Fox (Lying straight,
            without base) RW3570
Comm. by: Betzemann for
            mounting
U.S. $325.00
Can. $400.00
U.K.   £175.00

RW2998
HOUND (Lying, on straight base)
Modeller: Doris Lindner
Length: 4 ½", 11.9 cm
Colour: White with dark brown
            and black markings
Issued: 1932
Varieties: Hound (Lying straight,
            without base) RW3571
Comm. by: Betzemann for
            mounting
U.S. $325.00
Can. $400.00
U.K.   £175.00

RW2999
COLUMBINE
Style Three
Modeller: Doris Lindner
Height: 6 ½", 16.5 cm
Colour: 1. Lilac and green dress, green shawl with pink
                and yellow flowers
            2. Pale green dress; green shawl with pink and
                yellow flowers; green base
            3. Red and yellow dress; blue and green shawl;
                black base
            4. White dress; green shawl with pink and yellow
                flowers; grey base
Issued: 1932-by 1940

U.S. $600.00
Can. $725.00
U.K.   £325.00

RW3000
FOX AND HOUND CALENDAR
Modeller: Possibly Doris Lindner
Height: 5 ½", 14.0 cm
Colour: Unknown
Issued: 1932-by 1953
Comm. By: Betzemann

B/S:	Puce	Black
U.S.	$600.00	550.00
Can.	$725.00	675.00
U.K.	£325.00	300.00

RW3001
GIRL WITH KITTEN POWDER BOWL
Modeller: Anne Acheson
Height: 6", 15.0 cm
Colour: Girl: See model RW2930 for colour variations on dress Bowl: Grey with blue, yellow and green
Issued: 1932-by 1940
Varieties: RW2930 Betty

U.S. $ 825.00
Can. $1,000.00
U.K. £ 450.00

RW3006
SWEET NELL OF OLD DRURY
Modeller: Anne Acheson
Height: 9", 22.9 cm
Colour: 1. Green dress with white collar and bows
2. Grey-green dress
3. Mauve dress
4. Red dress with white collar, blue bows
5. Shaded pink dress with yellow collar, pale blue bows
6. Shot green and gold dress
7. Turquoise dress with white collar, lilac bows
8. Turquoise dress with white collar and sleeves, red bows
9. Yellow dress with green collar and bows
Issued: 1933-by 1940

U.S. $ 925.00
Can. $1,100.00
U.K. £ 500.00

RW3008
SEA BREEZE
Modeller: Freda Doughty
Height: 8 ½", 21.6 cm
Colour: 1. Blue-green dress; brown and blue base
2. Green and pink dress; brown and blue base
3. Mauve dress; brown and blue base
4. Pink and blue dress; green and blue base
5. Yellow and green dress; green and brown base
Issued: 1933-1959

B/S:	Puce	Black
U.S.	$800.00	700.00
Can.	$950.00	850.00
U.K.	£425.00	375.00

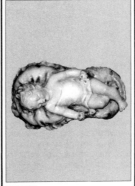

RW3009
THE TREASURE
Modeller: Freda Doughty
Height: 5", 12.7 cm
Colour: Fleshtones; pale pink clothing; deep pink cushion; white daisies; green-brown base
Issued: 1932-by 1948
Varieties: Also called "Baby on Cushion" or "Sleeping Baby"

U.S.
Can. Extremely rare
U.K.

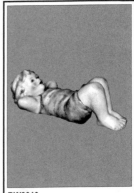

RW3010
HAPPY BOY
Modeller: Freda Doughty
Length: 5", 12.7 cm
Colour: 1. Mauve bathing suit with green trim; blonde hair
2. Pink bathing suit with yellow trim; blonde hair
Issued: 1932-1948

B/S:	Puce	Black
U.S.	$1,000.00	925.00
Can.	$1,200.00	1,100.00
U.K.	£ 550.00	500.00

RW3011
PETER PAN
Modeller:	Frederick M. Gertner
Height:	8", 20.3 cm
Colour:	1. Blue shirt and shorts, brown hair
	2. Green shirt and shorts, brown hair
	3. Pink shirt, brown shorts, yellow hair
	4. Red shirt, ultramarine shorts, brown hair
Issued:	1933-by 1958

B/S:	Puce	Black
U.S.	$650.00	550.00
Can.	$750.00	650.00
U.K.	£350.00	300.00

RW3012
SPRING
Style One
Modeller:	Freda Doughty
Height:	9", 22.9 cm
Colour:	1. Blue dress
	2. Lavender dress
	3. Pink dress
	4. Yellow dress
Issued:	1933-1959

B/S:	Puce	Black
U.S.	$650.00	550.00
Can.	$750.00	650.00
U.K.	£350.00	300.00

RW3013
SEAL
Modeller:	Unknown
Height:	Unknown
Colour:	Unknown
Issued:	1932
U.S.	Possibly
Can.	not put into
U.K.	production

RW3014
MY FAVOURITE
Modeller:	Freda Doughty
Height:	5 ½", 14.0 cm
Colour:	1. Blue dress with pink dots; yellow hair; white rabbits; green base
	2. Blue dress with mauve highlights; yellow hair; brown and white rabbits; green base
	3. Chrome green dress; yellow hair; white rabbits; yellow flowers on base
	4. Dark green dress; yellow hair; white rabbits; yellow flowers on base
	5. Pink dress; yellow hair; white rabbits; pink flowers on green base
	6. White dress with blue dots; blue hairband; black and white rabbits
	7. Yellow dress; white rabbits; yellow flowers on base
Issued:	1932-1959

B/S:	Puce	Black
U.S.	$ 925.00	800.00
Can.	$1,100.00	950.00
U.K.	£ 500.00	425.00

RW3024
FOX HEAD (Wall mount)

Modeller:	Doris Lindner	
Height:	4", 10.1 cm	
Colour:	Red-brown and white	
Issued:	1933-by 1960s	
Series:	Wall Mounts	

B/S:	Puce	Black
U.S.	$175.00	175.00
Can.	$450.00	450.00
U.K.	£200.00	200.00

Note: The head of model RW2993 was used to make this wall mount.

RW3025
HOUND HEAD (Wall mount)

Modeller:	Doris Lindner	
Height:	4", 10.1 cm	
Colour:	White and brown	
Issued:	1933-by 1960s	
Series:	Wall Mounts	

B/S:	Puce	Black
U.S.	$175.00	175.00
Can.	$450.00	450.00
U.K.	£200.00	200.00

Note: The head of model RW2994 was used to make this wall mount.

RW3026
AIREDALE TERRIER / WIRE-HAIRED TERRIER
(Standing, head to right, without plinth)

Modeller:	Doris Lindner
Height:	2 ½", 6.4 cm
Colour:	1. **Airedale Terrier:** Golden and dark brown
	2. **Wire-Haired Terrier:** White with reddish-brown
Issued:	1933-1957
Varieties:	Terrier (on plinth) RW2870
	Terrier Powder Bowl / Bon Bon Box RW2927
Series:	Small Dogs

Name:	Airedale Puce	Airedale Black	Wire-Haired Puce	Wire-Haired Black
U.S.	$275.00	225.00	275.00	225.00
Can.	$325.00	275.00	325.00	275.00
U.K.	£150.00	125.00	150.00	125.00

RW3027
AIREDALE TERRIER / WIRE-HAIRED TERRIER (Standing, head to left)

Modeller:	Doris Lindner
Height:	2 ¾", 6.9 cm
Colour:	1. **Airedale Terrier:** Golden brown with darker brown shading
	2. **Wire-Haired Terrier:** White with reddish-brown and black patches
Issued:	1933-1957
Series:	Small Dogs

Name:	Airedale Puce	Airedale Black	Wire-Haired Puce	Wire-Haired Black
U.S.	$275.00	225.00	275.00	225.00
Can.	$325.00	275.00	325.00	275.00
U.K.	£150.00	125.00	150.00	125.00

RW3028
SEALYHAM TERRIER

Modeller:	Doris Lindner
Height:	2", 5.0 cm
Colour:	White with golden brown markings
Issued:	1933-1957
Series:	Small Dogs

B/S:	Puce	Black
U.S.	$275.00	225.00
Can.	$325.00	275.00
U.K.	£150.00	125.00

RW3029
SCOTTISH TERRIER (Seated)

Modeller:	Doris Lindner
Height:	2", 5.0 cm
Colour:	1. Black
	2. White
Issued:	1933-by 1957
Series:	Small Dogs

	Black	White
U.S.	$275.00	225.00
Can.	$325.00	275.00
U.K.	£150.00	125.00

RW3030
NAIAD

Modeller:	Doris Lindner
Height:	4 ½", 11.9 cm
Colour:	Fleshtones; blonde hair
Issued:	1933-by 1948
Varieties:	RW2698 Naiad (on plinth); RW2783 Naiad Powder Bowl (First Version); RW2820 Naiad Powder Bowl (Second Version)
Comm. by:	Aspreys, London, England
U.S.	$650.00
Can.	$775.00
U.K.	£350.00

Note: Originally, this figure sat on a mirror.

RW3031
SALMON
Style One

Modeller:	Unknown
Size:	Large
Colour:	1. Coloured
	2. White
Issued:	1933
Comm. by:	H. Grant, Torquay

	Coloured	White
U.S.	$550.00	175.00
Can.	$675.00	200.00
U.K.	£300.00	100.00

RW3032
TROUT
Style One

Modeller:	Unknown
Size:	Large
Colour:	1. Coloured
	2. White
Issued:	1933
Comm. by:	H. Grant, Torquay

	Coloured	White
U.S.	$550.00	175.00
Can.	$675.00	200.00
U.K.	£300.00	100.00

RW3033
COCKER SPANIEL
Style Two (Front legs apart)

Modeller:	Doris Lindner
Height:	2", 5.0 cm
Colour:	1. Black
	2. Golden
	3. White with black markings
	4. White with dark brown markings
Issued:	1933-1957
Series:	Small Dogs

B/S:	Puce	Black
U.S.	$275.00	225.00
Can.	$325.00	275.00
U.K.	£150.00	125.00

RW3034
PEKINESE (Seated)

Modeller:	Doris Lindner
Height:	2", 5.0 cm
Colour:	Golden brown and cream
Issued:	1933-1957
Series:	Small Dogs

B/S:	Puce	Black
U.S.	$275.00	225.00
Can.	$325.00	275.00
U.K.	£150.00	125.00

RW3035
SALMON
Style Two

Modeller:	Unknown
Size:	Small
Colour:	1. Coloured
	2. White
Issued:	1933
Comm. by:	H. Grant, Torquay

	Coloured	White
U.S.	$550.00	175.00
Can.	$675.00	200.00
U.K.	£300.00	100.00

RW3036
PIKE

Modeller:	Unknown
Size:	Small
Colour:	1. Coloured
	2. White
Issued:	1933
Comm. by:	H. Grant, Torquay

	Coloured	White
U.S.	$550.00	175.00
Can.	$675.00	200.00
U.K.	£300.00	100.00

RW3037
TROUT
Style Two

Modeller:	Unknown
Size:	Small
Colour:	1. Coloured
	2. White
Issued:	1933
Comm. by:	H. Grant, Torquay

	Coloured	White
U.S.	$550.00	175.00
Can.	$675.00	200.00
U.K.	£300.00	100.00

RW3038
ROACH

Modeller:	Unknown
Size:	Small
Colour:	1. Coloured
	2. White
Issued:	1933
Comm. by:	H. Grant, Torquay

	Coloured	White
U.S.	$550.00	175.00
Can.	$675.00	200.00
U.K.	£300.00	100.00

RW3039
CARP

Modeller:	Unknown
Size:	Small
Colour:	1. Coloured
	2. White
Issued:	1933
Comm. by:	H. Grant, Torquay

	Coloured	White
U.S.	$550.00	175.00
Can.	$675.00	200.00
U.K.	£300.00	100.00

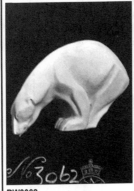

RW3040
THE KISS

Modeller:	Possibly Doris Lindner
Height:	4 ¾", 12.1 cm
Colour:	1. Green, pink and
	blue dress
	2. Ivory (matt)
	3. Peacock blue dress
Issued:	1933-by 1940

U.S.	
Can.	Extremely rare
U.K.	

RW3062
POLAR BEAR BOOKEND
(Bear bending)

Modeller:	Doris Lindner
Height:	3 ¼", 8.3 cm
Colour:	White; brown and
	purple highlights
Issued:	1934
Varieties:	Polar Bear Ashtray
	(Bear bending)
	RW3185
Comm. by:	H. Grant, Torquay

U.S.	$750.00
Can.	$900.00
U.K.	£400.00

RW3063
POLAR BEAR BOOKEND
(Bear seated, looking up)

Modeller:	Doris Lindner
Height:	4 ¾", 12.1 cm
Colour:	White; brown and
	purple highlights
Issued:	1934
Varieties:	Polar Bear Ashtray
	(Bear seated, looking
	up) RW3184
Comm. by:	H. Grant, Torquay

U.S.	$750.00
Can.	$900.00
U.K.	£400.00

RW3066
EGYPT

Designer:	Unknown
Modeller:	Freda Doughty
Height:	6", 15.0 cm
Colour:	Yellow robe with
	mauve and green
	stripes; red fez; orange
	shoes; brown mound
Issued:	1934-1959
Series:	Children of the Nations

B/S:	Puce	Black
U.S.	$550.00	500.00
Can.	$675.00	600.00
U.K.	£300.00	275.00

RW3067
ITALY / FLOWER GIRL (Style Two)
Modeller: Freda Doughty
Height: 3 ¾", 9.5 cm
Colour: 1. **Italy:** Green blouse; white fichu and apron; yellow and pink headscarf; pink and purple flowers
2. **Flower Girl:** Green blouse with purple decoration; mauve fichu and apron; yellow and pink kerchief; red, turquoise and purple flowers
Issued: 1934-1959
Series: **Italy:** Children of the Nations

Name:	Italy		Flower Girl	
	Puce	Black	Puce	Black
U.S.	$650.00	550.00	650.00	550.00
Can.	$775.00	675.00	775.00	675.00
U.K.	£350.00	300.00	350.00	300.00

RW3068
BURMAH
Modeller: Freda Doughty
Height: 5", 12.7 cm
Colour: Light blue loincloth with dark blue highlights; red necklace and bracelets; brown and green base
Issued: 1934-1972
Series: Children of the Nations

B/S:	Puce	Black
U.S.	$325.00	275.00
Can.	$400.00	325.00
U.K.	£175.00	150.00

RW3069
GREECE
Modeller: Freda Doughty
Height: 5 ½", 14.0 cm
Colour: Yellow blouse and stockings; black vest with orange and white trim; red sash; white skirt; red cap; brown base
Issued: 1934-1959
Series: Children of the Nations

B/S:	Puce	Black
U.S.	$550.00	500.00
Can.	$675.00	600.00
U.K.	£300.00	275.00

RW3070
SPAIN
Modeller: Freda Doughty
Height: 5 ¼", 13.3 cm
Colour: Pink dress; white apron with yellow and purple flowers; black sash; dark brown hair; yellow and mauve parasol
Issued: 1934-1959
Series: Children of the Nations

B/S:	Puce	Black
U.S.	$550.00	500.00
Can.	$675.00	600.00
U.K.	£300.00	275.00

RW3071
INDIA
Modeller: Freda Doughty
Height: 3 ½", 8.9 cm
Colour: 1.   White robe with purple highlights; blue turban; metal pipe
           2.   Yellow robe with purple highlights; blue turban; metal pipe
Issued: 1934-1959
Series: Children of the Nations

B/S:	Puce	Black
U.S.	$325.00	275.00
Can.	$400.00	325.00
U.K.	£175.00	150.00

RW3072
JAPAN
Modeller: Freda Doughty
Height: 3 ½", 8.9 cm
Colour: Flowered pink kimono; light green obi; dark brown hair;
           yellow fan
Issued: 1934-1959
Series: Children of the Nations

B/S:	Puce	Black
U.S.	$ 825.00	750.00
Can.	$1,000.00	900.00
U.K.	£ 450.00	400.00

RW3073
CHINA
Modeller: Freda Doughty
Height: 2 ½", 6.4 cm
Colour: 1.   Light green shirt with blue-green highlights; lavender
           trousers; maroon shoes; beige bowl
          2.   Yellow shirt; blue trousers; purple shoes; turquoise bowl
Issued: 1934-1959
Series: Children of the Nations

B/S:	Puce	Black
U.S.	$325.00	275.00
Can.	$400.00	325.00
U.K.	£175.00	150.00

RW3074
HOLLAND
Modeller: Freda Doughty
Height: 5 ½", 14 cm
Colour: Blue blouse; white skirt with blue checks; pink and white scarf;
           white hat; fawn clogs
Issued: 1934-1959
Series: Children of the Nations

B/S:	Puce	Black
U.S.	$650.00	550.00
Can.	$775.00	675.00
U.K.	£350.00	300.00

RW3075
ENGLAND
Modeller: Freda Doughty
Height: 5 ¾", 14.6 cm
Colour: 1. Blue dress; yellow hair; white flowers; white flowers on
                  green and yellow base
              2. Pink dress; yellow hair; white flowers; white flowers on
                  green and yellow base
Issued: 1934-1959
Series: Children of the Nations

B/S:	Puce	Black
U.S.	$650.00	550.00
Can.	$775.00	675.00
U.K.	£350.00	300.00

RW3076
WOODLAND DANCE
Modeller: Freda Doughty
Height: 4", 10.1 cm
Colour: 1. Blue dress; brown hair; light brown rabbits; red-brown
                  squirrel
              2. Pink dress; yellow hair; light brown rabbits; brown squirrel
              3. Sea-green dress; brown hair; light brown rabbits;
                  brown squirrel
              4. Yellow dress; yellow hair; brown rabbits; red squirrel
Issued: 1934-1972

B/S:	Puce	Black
U.S.	$550.00	450.00
Can.	$675.00	550.00
U.K.	£300.00	250.00

RW3081
GRANDMOTHER'S DRESS
Modeller: Freda Doughty
Height: 6 ½", 16.5 cm
Colour: 1. Blue dress, white frills; white mob cap with blue ribbon; gloss
              2. Blue dress, white frills; blue mob cap; gold highlights; matt
              3. Creamy-yellow dress, blue frills and hem; white mob cap
                  with blue frill; gloss
              4. Creamy-yellow dress, pink frills and hem; white mob cap
                  with pink frill; gloss
              5. Green dress, white frills; white mob cap with green ribbon; gloss
              6. Green dress, white frills; green mob cap; gold highlights; matt
              7. Pink dress, white frills; white mob cap with pink ribbon; gloss
              8. Pink dress, white frills; pink mob cap; gold highlights; matt
              9. Red dress, white frills; red mob cap; gloss
              10. Red dress, white frills; red mob cap; gold highlights; matt
              11. Yellow dress; white frills, white mob cap, yellow ribbon; gloss
              12. Yellow dress; white frills; yellow mob cap; gold highlights; matt
Issued: 1935-1983

B/S:	Puce	Black
U.S.	$275.00	175.00
Can.	$325.00	200.00
U.K.	£150.00	100.00

Note: This model is also known with the left hand flat to the dress.
          See also miniature version RW4155 Little Grandmother's Dress.

RW3082
THE FIRST CUCKOO
Modeller:	Freda Doughty	
Height:	6 ½", 16.5 cm	
Colour:	1.	Blue dress
	2.	Mauve dress
	3.	Pink dress; white petticoat; blonde hair; yellow flowers
	4.	White dress shaded in yellow; turquoise and purple trim
	5.	Yellow dress; purple flowers
Issued:	1935-1959	

B/S:	Puce	Black
U.S.	$750.00	650.00
Can.	$900.00	775.00
U.K.	£400.00	350.00

RW3083
SUNSHINE
Modeller:	Freda Doughty	
Height:	5", 12.7 cm	
Colour:	1.	Ivory dress; mauve flowers
	2.	Pink fress; mauve flowers
	3.	Turquoise dress; yellow flowers
	4.	Yellow dress; mauve flowers
	5.	Yellow dress; orange-brown flowers
Issued:	1935-1959	

B/S:	Puce	Black
U.S.	$ 875.00	825.00
Can.	$1,050.00	950.00
U.K.	£ 475.00	425.00

RW3084
THE DANDELION
Modeller:	Freda Doughty	
Height:	4", 10.1 cm	
Colour:	1.	Pale blue suit; blonde hair; yellow dandelion; white rabbits; green base
	2.	Yellow suit; blonde hair; yellow dandelion; white rabbits; green base
Issued:	1935-1959	

B/S:	Puce	Black
U.S.	$ 875.00	800.00
Can.	$1,050.00	950.00
U.K.	£ 475.00	425.00

RW3085
POODLE, CHAMPION
"SPRIGGAN BELL"
Modeller:	Doris Lindner	
Height:	8 ½", 21.6 cm	
Colour:	1.	Dark and light brown
	2.	White
Issued:	1935	

	Coloured	White
U.S.	$ 925.00	750.00
Can.	$1,100.00	900.00
U.K.	£ 500.00	400.00

RW3086
LADY WITH A ROSE
Modeller:	Doris Lindner	
Height:	8", 20.3 cm	
Colour:	1.	Blue-grey dress, gold shading; blonde hair; red shoes
	2.	Ivory dress, gold lustre (matt)
Issued:	1935-by 1940	

U.S.	$1,025.00	
Can.	$1,775.00	
U.K.	£ 800.00	

RW3087
BOY WITH PARAKEET
Modeller: Freda Doughty
Height: 6 ½", 16.5 cm
Colour: 1. Blue suit with white frills; lavender bird; gloss
              2. Blue suit with white frills; gold highlights; lavender bird; matt
              3. Creamy-yellow suite with blue frills; yellow bird; gloss
              4   Pink suit with white frills; purple bird; gloss
              5. Pink suit with white frills; gold highlights; purple bird; matt
              6. Red suit with white frills; grey bird; gloss
              7. Red suit with white frills; gold highlights; grey bird; matt
              8. Yellow suit with white frills; green bird; gloss
              9. Yellow suit with white frills; gold highlights; green bird; matt
Issued: 1935-1983
Varieties: Also called "Parakeet"

B/S:	Puce	Black
U.S.	$275.00	175.00
Can.	$325.00	200.00
U.K.	£150.00	100.00

Note: See also miniature version RW4163 Little Parakeet Boy.

RW3088
DANCE
Modeller: Doris Lindner
Height: 8 ½", 21.6 cm
Colour: 1. Gold dress; red
               shoes; blonde hair
           2. Ivory dress with
               gold lustre; matt
           3. Mottled grey
Issued: 1935-by 1940

U.S. $1,575.00
Can. $1,900.00
U.K.   £ 850.00

RW3089
KING GEORGE V
Modeller: Gwendolen Parnell
Height: 9", 22.9 cm
Colour: Blue uniform with gold
           trim; red sash
Issued: 1935 in a limited
           edition of 250

U.S. $1,525.00
Can. $1,825.00
U.K.   £ 825.00

Note: Only 72 pairs (RW3089 and RW3090) were issued.

RW3090
QUEEN MARY
Modeller: Gwendolen Parnell
Height: 9", 22.9 cm
Colour: White gown, blue cape
           and sash
Issued: 1935 in a limited
           edition of 250

U.S. $1,525.00
Can. $1,825.00
U.K.   £ 825.00

Note: Only 72 pairs (RW3089 and RW3090) were issued.

RW3091
KING GEORGE V (Bust)
Modeller: Gwendolen Parnell
Height: 1. 4 ½", 11.9 cm (with
                porcelain plinth)
            2. 2 ½", 6.4 cm (with
                wooden base)
Colour: 1. Navy jacket, blue
                sash; gold collar
                epaulettes
            2. White Parian
Issued: 1935-1935

	Porcelain	Parian
U.S.	$500.00	175.00
Can.	$600.00	200.00
U.K.	£275.00	100.00

RW3092
QUEEN MARY (Bust)
Modeller: Gwendolen Parnell
Height: 1. 4 ½", 11.9 cm (with porcelain plinth)
2. 2 ½", 6.4 cm (with wooden base)
Colour: 1. White gown, blue sash
2. White Parian
Issued: 1935-1935

	Porcelain	Parian
U.S.	$500.00	175.00
Can.	$600.00	200.00
U.K.	£275.00	100.00

RW3093
PENGUIN (Head forward)
Modeller: Doris Lindner
Height: 4 ¾", 12.1 cm
Colour: White with blue-grey, yellow and black markings; orange beak
Issued: 1935-by 1940
U.S. $550.00
Can. $675.00
U.K. £300.00

RW3094
PENGUIN (Raised beak)
Modeller: Doris Lindner
Height: 4 ¾", 12.1 cm
Colour: White with blue-grey, yellow and black markings; orange beak
Issued: 1935-by 1940
U.S. $550.00
Can. $675.00
U.K. £300.00

RW3095
"GOOD LUCK TO YOUR FISHING"
Modeller: Gwendolen Parnell
Height: 5 ¾", 14.6 cm
Colour: Fleshtone body; pink wings; blonde hair; blue water; marbled white base with inscribed title in black
Issued: 1935-by 1948
U.S. $800.00
Can. $950.00
U.K. £425.00

RW3096
ELEPHANT
Style One
Modeller: E. Evans
Height: 3 ½", 8.9 cm
Size: Large
Colour: 1. Green enamel
2. White
Issued: 1935

	Coloured	White
U.S.	$650.00	275.00
Can.	$775.00	325.00
U.K.	£350.00	150.00

RW3097
LADY BOUNTIFUL
Modeller: Gwendolen Parnell
Height: 7 ¾", 19.7 cm
Colour: 1. Blue jacket; white cuffs and bodice; white skirt with pink flower print; yellow bonnet
2. Green jacket; pink skirt; white bodice with blue design; white bonnet
Issued: 1935-by 1959

B/S:	Puce	Black
U.S.	$650.00	600.00
Can.	$775.00	725.00
U.K.	£350.00	325.00

RW3099
FLOWER GIRL
Style Three
Modeller: Miss Stewart
Height: 7 ½", 19.1 cm
Colour: Unknown
Issued: 1935
U.S.
Can. Extremely rare
U.K.

RW3100
LION
Modeller:	E. Evans
Height:	3", 7.6 cm
Colour:	Golden brown
Issued:	1935-by 1940
U.S.	$450.00
Can.	$550.00
U.K.	£250.00

RW3101
TIGER
Modeller:	E. Evans
Height:	2 ½", 6.4 cm
Colour:	Unknown
Issued:	1935-by 1940
U.S.	$450.00
Can.	$550.00
U.K.	£250.00

RW3102
ELEPHANT
Style Two
Modeller:	E. Evans
Height:	2 ½", 6.4 cm
Size:	Small
Colour:	1. Green enamel
	2. White
Issued:	1935

	Coloured	White
U.S.	$650.00	275.00
Can.	$775.00	325.00
U.K.	£350.00	150.00

RW3103
WALES
Modeller:	Freda Doughty
Height:	5 ½", 14 cm
Colour:	Pink dress; white apron; black hat; yellow flowers; green and yellow base
Issued:	1935-1959
Series:	Children of the Nations

B/S:	Puce	Black
U.S.	$650.00	600.00
Can.	$775.00	725.00
U.K.	£350.00	325.00

RW3104
SCOTLAND
Modeller:	Freda Doughty
Height:	5 ½", 14 cm
Colour:	Deep rose jacket; green and yellow kilt; brown and beige sporran; yellow hair; purple and green base
Issued:	1935-1959
Series:	Children of the Nations

B/S:	Puce	Black
U.S.	$650.00	600.00
Can.	$775.00	725.00
U.K.	£350.00	325.00

RW3105
"HIT!"
Modeller:	Gwendolen Parnell
Height:	7 ¼", 18.4 cm
Colour:	1. Blue tunic; red sandals; brown bow
	2. White tunic; red sandals; purple bow
	3. White tunic; pink sandals; blue and brown bow
Issued:	1935-by 1948
U.S.	$ 825.00
Can.	$1,000.00
U.K.	£ 450.00

RW3106
THE DUCHESS' DRESS
First Version (Hand beneath rose - 9")
Modeller: Freda Doughty
Height: 9 ½", 24.0 cmm
Colour: 1. Pink dress with red and green flower design
2. Rose-pink dress
3. Turquoise dress with mauve highlights
4. Yellow dress
Issued: 1935-1959

U.S.	$ 800.00	525.00
Can.	$1,000.00	675.00
U.K.	£ 400.00	300.00

Second Version (Hand to the side of rose - 6 ½")
Modeller: Freda Doughty
Height: 6 ½", 16.5 cm
Colour: 1. Pink dress with red and green flower design
2. Rose-pink dress
3. Turquoise dress with mauve highlights
4. Yellow dress
Issued: 1935-1959

B/S:	Puce	Black
U.S.	$450.00	425.00
Can.	$550.00	500.00
U.K.	£250.00	225.00

First Version
Hand beneath rose

Second Version
Hand to the side of rose

RW3107
APPLAUSE
Modeller: Gwendolen Parnell
Height: 7 ¼", 18.4 cm
Colour: 1. Green dress with floral pattern; black hair
2. Pink dress; ivory and turquoise fringe
3. Yellow bodice and peplum with flower print; green skirts; yellow gloves; black hair
Issued: 1935-by 1948

U.S.	$750.00
Can.	$900.00
U.K.	£400.00

RW3108
AMARYLLIS
Modeller: Gwendolen Parnell
Height: 9 ¾", 24.7 cm
Colour: 1. Black, yellow, green and white
2. Green and yellow dress
3. Pink dress; white skirt with orange
4. Turquoise dress; white skirt with orange flowers
5. Yellow, purple, white and green
Issued: 1935-by 1959

B/S:	Puce	Black
U.S.	$ 925.00	800.00
Can.	$1,100.00	950.00
U.K.	£ 500.00	425.00

RW3110
BEAR
Modeller: Possibly E. Evans
Height: 2 ½", 6.4 cm
Colour: Brown
Issued: 1935-by 1940

U.S.	$500.00
Can.	$600.00
U.K.	£275.00

RW3111
BAL MASQUÉ
Modeller: Gwendolen Parnell
Height: 9 ½", 24.0 cm
Colour:
1. Blue and green dress; mauve and pink underskirt; green shoes
2. Pink dress; green, yellow and grey underskirt; yellow shoes
3. Pink dress; turquoise, green and yellow underskirt; yellow shoes
4. Shot green dress; ivory and claret underskirt; green shoes
5. Turquoise dress; mauve, yellow and grey underskirt; green shoes

Issued: 1935-c.1965

B/S:	Puce	Black
U.S.	$ 925.00	825.00
Can.	$1,100.00	1,000.00
U.K.	£ 500.00	450.00

Note: Earlier models had a square base, later models an oval base.

RW3112
AMERICAN REDSTART (Cock)
(Setophaga Ruticilla)
Modeller: Dorothy Doughty
Height: 7 ¾", 19.7 cm
Colour: Purple and pink bird; green fir branches
Issued: 1935 in a limited edition of 66
Series: Doughty American Birds
Comm. by: Alex Dickens U.S.A.

U.S.	$1,475.00
Can.	$1,775.00
U.K.	£ 800.00

RW3113
AMERICAN REDSTART (Hen)
(Setophaga Ruticilla)
Modeller: Dorothy Doughty
Height: 7 ¾", 19.7 cm
Colour: Yellowish-green and grey-brown; green fir branches
Issued: 1935 in a limited edition of 66
Series: Doughty American Birds
Comm. by: Alex Dickens U.S.A.

U.S.	$1,475.00
Can.	$1,775.00
U.K.	£ 800.00

RW3114
AT THE MEET
Modeller: Doris Lindner
Height: 7 ¼", 18.4 cm
Colour:
1: Rider: Black habit, hat and boots
   Horse: Grey
2. Rider: Navy habit, hat and boots
   Horse: Bay
3. White
Issued: 1935-1981
Series: Equestrian

	Black/grey	Navy/Bay	White
U.S.	$1,850.00	1,850.00	1,000.00
Can.	$2.200.00	2,200.00	1,200.00
U.K.	£1,000.00	1,000.00	500.00

Note: Available with or without a wooden plinth.

RW3115
HUNTSMAN AND HOUNDS
Modeller:	Doris Lindner
Height:	Without plinth: 7 ½", 19.1 cm
	With plinth: 9", 22.9 cm
Colour:	1. Rider: Red riding habit; white jodhpurs and cravat; black hat; metal whip: Horse: Light grey Dogs: White with light brown and black patches
	2. White
Issued:	1936-1981
Series:	Equestrian

	Coloured	White
U.S.	$1,850.00	1,100.00
Can.	$2,200.00	1,350.00
U.K.	£1,000.00	600.00

Note: Available with or without a wooden plinth.

RW3116
OVER THE STICKS
Modeller:	Doris Lindner
Height:	Without plinth: 7 ¼", 18.4 cm
	With plinth: 9 ¾", 24.7 cm
Colour:	1. Rider: Various coloured silks Horse: Chestnut
	2. White
Issued:	1936-1986
Series:	Equestrian

	Coloured	White
U.S.	$1,850.00	1,100.00
Can.	$2,200.00	1,350.00
U.K.	£1,000.00	600.00

Note: Many colourway variations of this model may exist as the rider's silks could be painted to order. Available with or without a wooden plinth.

RW3117
CANTERING TO THE POST
Modeller:	Doris Lindner
Height:	Without plinth: 6 ¼", 15.9 cm
	With plinth: 7 ¼", 18.4 cm
Colour:	1. Rider: Various coloured silks Horse: Bay
	2. White
Issued:	1936-1986
Series:	Equestrian

	Coloured	White
U.S.	$1,850.00	1,100.00
Can.	$2,200.00	1,350.00
U.K.	£1,000.00	600.00

Note: Many colourway variations of this model may exist as the rider's silks could be painted to order. Available with or without a wooden plinth.

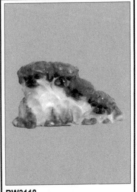

RW3118
PEKINESE PUPPIES (Four)
Modeller:	Doris Lindner
Height:	2 ½", 6.4 cm
Colour:	1. Golden brown and cream
	2. White
Issued:	1935-c.1950s

	Coloured	White
U.S.	$550.00	450.00
Can.	$675.00	550.00
U.K.	£300.00	250.00

RW3119
SEALYHAM TERRIER PUPPIES CIGARETTE BOX
Modeller:	Doris Lindner
Height:	3 ¼", 8.3 cm
Colour:	Dogs: White with brown highlights Box: Brown
Issued:	1936-by 1953

B/S:	Puce	Black
U.S.	$750.00	700.00
Can.	$900.00	850.00
U.K.	£400.00	375.00

RW3120
SPANIELS' CALENDAR
Modeller:	Doris Lindner
Height:	3 ½", 8.9 cm
Colour:	Black and blue roan spaniels; green base
Issued:	1936-by 1953
Comm. by:	Betzemann for mounting

B/S:	Puce	Black
U.S.	$550.00	500.00
Can.	$675.00	600.00
U.K.	£300.00	275.00

RW3121
TIGER (On plinth)
Modeller:	Guéro
Height:	5 ¼", 13.3 cm
Colour:	White
Issued:	1936

U.S.	$750.00
Can.	$900.00
U.K.	£400.00

Note: Available with or without a wooden plinth.

RW3123
MAYTIME (With base)
Modeller:	Doris Lindner
Height:	3 ¾", 9.5 cm
Colour:	1. Creamy white; black feet, nose, eyes, inner ear; green base
	2. White
Issued:	1936-c.1950s
Varieties:	Maytime (Without base) RW3516

	Coloured	White
U.S.	$550.00	175.00
Can.	$675.00	200.00
U.K.	£300.00	100.00

Note: A wooden plinth was available for this model.

RW3124
GOAT (Licking hind leg, with base)
Modeller:	Henri Bargas
Height:	5", 12.7 cm
Colour:	1. Creamy-white with black markings, green base
	2. White
Issued:	1936-c.1950s
Varieties:	Goat (Licking hind leg, without base) RW3531
Series:	Goats

	Coloured	White
U.S.	$550.00	175.00
Can.	$675.00	200.00
U.K.	£300.00	100.00

Note: A wooden plinth was available for this model.

RW3125
GOAT (Head raised, with base)
Modeller:	Henri Bargas
Height:	5 ½", 14.0 cm
Colour:	1. Creamy with black markings; green base
	2. White
Issued:	1936-c.1950s
Varieties:	Goat (Head raised, without base) RW3530
Series:	Goats

	Coloured	White
U.S.	$550.00	175.00
Can.	$675.00	200.00
U.K.	£300.00	100.00

Note: A wooden plinth was available for this model.

RW3126
PIERROT PUFF BOWL
Modeller:	Henri Bargas
Height:	6 ½" , 16.5 cm
Colour:	Girl: Aquamarine dress with pink lining
	Pierrot: Fawn top with clover ruff; yellow pants with clover design; clover shoes; black hat and pompons
Issued:	1936-by 1940
U.S.	
Can.	Extremely rare
U.K.	

RW3127
BABY BON BON BOX / POWDER BOWL
Modeller:	Henri Bargas
Height:	5", 12.7 cm
Colour:	Baby: Fleshtones
	Bowl: Cream with embossed leaves and fruits
Issued:	1936-by 1940
U.S.	
Can.	Extremely rare
U.K.	

RW3130
SPANIEL PUPPIES (Three)
Modeller:	Doris Lindner
Height:	2", 5.0 cm
Colour:	1. Two black and one golden brown
	2. Two golden brown and one black
Issued:	1936-c.1950s

B/S:	Puce	Black
U.S.	$500.00	450.00
Can.	$600.00	550.00
U.K.	£275.00	250.00

RW3131
YOUNG FOXES (Three)
Modeller:	Doris Lindner
Height:	2 ½", 6.4 cm
Colour:	Reddish-brown and white
Issued:	1936-c.1950s

B/S:	Puce	Black
U.S.	$500.00	450.00
Can.	$600.00	550.00
U.K.	£275.00	250.00

RW3132
FOXHOUND PUPPIES (Three)
Modeller:	Doris Lindner
Height:	2 ½", 6.4 cm
Colour:	White with light brown faces
Issued:	1936-c.1950s

B/S:	Puce	Black
U.S.	$550.00	500.00
Can.	$675.00	600.00
U.K.	£300.00	275.00

RW3133
BULLDOG PUPPIES (Two)
Modeller:	Doris Lindner
Height:	2", 5.0 cm
Colour:	1. Left puppy: White with light brown patches
	Right puppy: White with dark brown patches; name on bowl "Puppy"
	2. Left puppy: White with light brown patches
	Right puppy: Brindle; name on bowl "Puppy"
Issued:	1936-c.1950s

B/S:	Puce	Black
U.S.	$600.00	550.00
Can.	$725.00	675.00
U.K.	£325.00	300.00

RW3134
AMERICAN GOLDFINCH AND THISTLE (Cock)
(Spinus Tristis Tristis)
Modeller:	Dorothy Doughty
Height:	6 ½", 16.5 cm
Colour:	Yellow and brown bird; grey and green thistle
Plinth:	Wooden
Issued:	1936 in a limited edition of 250
Series:	Doughty American Birds
Comm. by:	Alex Dickens, U.S.A.
U.S.	$1,100.00
Can.	$1,325.00
U.K.	£ 600.00

RW3135
AMERICAN GOLDFINCH AND THISTLE (Hen)
(Spinus Tristis Tristis)
Modeller:	Dorothy Doughty
Height:	6 ½", 16.5cm
Colour:	Yellow and brown bird; mauve and green thistle
Plinth:	Wooden
Issued:	1936 in a limited edition of 250
Series:	Doughty American Birds
Comm. by:	Alex Dickens, U.S.A.
U.S.	$1,100.00
Can.	$1,325.00
U.K.	£ 600.00

RW3136
BLUEBIRD AND APPLE BLOSSOM (Hen)
(Sialia Sialis)
Modeller:	Dorothy Doughty
Height:	9 ½", 24.0 cm
Colour:	Blue and russet bird with twig in its mouth; pink and white apple blossom; green leaves
Plinth:	Wooden
Issued:	1936 in a limited edition of 350
Series:	Doughty American Birds
Comm. by:	Alex Dickens, U.S.A.
U.S.	$1,100.00
Can.	$1,325.00
U.K.	£ 600.00

RW3137
BLUEBIRD AND APPLE BLOSSOM (Cock)
(Sialia Sialis)
Modeller:	Dorothy Doughty
Height:	9 ½", 24.0 cm
Colour:	Blue and russet bird; pink and white blossom; green leaves
Plinth:	Wooden
Issued:	1936 in a limited edition of 350
Series:	Doughty American Birds
Comm. by:	Alex Dickens, U.S.A.
U.S.	$1,100.00
Can.	$1,325.00
U.K.	£ 600.00

RW3138
THE PLANTER'S DAUGHTER
Modeller: Gwendolen Parnell
Height: 7 ½", 19.1 cm
Colour: Daughter: Pink and white dress; fawn bodice;
             blue and green hair ribbons
             Servant: Purple coat; green shoes; white and green turban
Issued: 1936- by 1948

U.S. $1,650.00
Can. $1,900.00
U.K.   £ 850.00

RW3139
RECOLLECTIONS
Modeller: Gwendolen Parnell
Height: 12", 30.5 cm
Colour: 1. White coat with pink and brown designs; black and
                 gold hat; black shoes; white plinth
             2. Yellow coat; black and green hat and shoes; marbled plinth
Issued: 1936

U.S.
Can.   Extremely rare
U.K.

Note: Possibly issued as a bookend.

RW3140
THE POWDERING MASK
Modeller: Gwendolen Parnell
Height: 7", 17.8 cm
Colour: Woman: Blue dress, white skirt with brown pattern; blue
             headdress; white cloth over shoulders; brown chair and mirror
             Servant: Yellow coat; pale brown pants; white turban; white
             sash with purple fringes
Issued: 1936-by 1948

U.S. $1,625.00
Can. $1,900.00
U.K.   £ 850.00

RW3141
KITTENS (Three)
Modeller: Doris Lindner
Height: 2 ¼", 6.4 cm
Colour: Black and white kitten;
             brown and white kitten;
             grey and white kitten
Issued: 1936-c.1950s

B/S:	Puce	Black
U.S.	$750.00	650.00
Can.	$900.00	775.00
U.K.	£400.00	350.00

RW3142
THE FROG
Modeller: Gwendolen Parnell
Height: 7 ¾", 19.7 cm
Colour: Primrose and white
             dress; black hat and
             shoes; green frog
Issued: 1936

U.S. $ 925.00
Can. $1,100.00
U.K.   £ 500.00

RW3143
THE SUMMIT
Modeller:	Gwendolen Parnell
Height:	9", 22.9 cm
Colour:	Unknown
Issued:	1936

U.S.	
Can.	Extremely Rare
U.K.	

RW3144
MAGNOLIA BUD
Modeller:	Gwendolen Parnell
Height:	4 ½", 11.9 cm
Colour:	1. Pink, white and blue tabard; pink headdress
	2. Turquoise tabard with pink edging
Issued:	1936-c.1955

B/S:	Puce	Black
U.S.	$425.00	375.00
Can.	$500.00	450.00
U.K.	£225.00	200.00

RW3145
THE THIEF
Modeller:	Gwendolen Parnell
Height:	4 ½", 11.9 cm
Colour:	1. Pink skirt; spotted and striped pink and white turban; marbled white plinth
	2. Turquoise skirt with pink edging; marbled white plinth
Issued:	1936-c.1955

B/S:	Puce	Black
U.S.	$425.00	375.00
Can.	$500.00	450.00
U.K.	£225.00	200.00

RW3146
CALVES (With base)
Modeller:	Doris Lindner
Height:	4", 10.1 cm
Colour:	Red-brown and white
Issued:	1936-c.1950s
Varieties:	Calves (Without base) RW3515

U.S.	$550.00
Can.	$675.00
U.K.	£300.00

RW3147
CHILD WITH LAMB, FLOWERS IN ARMS
Modeller:	Guero
Height:	Unknown
Colour:	Unknown
Issued:	1936

U.S.	
Can.	Extremely rare
U.K.	

RW3148
CHILD WITH LAMB IN ARMS
Modeller:	Guero
Height:	Unknown
Colour:	Unknown
Issued:	1936

U.S.	
Can.	Extremely rare
U.K.	

RW3149
SISTER

Modeller:	Freda Doughty
Height:	6 ¾", 17.2 cm
Colour:	1. Sister: Pink dress Brother: Green jacket; white trousers
	2. Sister: Rose-pink dress; Brother: Yellow suit
	3. Sister: Yellow dress with red flower design Brother: Blue suit
	4. Sister: White dress with red flower design Brother: Blue suit
Issued:	1936-1959

B/S:	Puce	Black
U.S.	$ 925.00	825.00
Can.	$1,100.00	1,000.00
U.K.	£ 500.00	450.00

RW3150
TWO BABIES

Modeller:	Freda Doughty
Height:	3 ¾", 9.5 cm
Colour:	1. Blue vest; yellow shorts; white and brown puppy; yellow flowers on green and brown base
	2. White vest with blue trim; white and grey puppy; yellow flowers on green and brown base
Issued:	1936-by 1959

B/S:	Puce	Black
U.S.	$750.00	700.00
Can.	$900.00	850.00
U.K.	£400.00	375.00

RW3151
WATER BABY

Modeller:	Freda Doughty
Height:	6 ¼", 15.9 cm
Colour:	Flesh colouring; yellow hair; brown rock; blue and turquoise base
Issued:	1936-1959

B/S:	Puce	Black
U.S.	$750.00	700.00
Can.	$900.00	850.00
U.K.	£400.00	375.00

RW3152
FOALS (With base)

Modeller:	Doris Lindner
Height:	5 ½", 14.0 cm
Colour:	Light tan; dark tan; light green base
Issued:	1936-c.1950s
Varieties:	Foals (Without base) RW3514

U.S.	$ 825.00	
Can.	$1,000.00	
U.K.	£ 450.00	

RW3153
KIDS AT PLAY (With base)

Modeller:	Doris Lindner
Height:	4 ¾", 12.1 cm
Colour:	Grey-blue, black and white; light green base
Issued:	1936-c.1950s
Varieties:	Kids at Play (Without base) RW3517
Series:	Goats

U.S.	$550.00
Can.	$675.00
U.K.	£300.00

RW3154
THE DRUMMER
Modeller: Gwendolen Parnell
Height: 7", 17.8 cm
Colour: 1.   Imperial red and golden orange dress; dark brown gloves
            2.   Ivory and red dress; green gloves
            3.   Yellow dress with red and black decoration; green gloves
Issued: 1936-by 1959
Varieties: Also called "The Drum"

B/S:	Puce	Black
U.S.	$800.00	700.00
Can.	$950.00	900.00
U.K.	£425.00	400.00

RW3155
SHEEP
Modeller: Henri Bargas
Height: 5", 12.7 cm
Colour: 1.   Creamy-white with black markings; green base
            2.   White
Issued: 1936-c.1950s

	Coloured	White
U.S.	$325.00	135.00
Can.	$400.00	165.00
U.K.	£175.00	75.00

Note: A wooden plinth was available for this model.

RW3156
ASHTRAY (with dog)
Modeller: Doris Lindner
Size: 3 ½" x 4 ½", 8.9 x 11.9 cm
Colour: Light green ashtray; various dogs
Issued: 1933-c.1940s

U.S.	$450.00
Can.	$550.00
U.K.	£250.00

Note: This ashtray base was available with 'assorted' dogs.

RW3157
CHILD WITH BUTTERFLY
Modeller: Anne Acheson
Height: 4 ¾", 12.1 cm
Colour: 1.   Blue butterfly; checkered clothing; turquoise and yellow base
            2.   Pink butterfly; flowered clothing; turquoise and green base
Issued: 1936-by 1959

B/S:	Puce	Black
U.S.	$ 925.00	875.00
Can.	$1,100.00	1,050.00
U.K.	£ 500.00	475.00

RW3160
BUBBLES
Modeller: Freda Doughty
Height: 6 ½", 16.5 cm
Colour: 1.   Pale blue dress; white bowl with blue band; white circular base with blue band
            2.   Pink dress; white bowl with pink band; white circular base with pink band
            3.   Pink dress; white bowl with pink band; white circular base with pink, yellow and white patterned band
Issued: 1936-1959

B/S:	Puce	Black
U.S.	$1,000.00	925.00
Can.	$1,200.00	1,100.00
U.K.	£ 550.00	500.00

Note: The glass bubble, which was made at Stourbridge Glass Works, was added separately.

RW3161
MERMAID
Modeller:	Anne Acheson
Height:	5 ¼", 13.3 cm
Colour:	1. Fleshtone skin with orange on tail; blonde hair; pale turquoise fish and waves
	2. Fleshtone skin with sea-green on tail; blonde hair; sea-green fish and waves
	3. All-over sea-green
Issued:	1936

B/S:	Puce	Black
U.S.	$1,100.00	1,000.00
Can.	$1,300.00	1,200.00
U.K.	£ 600.00	550.00

Photograph not
available
at press time

RW3162
**SCOTTISH TERRIER PUPPIES ON
CIGARETTE BOX**
Modeller:	Doris Lindner
Height:	3 ½, 8.9 cm
Colour:	Unknown
Issued:	1936

U.S.	$750.00
Can.	$900.00
U.K.	£400.00

RW3163
POLO PLAYER
Modeller:	Doris Lindner
Height:	1. Without plinth: 6 ¾", 17.2 cm
	2. With plinth: 8 ¼", 21.0 cm
Colour:	1. Jockey: Blue, red and yellow shirt; white jodhpurs and cap; black boots
	Horse: Chestnut (gloss or matt)
	2. Jockey: Yellow shirt; white jodhpurs and cap; brown metal polo stick, reins;
	Horse: Chestnut (gloss or matt)
Issued:	1936-1981

B/S:	Puce	Black
U.S.	$2,200.00	2,000.00
Can.	$2,600.00	2,400.00
U.K.	£1,200.00	1,100.00

RW3164
HOG HUNTING
Modeller:	Doris Lindner
Height:	6 ¾", 17.2 cm (no plinth)
	8 ½", 21.6 cm (plinth)
Colour:	Rider: Khaki clothes and hat; painted metal spear: Horse: Bay Hog: Dark grey
Issued:	1936-1981

B/S:	Puce	Black
U.S.	$1,850.00	1,600.00
Can.	$2,200.00	2,000.00
U.K.	£1,000.00	900.00

RW3165
BANBURY CROSS
Modeller:	Geraldine Blake
Height:	8", 20.3 cm
Colour:	Unknown
Issued:	1936-c.1950s

U.S.	$2,200.00
Can.	$2,600.00
U.K.	£1,200.00

Note: This model was available with or without a wooden plinth.

RW3166
HIGHWAYMAN
Modeller: Geraldine Blake
Height: 8 ½", 21.6 cm
Colour: Rider: Pale blue jacket;
green shirt; black hat,
eye mask, boots
Horse: Black; brown
saddle
Issued: 1936-c.1950s

U.S. $1,850.00
Can. $2,200.00
U.K. £1,000.00

Note: This model was available with
or without a wooden plinth.

RW3167
YONDER HE GOES
Modeller: Geraldine Blake
Height: 8", 20.3 cm
Colour: Rider: Red riding habit;
white jodhpurs; black
hat and boots
Horse: Black
Issued: 1936-c.1950s

U.S. $1,850.00
Can. $2,200.00
U.K. £1,000.00

Note: This model was available with
or without a wooden plinth.

RW3168
BENGAL LANCER
Modeller: Geraldine Blake
Height: 8 ½", 21.6 cm
Colour: Rider: Blue tunic and
leggings; brown sash
and belt; white turban
with blue stripes
Horse: Brown
Issued: 1936-c.1950s

U.S. $1,850.00
Can. $2,200.00
U.K. £1,000.00

Note: This model was available with
or without a wooden plinth.

RW3169
YOUNG ENTRY
Modeller: Geraldine Blake
Height: 7", 17.8 cm
Colour: Rider: Dark yellow
habit; black riding hat
Horse: White with
brown patches
Issued: 1936-c.1950s

U.S. $1,850.00
Can. $2,200.00
U.K. £1,000.00

Note: This model was available with
or without a wooden plinth.

RW3170
MARE AND FOAL
Modeller: Geraldine Blake
Height: 8 ½", 21.6 cm
Colour: Mare: Dark brown
Foal: Light brown
Issued: 1936-c.1950s

	Puce	Black
U.S.	$1,675.00	1,575.00
Can.	$2,010.00	1,900.00
U.K.	£ 900.00	850.00

Note: This model was available with or without a wooden plinth.

RW3171
ANITA / SOUBRETTE
Modeller: Rachel Greaves
Height: 5 ¾", 14.6 cm
Colour: **Anita:** 1. Asprey grey dress
2. Blue-green dress
3. Sea green dress; blue slippers
Soubrette: White; gold lined base
Issued: **Anita:** 1936
Soubrette: 1982-1985
Series: **Anita:** Ballet Dancers
Soubrette: Art Deco

Name:	Anita	Soubrette
U.S.		$550.00
Can.	Extremely	$675.00
U.K.	Rare	£300.00

RW3172
TAMARA / JOY (Style One)

Modeller:	Rachel Greaves	
Height:	5 ¾", 14.6 cm	
Colour:	**Tamara:**	1. Asprey grey dress
		2. Blue-green dress
		3. Sea green dress
	Joy: White; gold lined base	
Issued:	**Tamara:** 1936:	
	Joy: 1982-1985	
Series:	**Tamara:** Ballet Dancers	
	Joy: Art Deco	

Name:	**Tamara**	**Joy (Style One)**
U.S.		$425.00
Can.	Extremely Rare	$500.00
U.K.		£225.00

RW3173
TATIANA

Modeller:	Rachel Greaves	
Height:	5 ¾", 14.6 cm	
Colour:	1. Asprey grey dress	
	2. Blue-green dress	
	3. Sea green dress	
Issued:	1936	
Series:	Ballet Dancers	
U.S.		
Can.	Extremely Rare	
U.K.		

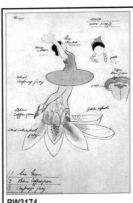

RW3174
ANNA
Style One

Modeller:	Rachel Greaves	
Height:	6 ½", 16.5 cm	
Colour:	1. Asprey grey dress	
	2. Blue-green dress	
	3. Sea green dress	
Issued:	1936	
Series:	Ballet Dancers	
U.S.		
Can.	Extremely Rare	
U.K.		

RW3175
ALICIA / BLITHE SPIRIT

Modeller:	Rachel Greaves	
Height:	5 ¼", 13.3 cm	
Colour:	**Alicia:**	1. Asprey grey dress
		2. Blue-green dress
		3. Sea green dress
	Blithe Spirit: White; gold lined base	
Issued:	**Alicia:** 1936	
	Blithe Spirit: 1982-1985	
Series:	**Alicia:** Ballet Dancers	
	Blithe Spirit: Art Deco	

Name:	**Alicia**	**Blithe Spirit**
U.S.		$550.00
Can.	Extremely Rare	$675.00
U.K.		£300.00

RW3176
NATASHA (Style One) / PIROUETTE

Modeller:	Rachel Greaves	
Height:	6 ½", 16.5 cm	
Colour:	**Natashia:**	1. Asprey grey dress
		2. Blue-green dress
		3. Sea green dress
	Pirouette: White; gold lined base	
Issued:	**Natashia:** 1936	
	Pirouette: 1982-1985	
Series:	**Natashia:** Ballet Dancers	
	Pirouette: Art Deco	

Name:	**Natasha**	**Pirouette**
U.S.		$425.00
Can.	Extremely Rare	$500.00
U.K.		£225.00

RW3177
IRINA / GRACE (Style Two)
Modeller: Rachel Greaves
Height: 5 ¾", 14.6 cm
Colour: **Irina:** 1. Asprey grey dress
                     2. Blue-green dress
                     3. Sea green dress
            Grace: White; gold lined base
Issued: **Irina:** 1936
            Grace: 1982-1985
Series: **Irina:** Ballet Dancers
            Grace: Art Deco

Name:	Irina	Grace
U.S.		$550.00
Can.	Extremely Rare	$675.00
U.K.		£300.00

RW3178
IRELAND
Modeller: Freda Doughty
Height: 5 ¾", 14.6 cm
Colour: 1. Green dress and scarf; white apron; brown hair; light brown basket
            2. Green and white striped dress; pink scarf; white apron; brown hair; brown basket
Issued: 1936-1959
Series: Children of the Nations

B/S:	Puce	Black
U.S.	$650.00	625.00
Can.	$775.00	750.00
U.K.	£350.00	325.00

RW3179
CIRCUS HORSES (Three)
Modeller: Doris Lindner
Height: Without plinth:
                 10 ¾", 27.8 cm
            With plinth:
                 14 ¾", 37.5 cm
Colour: Grey horses; red reins and breastplates
Plinth: Wooden
Issued: 1936-c.1970s

B/S:	Puce	Black
U.S.	$4,500.00	4,500.00
Can.	$5,500.00	5,500.00
U.K.	£2,500.00	2,500.00

RW3180
IN THE RING
Modeller: Doris Lindner
Height: With plinth: 14 ¾", 37.5 cm
                Without plinth: 10 ¼", 26.0 cm
Colour: Rider: Yellow dress with red stars and white trim; white and yellow plume
            Horses: Grey
Issued: 1936-c.1970

B/S:	Puce	Black
U.S.	$6,500.00	6,500.00
Can.	$7,250.00	7,250.00
U.K.	£3,500.00	3,500.00

RW3184
POLAR BEAR ASHTRAY
(Bear seated, looking up)
Modeller: Doris Lindner
Size: 7" x 5", 17.8 x 12.7 cm
Colour: White with grey shading
Issued: 1937-c.1940s
Varieties: Polar Bear Bookend
            (Bear seated, looking up) RW3063

U.S.	$650.00
Can.	$775.00
U.K.	£350.00

RW3185
POLAR BEAR ASHTRAY
(Bear bending)
Modeller:	Doris Lindner
Size:	6" x 3 ¾",
	15.0 x 9.5 cm
Colour:	White with grey shading
Issued:	1937-c.1940s
Varieties:	Polar Bear Bookend
	(Bear bending) RW3062

U.S.	$650.00
Can.	$775.00
U.K.	£350.00

RW3186
BALLET DANCER
Style One
Modeller:	Dorothea Charol
Height:	11 ¼", 28.5 cm
Colour:	1. Asprey grey bodice
	with blue bows; blue
	skirt and slippers
	2. Ivory with blue bows
Issued:	1937-by 1948

U.S.	
Can.	Extremely Rare
U.K.	

RW3187
FOAL
Modeller:	Geraldine Blake
Height:	7 ¾", 19.7 cm
Colour:	Brown with white
	markings; turquoise
	base
Issued:	1937-c.1950s

B/S:	Puce	Black
U.S.	$ 700.00	575.00
Can.	$1,000.00	800.00
U.K.	£ 500.00	400.00

Note: Available with or without a
wooden plinth. The foal from
model RW3170 was used to
make model RW3187.

RW3188
FOXHOUND CALENDAR WITH
FITTINGS
Modeller:	Doris Lindner
Height:	4 ¾", 12.1 cm
Colour:	1. Coloured
	2. White
Issued:	1937

	Coloured	White
U.S.	$550.00	275.00
Can.	$675.00	325.00
U.K.	£300.00	150.00

RW3190
VIRGINIA CARDINAL AND ORANGE BLOSSOM (Cock)
(Richmondena Cardinalis)
Modeller:	Dorothy Doughty
Height:	11 ½", 29.2 cm
Colour:	Red with brown shading; pink flowers and buds; green leaves;
	brown branch
Plinth:	Wooden
Issued:	1937 in a limited edition of 500
Series:	Doughty American Birds
Comm. by:	Alex Dickens, U.S.A.

U.S.	$1,300.00
Can.	$1,550.00
U.K.	£ 700.00

RW3191
VIRGINIA CARDINAL AND ORANGE BLOSSOM (Hen)
(Richmondena Cardinalis)
Modeller:	Dorothy Doughty
Height:	11 ½", 29.2 cm
Colour:	Red with brown shading; pink flowers; green leaves;
	brown branch
Plinth:	Wooden
Issued:	1937 in a limited edition of 500
Series:	Doughty American Birds
Comm. by:	Alex Dickens, U.S.A.

U.S.	$1,300.00
Can.	$1,550.00
U.K.	£ 700.00

RW3192
BALLET DANCER
Style Two
Modeller:	Dorothea Charol
Height:	10 ¼", 26.0 cm
Colour:	1. Grey and gold costume; blue shoes
	2. Grey and pink costume; pink shoes
	3. Lilac and white costume; pink shoes
	4. Turquoise costume and shoes
Issued:	1937-by 1948
U.S.	
Can.	Extremely Rare
U.K.	

RW3193
THE QUEEN IN THE PARLOUR
Modeller:	Anne Acheson
Height:	6", 15.0 cm
Colour:	Pink dress and shoes; turquoise cloak; gold, fawn and pink headdress
Issued:	1937-by 1948
U.S.	
Can.	Extremely Rare
U.K.	

RW3194
CHINESE DANCER (Male)
Modeller:	Gwendolen Parnell
Height:	9 ½", 24.0 cm
Colour:	Black, green, grey and cream; edged in red
Issued:	1937-by 1948
Series:	Chinese Dancers
U.S.	$1,475.00
Can.	$1,775.00
U.K.	£ 800.00

RW3195
CHINESE DANCER (Female)
Modeller:	Gwendolen Parnell
Height:	9 ½", 24.0 cm
Colour:	Black, green, grey and cream; edged in red
Issued:	1937-by 1948
Series:	Chinese Dancers
U.S.	$1,475.00
Can.	$1,775.00
U.K.	£ 800.00

RW3197
ROBIN
Modeller:	Eva Soper
Height:	2 ¾", 7.0 cm
Colour:	Red breast, brown feathers; red berries, green holly leaves; gloss or matt
Issued:	1937-1986
Series:	British Birds, Series One

	Gloss	Matt
U.S.	$100.00	90.00
Can.	$125.00	100.00
U.K.	£ 60.00	50.00

RW3198
WREN
Modeller:	Eva Soper
Height:	2 ¼", 5.7 cm
Colour:	Browns and green; gloss or matt
Issued:	1937-1986
Series:	British Birds, Series One

	Gloss	Matt
U.S.	$100.00	90.00
Can.	$125.00	100.00
U.K.	£ 60.00	50.00

RW3199
BLUE TIT
Modeller:	Eva Soper
Height:	2 ¼", 5.7 cm
Colour:	Light brown, blue, and cream; gloss or matt
Issued:	1937-1986
Series:	British Birds, Series One

	Gloss	Matt
U.S.	$100.00	90.00
Can.	$125.00	100.00
U.K.	£ 60.00	50.00

RW3200
WOOD WARBLER
Modeller: Eva Soper
Height: 2 ¾", 7.0 cm
Colour: Yellow with green markings; pink base; gloss or matt
Issued: 1937-1986
Series: British Birds, Series One

	Gloss	Matt
U.S.	$100.00	90.00
Can.	$125.00	100.00
U.K.	£ 60.00	50.00

RW3202
PIERROT GROUP
Modeller: Dorothea Charol
Height: 10 ½", 26.7 cm
Colour: Pierrot: Grey suit; black shoes
Columbine: White dress with pink bows and roses
Issued: 1937-by 1948

U.S.
Can. Extremely rare
U.K.

RW3222
THE CANDLESTICK
Modeller: Gwendolen Parnell
Height: 10", 25.4 cm
Colour: Unknown
Issued: 1937-by 1959

B/S:	Puce	Black
U.S.	$ 925.00	825.00
Can.	$1,100.00	1,000.00
U.K.	£ 500.00	450.00

RW3223
INDIGO BUNTING ON PLUM TREE (Single)
(Passerina Cyanea)
Modeller: Dorothy Doughty
Height: 9 ½", 24.0 cm
Colour: Blue and turquoise bird; green leaves; brown branch
Issued: 1937 in a limited edition of 6
Series: Doughty American Birds
Comm. by: Alex Dickens, U.S.A.

U.S.	$1,400.00
Can.	$1,675.00
U.K.	£ 750.00

RW3224
THE BRIDESMAID
Style One
Modeller: Freda Ddoughty
Height: 8 ¼", 21.0 cm
Colour: 1. Blue dress with white highlights; yellow shoe; pink flowers; brown hair; blue headband
2. White dress; green shoe; pink flowers; brown hair; green headband
3. Yellow dress; green shoe; purple flowers; brown hair; green headband
Issued: 1938-1955
Varieties: Also called "Rose Maiden"

B/S:	Puce	Black
U.S.	$ 925.00	825.00
Can.	$1,100.00	1,000.00
U.K.	£ 500.00	450.00

RW3225
DANCING WAVES
Modeller:	Freda Doughty
Height:	8 ¾", 22.2 cm
Colour:	1. Pink dress; blue, yellow and white base
	2. Turquoise dress; blue and white base
Issued:	1938-1959

B/S:	Puce	Black
U.S.	$1,000.00	925.00
Can.	$1,200.00	1,000.00
U.K.	£ 550.00	500.00

RW3226
ONLY ME
Modeller:	Freda Doughty
Height:	5 ½", 14.0 cm
Colour:	1. Pink and rose dress; lilac base
	2. Pink dress with deep pink star design; brown hair; pink base with star design
	3. White dress with pink bodice and pink dots on skirt; white base
Issued:	1938-1972

B/S:	Puce	Black
U.S.	$450.00	375.00
Can.	$550.00	450.00
U.K.	£250.00	200.00

Note: See also miniature version RW4206 Solitaire.

RW3227
"DELICATE COWCUMBERS TO PICKLE"
Modeller:	Gwendolen Parnell
Height:	6 ¼", 15.9 cm
Colour:	Pink coat; brown skirt; green apron; fawn hat
Issued:	1938-by 1948
Series:	The Cries of London

B/S:	Puce	Black
U.S.	$ 925.00	825.00
Can.	$1,100.00	1,000.00
U.K.	£ 500.00	450.00

RW3228
IRISH SETTER / RED SETTER (With base)
Modeller:	Doris Lindner
Height:	4 ½", 11.9 cm
Colour:	1. Irish Setter: Chocolate brown dog; green-brown base
	2. Irish Setter: Chocolate brown dog; gold line around base
	3. Red Setter: Red-brown; green base
	4. Red Setter: Red-brown; gold line around base
Issued:	1. 1938-c.1950s 3. 1938-c.1955
	2. 1976-1980 4. 1976-1980
Varieties:	Red Setter (Without base) RW3307
Series:	Sporting Dogs

	Green base	Gold line/base
U.S.	$450.00	425.00
Can.	$550.00	500.00
U.K.	£250.00	225.00

RW3229
ENGLISH POINTER (With base)
Modeller:	Doris Lindner
Height:	4 ½", 11.9 cm
Colour:	1. White with dark brown markings; green-brown base
	2. White with dark brown markings; gold line around base
Issued:	1. 1938-c.1950s
	2. 1976-1980
Varieties:	English Pointer (Without base) RW3308
Series:	Sporting Dogs

	Green base	Gold line/base
U.S.	$450.00	425.00
Can.	$550.00	500.00
U.K.	£250.00	225.00

RW3230
GOLDEN RETRIEVER (With base)

Modeller:	Doris Lindner
Height:	4 ½", 11.9 cm
Colour:	1. Golden brown; blue-green base
	2. Golden brown; gold line around base
Issued:	1. 1938-c.1950s
	2. 1976-1980
Varieties:	Golden Retriever (Without base) RW3309
Series:	Sporting Dogs

	Blue-green base	Gold line/base
U.S.	$375.00	325.00
Can.	$450.00	400.00
U.K.	£200.00	175.00

RW3231
COCKER SPANIEL, Style Three (With base)

Modeller:	Doris Lindner
Height:	4 ½", 11.9 cm
Colour:	1. Black and white dog; fawn rabbit; green base
	2. Black and white dog; fawn rabbit; gold line around base
	3. Blue roan dog; fawn rabbit; green-brown base
	4. Blue roan dog; fawn rabbit; gold line around base
Issued:	1. 1938-c.1955 3. 1938-c.1955
	2. 1976-1980 4. 1976-1980
Varieties:	Cocker Spaniel (Without base) RW3310
Series:	Sporting Dogs

	Green base	Gold line/ base
U.S.	$375.00	325.00
Can.	$450.00	400.00
U.K.	£200.00	175.00

RW3232
CLUMBER SPANIEL / ENGLISH SPRINGER SPANIEL (With base)

Modeller:	Doris Lindner
Height:	4 ½", 11.9 cm
Colour:	1. Grey-blue and white spaniel; green, red and yellow fowl
	2. Grey-blue and white spaniel; gold line around base
	3. Liver and white spaniel; green, red and yellow fowl
	4. Liver and white spaniel; gold line around base
Issued:	1. 1938-c.1955 3. 1938-c.1955
	2. 1976-1980 4. 1976-1980
Varieties:	Clumber Spaniel (Without base) RW3311
Series:	Sporting Dogs

	Grey-blue	Liver/white	Gold line/base
U.S.	$375.00	375.00	325.00
Can.	$450.00	450.00	400.00
U.K.	£200.00	200.00	175.00

RW3233
LABRADOR RETRIEVER (With base)

Modeller:	Doris Lindner
Height:	4 ½", 11.9 cm
Colour:	1. Black
	2. Black; gold line around base
	3. Golden
	4. Golden; gold line around base
Issued:	1. 1938-c.1955 3. 1938-c.1955
	2. 1976-1980 4. 1976-1980
Varieties:	Labrador Retriever (Without base) RW3312
Series:	Sporting Dogs

	Black	Golden	Gold line/base
U.S.	$375.00	375.00	325.00
Can.	$450.00	450.00	400.00
U.K.	£200.00	200.00	175.00

RW3234
THRUSH
Style One

Modeller:	Eva Soper
Height:	4 ¾", 12.1 cm
Colour:	Light and dark brown thrush; red berries and orange leaves on base; gloss or matt
Issued:	1938-1986
Series:	British Birds, Series One

	Gloss	Matt
U.S.	$125.00	100.00
Can.	$150.00	125.00
U.K.	£ 75.00	65.00

RW3235
KINGFISHER

Modeller:	Eva Soper
Height:	3 ¼", 8.3 cm
Colour:	Blue and orange-brown; gloss or matt
Issued:	1938-1986
Series:	British Birds, Series One

	Gloss	Matt
U.S.	$175.00	165.00
Can.	$225.00	200.00
U.K.	£100.00	90.00

RW3236
SPARROW

Modeller:	Eva Soper
Height:	3 ½", 8.9 cm
Colour:	Brown and grey sparrow; green leaves and red berries on base; gloss or matt
Issued:	1938-1986
Series:	British Birds, Series One

	Gloss	Matt
U.S.	$100.00	90.00
Can.	$125.00	110.00
U.K.	£ 65.00	50.00

RW3238
BULLFINCH

Modeller:	Eva Soper
Height:	3", 7.6 cm
Colour:	Brown, black and grey finch; light green base; gloss or matt
Issued:	1938-1986
Series:	British Birds, Series One

	Gloss	Matt
U.S.	$100.00	90.00
Can.	$125.00	110.00
U.K.	£ 65.00	50.00

RW3239
GOLDFINCH

Modeller:	Eva Soper
Height:	2 ¼", 5.7 cm
Colour:	Browns, red, yellow and white finch; beige, maroon and grey base; gloss or matt
Issued:	1938-1986
Series:	British Birds, Series One

	Gloss	Matt
U.S.	$100.00	90.00
Can.	$125.00	110.00
U.K.	£ 65.00	50.00

RW3240
CHAFFINCH
Style One

Modeller:	Eva Soper
Height:	3 ¼", 8.3 cm
Colour:	Orange, grey and black finch; green leaves; gloss or matt
Issued:	1938-1986
Series:	British Birds, Series One

	Gloss	Matt
U.S.	$100.00	90.00
Can.	$125.00	110.00
U.K.	£ 65.00	50.00

RW3241
CHICKADEE AND LARCH (Cock)
(Parus Atricapillus)

Modeller:	Dorothy Doughty
Height:	9 ½", 24.0 cm
Colour:	Brown and grey bird; brown cones; green spikes; brown and grey branch
Plinth:	Wooden
Issued:	1938 in a limited edition of 325
Series:	Doughty American Birds
Comm. by:	Alex Dickens, U.S.A.

U.S.	$ 825.00
Can.	$1,000.00
U.K.	£ 450.00

RW3242
CHICKADEE AND LARCH (Hen)
(Parus Atricapillus)
Modeller:	Dorothy Doughty
Height:	9 ½", 24.0 cm
Colour:	Brown and grey bird; brown cones; green spikes; brown and grey branch
Plinth:	Wooden
Issued:	1938 in a limited edition of 325
Series:	Doughty American Birds
Comm. by:	Alex Dickens, U.S.A.

U.S.	$1,000.00
Can.	$1,250.00
U.K.	£ 550.00

RW3243
WELSH CORGI
Modeller:	Doris Lindner
Height:	2", 5.0 cm
Colour:	Red-brown and cream
Issued:	1938-c.1950s
Series:	Small Dogs

U.S.	$275.00
Can.	$325.00
U.K.	£150.00

RW3246
AUTUMN (Bust)
Modeller:	Rachel Greaves
Height:	9", 22.9 cm
Colour:	Glazed cream bone china
Issued:	1938-by 1959

B/S:	Puce	Black
U.S.	$ 925.00	825.00
Can.	$1,100.00	1,000.00
U.K.	£ 500.00	450.00

RW3247
SPRING (Bust)
Modeller:	Rachel Greaves
Height:	9", 22.9 cm
Colour:	Glazed cream bone china
Issued:	1938-by 1959

B/S:	Puce	Black
U.S.	$ 925.00	825.00
Can.	$1,100.00	1,000.00
U.K.	£ 500.00	450.00

RW3248
JAY
Modeller:	Eva Soper
Height:	6 ¼", 15.9 cm
Colour:	Orange-brown with blue highlights; light green and beige base; gloss or matt
Issued:	1938-1986
Series:	British Birds, Series One

	Gloss	Matt
U.S.	$400.00	400.00
Can.	$475.00	475.00
U.K.	£225.00	225.00

RW3249
WOODPECKER
Modeller:	Eva Soper
Height:	7 ¼", 18.4 cm
Colour:	Light yellow, green, black and dark red; mauve and light brown base; gloss or matt
Issued:	1938-1986
Series:	British Birds, Series One

	Gloss	Matt
U.S.	$400.00	400.00
Can.	$475.00	475.00
U.K.	£225.00	225.00

RW3250
"RIPE 'SPERAGUS"

Modeller:	Gwendolen Parnell
Height:	6", 15.0 cm
Colour:	Sea green dress; orange apron; yellow cloak; clover shoe with red bows; purple and mauve hat
Issued:	1938
Series:	The Cries of London

B/S:	Puce	Black
U.S.	$ 925.00	825.00
Can.	$1,100.00	1,000.00
U.K.	£ 500.00	450.00

RW3252
"A MERY NEW SONG"

Modeller:	Gwendolen Parnell
Height:	6 ¼", 15.9 cm
Colour:	Pink, beige, yellow and blue
Issued:	1938-by 1959
Series:	The Cries of London

B/S:	Puce	Black
U.S.	$ 925.00	825.00
Can.	$1,100.00	1,000.00
U.K.	£ 500.00	450.00

RW3256
SUNDAY'S CHILD (Boy)

Modeller:	Freda Doughty
Height:	4 ¾", 12.1 cm
Colour:	Blue outfit; blonde hair; green ball with red and blue stripes; yellow sandy base
Issued:	1938-1984
Reissued:	1996-2002
Series:	The Days of the Week

B/S:	Blue	Black	Black circle	Black diamond
U.S.	$450.00	325.00	275.00	225.00
Can.	$550.00	400.00	325.00	275.00
U.K.	£250.00	175.00	150.00	125.00

Note: See also miniature version RW4164 Sunshine Days.

RW3257
MONDAY'S CHILD (Girl) / SUSIE

Modeller:	Freda Doughty
Height:	6 ½", 16.5 cm
Colour:	**Monday's Child:**

1. Blue dress trimmed with yellow frills and sash; white base with blue and yellow design
2. Creamy-white dress trimmed with blue frills and sash; light blue base

Susie:
Purple dress trimmed with yellow frills and sash

Issued:	**Monday's Child:** 1938-1984
	Susie: 1982-1983
Reissued:	**Monday's Child:** 1996-2002
Series:	**Monday's Child:** The Days of the Week

MONDAY'S CHILD

B/S:	Blue	Black	Black, circle	Black, diamond
U.S.	$450.00	325.00	275.00	225.00
Can.	$550.00	400.00	325.00	275.00
U.K.	£250.00	175.00	150.00	125.00

SUSIE:

B/S:	Black, circle
U.S.	
Can.	Very rare
U.K.	

Note: See also miniature version RW4194 Birthday Girl.

RW3258
TUESDAY'S CHILD (Girl) / RED SHOES

Modeller:	Freda Doughty
Height:	8 ½", 21.6 cm
Colour:	**Tuesday's Child:** Yellow and white tutu trimmed with orange; yellow and red slippers
	Red Shoes: White tutu; red slippers
Issued:	**Tuesday's Child:** 1938-1984
	Red Shoes: 1982-1983
Reissued:	**Tuesday's Child:** 1996-2002
Series:	**Tuesday's Child:** The Days of the Week

TUESDAY'S CHILD

B/S:	Blue	Black	Black, circle	Black, diamond
U.S.	$450.00	325.00	275.00	225.00
Can.	$550.00	400.00	325.00	275.00
U.K.	£250.00	175.00	150.00	125.00

RED SHOES

B/S:	Black, circle
U.S.	
Can.	Very rare
U.K.	

Note: See also miniature version RW4188 Ballerina.

RW3259
WEDNESDAY'S CHILD (Girl)

Modeller:	Freda Doughty
Height:	7", 17.8 cm
Colour:	Rose-pink dress; blue shoes; red hair; green base
Issued:	1938-1942
Series:	The Days of the Week

U.S.	$450.00
Can.	$550.00
U.K.	£250.00

Note: See also miniature version RW4200 Lost Slipper.

RW3260
THURSDAY'S CHILD (Boy) / SMILING THROUGH

Modeller:	Freda Doughty
Height:	6 ½", 16.5 cm
Colour:	**Thursday's Child:** Light blue coat; red hat, sandals; brown staff
	Smiling Through: Light blue coat; brown hat, sandals; brown staff
Issued:	**Thursday's Child:** 1938-1984
	Smiling Through: 1982-1983
Reissued:	**Thursday's Child:** 1996-2002
Series:	**Thursday's Child:** The Days of the Week

MONDAY'S CHILD

B/S:	Blue	Black	Black, circle	Black, diamond
U.S.	$450.00	325.00	275.00	225.00
Can.	$550.00	400.00	325.00	275.00
U.K.	£250.00	175.00	150.00	125.00

SMILING THROUGH

B/S:	Black, circle
U.S.	
Can.	Very rare
U.K.	

Note: See also miniature version RW4201 Country Boy.

RW3261
FRIDAY'S CHILD (Boy) / MY PET

Modeller:	Freda Doughty
Height:	7", 17.8 cm
Colour:	**Friday's Child:** Beige and white top; green shorts; orange sandals; grey kitten; green and white base
	My Pet: Turquoise shirt and shorts; golden brown hair; brown sandals; grey kitten
Issued:	**Friday's Child:** 1938-1984
	My Pet: 1982-1983
Reissued:	**Friday's Child:** 1996-2002
Series:	**Friday's Child:** The Days of the Week

FRIDAY'S CHILD

B/S:	Blue	Black	Black, circle	Black, diamond
U.S.	$450.00	325.00	275.00	225.00
Can.	$550.00	400.00	325.00	275.00
U.K.	£250.00	175.00	150.00	125.00

MY PET

B/S:	Black, circle
U.S.	
Can.	Extremely rare
U.K.	

Note: See also miniature version RW4193 Old Friends.

RW3262
SATURDAY'S CHILD (Girl)

Modeller:	Freda Doughty
Height:	7", 17.8 cm
Colour:	1. Blue dress; yellow wool; black and white kitten
	2. White dress trimmed with dark blue; red wool; black and white kitten; lavender base
Issued:	1938-1984
Reissued:	1996-2002
Series:	The Days of the Week

B/S:	Blue	Black	Black, circle	Black, diamond
U.S.	$450.00	325.00	275.00	225.00
Can.	$550.00	400.00	325.00	275.00
U.K.	£250.00	175.00	150.00	125.00

Note: See also miniature version RW4154 Katie.

See page 92 for this model without a base

RW3263
LEOPARDS, NELSON AND NORAH
(With base)

Modeller:	Doris Lindner
Height:	3 ½", 8.9 cm
Colour:	Light tan with spot; light green base
Issued:	1938-by 1953
Varieties:	Leopards, Nelson and Norah (Without base) RW3313
Series:	Zoo Babies

U.S.	$1,300.00
Can.	$1,550.00
U.K.	£ 700.00

See page 92 for this model without a base

RW3264
LIONS, OLIVER AND OCTOBER
(With base)

Modeller:	Doris Lindner
Height:	3 ½", 8.9 cm
Colour:	Light brown; light green base
Issued:	1938-by 1953
Varieties:	Lions, Oliver and October (Without base) RW3314
Series:	Zoo Babies

U.S.	$1,300.00
Can.	$1,550.00
U.K.	£ 700.00

RW3265
BEARS, MICK AND MACK
(With base)
Modeller: Doris Lindner
Height: 4 ¼", 10.8 cm
Colour: Brown; light green base
Issued: 1938-by 1953
Varieties: Bears, Mick and Mack
                 (Without base) RW3315
Series: Zoo Babies

U.S. $1,750.00
Can. $2,100.00
U.K.   £ 950.00

RW3266
FAWNS, YOUNG SPOTTED DEER (Rectangular base)
Modeller: Doris Lindner
Height: 4 ¾", 12.1 cm
Colour: Brown and white markings
Issued: 1938
Variations: Fawns, Young Spotted Deer (Oval base) RW3316
                 Fawns, Young Spotted Deer (Without base) RW3529
Series: Zoo Babies

U.S. $ 825.00
Can. $1,000.00
U.K.   £ 450.00

RW3268
BALTIMORE ORIOLE AND TULIP TREE (Cock)
(Icterus Galbula)
Modeller: Dorothy Doughty
Height: 9 ½", 24.0 cm
Colour: 1. Dark brown, red and yellow bird; yellow flowers;
                     green leaves
                 2. White
Plinth: Wooden
Issued: 1. Coloured: 1938 in a limited edition of 250
                 2. White: 1938 in a limited edition of 250
Series: Doughty American Birds
Comm. by: Alex Dickens, U.S.A.

	Coloured	White
U.S.	$1,200.00	225.00
Can.	$1,450.00	325.00
U.K.	£ 650.00	150.00

RW3269
BALTIMORE ORIOLE AND TULIP TREE (Hen)
(Icterus Galbula)

Modeller:	Dorothy Doughty
Height:	9 ½", 24.0 cm
Colour:	1. Browns, red and yellow bird; yellow flowers; green leaves
	2. White
Plinth:	Wooden
Issued:	1. Coloured: 1938 in a limited edition of 250
	2. White: 1938 in a limited edition of 250
Series:	Doughty American Birds
Comm. by:	Alex Dickens, U.S.A.

	Coloured	White
U.S.	$1,200.00	275.00
Can.	$1,450.00	325.00
U.K.	£ 650.00	150.00

RW3270
PLAYMATES

Modeller:	Freda Doughty
Height:	6 ¾", 17.2 cm
Colour:	1. Pink dress with white highlights; white and brown dog; green and brown base
	2. Pale blue dress with lavender highlights; white and brown dog; green and brown base
Issued:	1938-1959

B/S:	Puce	Black
U.S.	$ 925.00	825.00
Can.	$1,100.00	1,000.00
U.K.	£ 500.00	450.00

RW3271
"LONDON GAZETTE HERE"

Modeller:	Gwendolen Parnell
Height:	6 ¼", 15.9 cm
Colour:	Primrose and orange dress; clover cloak, hat and shoes
Issued:	1938
Series:	The Cries of London

B/S:	Puce	Black
U.S.	$ 925.00	875.00
Can.	$1,100.00	1,050.00
U.K.	£ 500.00	475.00

RW3272
REPOSE

Modeller:	Dorothea Charol
Height:	7", 17.8 cm
Colour:	1. Green dress; blonde hair
	2. Purple dress; blonde hair
	3. Turquoise dress; pink bodice; brown hair
Issued:	1938-by 1948

U.S.	
Can.	Extremely Rare
U.K.	

RW3273
KOALA BEARS, BILLY BLUEGUMS
(With base)

Modeller:	Doris Lindner
Height:	4 ¾", 12.1 cm
Colour:	Pale blue and white; green or beige base
Issued:	1938-by 1953
Varieties:	Koala Bears, Billy Bluegums (Without base) RW3317
Series:	Zoo Babies

U.S.	$ 950.00
Can.	$1,150.00
U.K.	£ 525.00

RW3274
TIGERS, MAURICE AND SONIA
(With base)

Modeller:	Doris Lindner
Height:	3 ½", 8.9 cm
Colour:	Golden brown with darker brown markings
Issued:	1938-by 1953
Varieties:	Tigers, Maurice and Sonia (Without base) RW3318
Series:	Zoo Babies

U.S.	$ 950.00
Can.	$1,150.00
U.K.	£ 525.00

RW3288
GIRL WITH BEADS
Modeller: Dorothea Charol
Height: 4", 10.1 cm
Colour: Golden fawn skin; shot
 tan hair and features;
 green necklace
Issued: 1939-by 1948
Varieties: Also called "The
 Necklace"
U.S.
Can. Extremely rare
U.K.

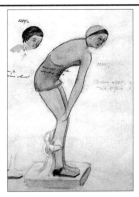

RW3289
BATHING GIRL
Modeller: Dorothea Charol
Height: 8 ¼", 21.0 cm
Colour: 1. Blue bathing suit; blue headband and sandals; blonde hair
 2. White bathing suit; red headband and sandals; brown hair
Issued: 1939-by 1948
Varieties: Also called "Hesitation"
U.S.
Can. Extremely rare
U.K.

RW3293
DALMATIAN
Modeller: Doris Lindner
Height: 3 ¼", 8.3 cm
Colour: 1. White with black
 spots
 2. White
Issued: 1939-c.1950s
Series: Small Dogs

	White/ Black	White
U.S.	$275.00	125.00
Can.	$325.00	145.00
U.K.	£150.00	65.00

RW3294
DACHSHUND
Modeller: Doris Lindner
Height: 2 ½", 6.4 cm
Colour: 1. Dark brown with
 golden brown
 underbody
 2. Golden brown
 3. White
Issued: 1939-c.1950s
Series: Small Dogs

	Coloured	White
U.S.	$275.00	125.00
Can.	$325.00	145.00
U.K.	£150.00	65.00

RW3295
ALSATIAN
Style One
Modeller: Doris Lindner
Height: 3 ½", 8.9 cm cm
Colour: Light brown with black
 shading
Issued: 1939-c.1950s
Series: Small Dogs
U.S. $275.00
Can. $325.00
U.K. £150.00

RW3296
HACKING IN THE PARK
Modeller: Doris Lindner
Height: 6 ¾", 17.2 cm
Colour: Rider: Light brown
 jacket; white jodhpurs;
 black boots
 Horse: Brown; tan
 saddle
Plinth: Wooden
Issued: 1939-by 1970

B/S:	Puce	Black
U.S.	$1,850.00	1,100.00
Can.	$2,250.00	1,325.00
U.K.	£1,000.00	600.00

RW3299
"FINE WRITEING INKES"
Modeller: Gwendolen Parnell
Height: 6", 15.0 cm
Colour: Mauve skirt;
 ultramarine apron;
 blue cloak; green
 shoes; white hat
Issued: 1940-by 1959
Series: The Cries of London

B/S:	Puce	Black
U.S.	$ 925.00	925.00
Can.	$1,100.00	1,100.00
U.K.	£ 500.00	500.00

RW3300
"FAIR CHERRYES"

Modeller:	Gwendolen Parnell
Height:	6 ½", 16.5 cm
Colour:	Yellow dress; pink pinafore; light green hat; blue shoes; red cherries; light grey base
Issued:	1940-by 1959
Series:	The Cries of London

B/S:	Puce	Black
U.S.	$ 925.00	875.00
Can.	$1,100.00	1,050.00
U.K.	£ 500.00	475.00

RW3301
LITTLE MISS MUFFET

Modeller:	Freda Doughty
Height:	4 ½", 11.9 cm
Colour:	1. Blue outer dress; yellow sleeves; cream underdress with red pattern; blue bowl; green tuffet; brown and black spider
	2. Rose outer dress; yellow sleeves; white underdress with pink and green pattern; blue bowl; green tuffet; brown and black spider
Issued:	1940-1959
Series:	Nursery Rhymes

B/S:	Puce	Black
U.S.	$650.00	550.00
Can.	$775.00	675.00
U.K.	£350.00	300.00

RW3302
BABES IN THE WOOD

Modeller:	Freda Doughty
Height:	6 ¼", 15.9 cm
Colour:	1. Older girl: Pink pinafore; lilac blouse and shoes
	Younger girl: Turquoise dress; lilac cap trimmed with white
	2. Older girl: Yellow pinafore; white blouse and shoes
	Younger girl: White dress with red pattern; pink cap trimmed with white
Issued:	1940-1959
Series:	Nursery Rhymes

B/S:	Puce	Black
U.S.	$ 825.00	750.00
Can.	$1,000.00	900.00
U.K.	£ 450.00	400.00

RW3303
POLLY PUT THE KETTLE ON

Modeller:	Freda Doughty
Height:	6", 15.0 cm
Colour:	1. White dress/cap; pink apron; gold kettle
	2. White dress/cap; pink apron; silver kettle
	3. Pink dress; green apron; gold kettle
	4. Pink dress; green apron; silver kettle
Issued:	1940-1983
Series:	Nursery Rhymes

B/S:	Puce	Black
U.S.	$425.00	375.00
Can.	$500.00	450.00
U.K.	£225.00	200.00

Note: Earlier versions of this model had either black or white kettles. See also miniature version RW4205 Mother's Helper.

RW3304
GOOSEY GOOSEY GANDER
Modeller: Freda Doughty
Height: 6", 15.0 cm
Colour: Yellow smock with
              white collar; green
              shorts; white and grey
              goose; orange beak,
              feet; green and beige
              base
Issued: 1940-1959
Series: Nursery Rhymes

B/S:	Puce	Black
U.S.	$750.00	650.00
Can.	$900.00	775.00
U.K.	£400.00	350.00

RW3305
LITTLE JACK HORNER
Modeller: Freda Doughty
Height: 4 ½", 11.9 cm
Colour: 1. Green and beige tunic; white blouse; yellow breeches;
                  green stockings; beige shoes; blonde hair
              2. Turquoise and yellow tunic; white blouse; yellow breeches;
                  turquoise stockings; orange shoes; blonde hair
Issued: 1940-1959
Series: Nursery Rhymes

B/S:	Puce	Black
U.S.	$750.00	650.00
Can.	$900.00	775.00
U.K.	£400.00	350.00

RW3306
LITTLE BOY BLUE
Modeller: Freda Doughty
Height: 3 ½", 8.9 cm
Colour: Blue suit with white
              collar, blue hat and
              shoes; yellow horn;
              white sheep with
              lavender and beige
              highlights; beige base
Issued: 1940-1959
Series: Nursery Rhymes

B/S:	Puce	Black
U.S.	$750.00	650.00
Can.	$900.00	775.00
U.K.	£400.00	350.00

RW3307
RED SETTER
(Without base)
Modeller: Doris Lindner
Size: 7" x 4 ¼",
              17.8 x 10.8 cm
Colour: Reddish-brown
Issued: 1940-c.1955
Varieties: Irish Setter / Red Setter
              (With base) RW3228
Series: Sporting Dogs

U.S. $450.00
Can. $550.00
U.K.   £250.00

RW3308
ENGLISH POINTER
(Without base)
Modeller: Doris Lindner
Height: 8" x 4", 20.3 x 10.1 cm
Colour: White with brown
              patches
Issued: 1940-c.1955
Varieties: English Pointer
              (With base) RW3229
Series: Sporting Dogs

U.S. $450.00
Can. $550.00
U.K.   £250.00

RW3309
GOLDEN RETRIEVER
(Without base)
Modeller: Doris Lindner
Size: 7 ½" x 3 ½",
              19.1 x 8.9 cm
Colour: Golden brown
Issued: 1940-c.1955
Varieties: Golden Retriever
              (With base) RW3230
Series: Sporting Dogs

U.S. $450.00
Can. $550.00
U.K.   £250.00

RW3310
COCKER SPANIEL
Style Three (Without base)
Modeller: Doris Lindner
Size: 5 ½" x 3 ¾",
              14.0 x 9.5 cm
Colour: White with black
              patches; brown rabbit
Issued: 1940-c.1955
Varieties: Cocker Spaniel
              (With base) RW3231
Series: Sporting Dogs

U.S. $450.00
Can. $550.00
U.K.   £250.00

RW3311
CLUMBER SPANIEL
(Without base)
Modeller:	Doris Lindner
Height:	6" x 4", 15.0 x 10.1 cm
Colour:	White with brown patches
Issued:	1940-c.1955
Varieties:	Clumber Spaniel(With base) / English Springer Spaniel (with Base) RW3232
Series:	Sporting Dogs
U.S.	$425.00
Can.	$500.00
U.K.	£225.00

RW3312
LABRADOR RETRIEVER
(Without base)
Modeller:	Doris Lindner
Height:	3 ¾", 9.5 cm
Colour:	Black
Issued:	1940-c.1955
Varieties:	Labrador Retriever (With base) RW3233
Series:	Sporting Dogs
U.S.	$425.00
Can.	$500.00
U.K.	£225.00

RW3313
LEOPARDS, NELSON AND NORAH
(Without base)
Modeller:	Doris Lindner
Height:	3 ½", 8.9 cm
Colour:	Golden brown, brown spots
Issued:	1940
Varieties:	Leopards, Nelson and Norah (With base) RW3263
Series:	Zoo Babies
U.S.	$1,000.00
Can.	$1,200.00
U.K.	£ 550.00

RW3314
LIONS, OLIVIA AND OCTOBER
(Without base)
Modeller:	Doris Lindner
Height:	3 ¼", 8.3 cm
Colour:	Golden brown
Issued:	1940
Varieties:	Lions, Oliver and October (With base) RW3264
Series:	Zoo Babies
U.S.	$1,000.00
Can.	$1,200.00
U.K.	£ 550.00

RW3315
BEARS, MICK AND MACK
(Without base)
Modeller:	Doris Lindner
Height:	3 ½", 8.9 cm
Colour:	Dark brown
Issued:	1940
Varieties:	Bears, Mick and Mack (With base) RW3265
Series:	Zoo Babies
U.S.	$1,800.00
Can.	$2,150.00
U.K.	£ 975.00

RW3316
FAWNS, YOUNG SPOTTED DEER (Oval base)
Modeller:	Doris Lindner
Height:	4 ¾", 12.1 cm
Colour:	Brown with white markings; light green oval base
Issued:	1940
Varieties:	Fawns, Young Spotted Deer (Rectangular base) RW3266 Fawns, Young Spotted Deer (Without base) RW3529
Series:	Zoo Babies

B/S:	Green	Puce
U.S.	$ 825.00	825.00
Can.	$1,000.00	1,000.00
U.K.	£ 450.00	450.00

RW3317
KOALA BEARS, BILLY BLUEGUMS
(Without base)
Modeller:	Doris Lindner
Height:	3 ½", 8.9 cm
Colour:	Pale blue and white
Issued:	1940
Varieties:	Koala Bears, Billy Bluegums (With base) RW3273
Series:	Zoo Babies
U.S.	$1,000.00
Can.	$1,200.00
U.K.	£ 550.00

RW3318
TIGERS, MAURICE AND SONIA
(Without base)
Modeller:	Doris Lindner
Height:	3 ½", 8.9 cm
Colour:	Golden brown with darker brown markings
Issued:	1940
Varieties:	Tigers, Maurice and Sonia (With base) RW3274
Series:	Zoo Babies

U.S.	$1,000.00
Can.	$1,200.00
U.K.	£ 550.00

RW3319
SCOTTISH TERRIER, DOG'S HEAD
(Wall Mount)
Modeller:	Doris Lindner
Height:	6", 15.0 cm
Colour:	Black
Issued:	1940
Series:	Wall Mounts

U.S.	$500.00
Can.	$600.00
U.K.	£275.00

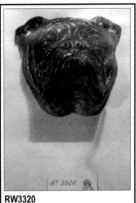

RW3320
BULLDOG, DOG'S HEAD
(Wall mount)
Modeller:	Doris Lindner
Height:	6", 15.0 cm
Colour:	Brown
Issued:	1940
Series:	Wall Mounts

U.S.	$500.00
Can.	$600.00
U.K.	£275.00

RW3321
SPANIEL, DOG'S HEAD
(Wall Mount)
Modeller:	Doris Lindner
Height:	6", 15.0 cm
Colour:	Brown and white
Issued:	1940
Series:	Wall Mounts

U.S.	$500.00
Can.	$600.00
U.K.	£275.00

RW3322
PEKINESE, DOG'S HEAD
(Wall mount)
Modeller:	Doris Lindner
Height:	6", 15.0 cm
Colour:	Brown
Issued:	1940
Series:	Wall mounts

U.S.	$500.00
Can.	$600.00
U.K.	£275.00

RW3323
BOB-WHITE QUAIL (Cock)
(Colinus Virginianus)
Style One
Modeller:	Dorothy Doughty
Height:	6", 15.0 cm
Colour:	Reddish-brown, grey and mauve
Issued:	1940 in a limited edition of 22
Series:	Doughty American Birds
Comm. by:	Alex Dickens, U.S.A.

U.S.	$1,500.00
Can.	$1,800.00
U.K.	£ 850.00

RW3324
BOB-WHITE QUAIL (Hen)
(Colinus Virginianus)
Style One
Modeller:	Dorothy Doughty
Height:	6", 15.0 cm
Colour:	Reddish-brown, grey and mauve hen with two chicks
Issued:	1940 in a limited edition of 22
Series:	Doughty American Birds
Comm. by:	Alex Dickens, U.S.A.

U.S.	$1,500.00
Can.	$1,800.00
U.K.	£ 850.00

RW3326
MOCKINGBIRD AND PEACH BLOSSOM (Cock)
(Mimus Polyglottos)
Modeller:	Dorothy Doughty
Height:	10 ½", 26.7 cm
Colour:	Blue-grey, yellow, brown and white bird; pink blossom; green-brown leaves
Plinth:	Wooden
Issued:	1940 in a limited edition of 500
Series:	Doughty American Birds
Comm. by:	Alex Dickens, U.S.A.
U.S.	$1,100.00
Can.	$1,300.00
U.K.	£ 600.00

RW3327
MOCKINGBIRD AND PEACH BLOSSOM (Hen)
(Mimus Polyglottos)
Modeller:	Dorothy Doughty
Height:	10 ½", 26.7 cm
Colour:	Blue-grey, yellow, brown and white bird; pink blossom; green-brown leaves
Plinth:	Wooden
Issued:	1940 in a limited edition of 500
Series:	Doughty American Birds
Comm. by:	Alex Dickens, U.S.A.
U.S.	$1,100.00
Can.	$1,300.00
U.K.	£ 600.00

RW3328
CRAB APPLE SPRAYS AND ONE BUTTERFLY
Modeller:	Dorothy Doughty
Height:	10", 25.4 cm
Colour:	Pink and white blossom; green leaves; brown branch; one blue butterfly
Plinth:	Wooden
Issued:	1940 in a limited edition of 250
U.S.	$700.00
Can.	$850.00
U.K.	£375.00

RW3329
CRAB APPLE SPRAYS AND TWO BUTTERFLIES
Modeller:	Dorothy Doughty
Height:	10", 25.4 cm
Colour:	Pink and white blossom; green leaves; brown branch; two blue butterflies
Plinth:	Wooden
Issued:	1940 in a limited edition of 250
U.S.	$700.00
Can.	$850.00
U.K.	£375.00

RW3330
BOGSKAR
Modeller:	Doris Lindner
Height:	9", 22.9 cm
Colour:	1. Rider: Blue and gold silks; white jodhpurs Horse: Brown
	2. White
Issued:	1940-by 1942
U.S.	
Can.	Extremely rare
U.K.	

Note: "Bogskar," owned by Lord Stalbridge, was the Grand National winner in 1940. Made exclusively for the U.S.A. market.

RW3331
CAIRN TERRIER "TOTO"
Modeller:	Aline Ellis
Height:	3 ½", 8.9 cm
Colour:	Black; red tongue; yellow brick road base
Issued:	1940
Comm. by:	Alex Dickens, U.S.A.
U.S.	$700.00
Can.	$850.00
U.K.	£375.00

Note: Made exclusively for the U.S.A. market.

RW3333
HEDGE SPARROW
Modeller:	Eva Soper	
Height:	2 ½", 6.4 cm	
Colour:	Red with brown markings; gloss or matt	
Issued:	1941-1986	
Series:	British Birds, Series One	

	Gloss	**Matt**
U.S.	$100.00	90.00
Can.	$125.00	100.00
U.K.	£ 60.00	50.00

RW3334
NUTHATCH
Modeller:	Eva Soper	
Height:	2 ½", 6.4 cm	
Colour:	Red, black and yellow; gloss or matt	
Issued:	1941-1986	
Series:	British Birds, Series One	

	Gloss	**Matt**
U.S.	$100.00	90.00
Can.	$125.00	100.00
U.K.	£ 60.00	50.00

RW3335
GREAT TIT
Modeller:	Eva Soper	
Height:	2 ½", 6.4 cm	
Colour:	Grey, yellow and green; gloss or matt	
Issued:	1941-1986	
Series:	British Birds, Series One	

	Gloss	**Matt**
U.S.	$100.00	90.00
Can.	$125.00	100.00
U.K.	£ 60.00	50.00

RW3336
MARSH TIT
Style One
Modeller:	Eva Soper	
Height:	2 ¼", 5.7 cm	
Colour:	Black and yellow; gloss or matt	
Issued:	1941-1986	
Series:	British Birds, Series One	

	Gloss	**Matt**
U.S.	$100.00	90.00
Can.	$125.00	100.00
U.K.	£ 60.00	50.00

RW3337
NIGHTINGALE
Modeller:	Eva Soper	
Height:	3 ½", 8.9 cm	
Colour:	Orangey-brown and cream; green leaf base; gloss or matt	
Issued:	1941-1986	
Series:	British Birds, Series One	

	Gloss	**Matt**
U.S.	$100.00	90.00
Can.	$125.00	100.00
U.K.	£ 60.00	50.00

RW3338
GOLDCREST
Modeller:	Eva Soper	
Height:	2 ¼", 5.7 cm	
Colour:	Browns and greys; gloss or matt	
Issued:	1941-1986	
Series:	British Birds, Series One	

	Gloss	**Matt**
U.S.	$100.00	90.00
Can.	$125.00	100.00
U.K.	£ 60.00	50.00

RW3339
SUMMER
Style One
Modeller:	Gwendolen Parnell	
Height:	4 ¾", 12.1 cm	
Colour:	1. Pink dress; green underskirt with white dots; white apron with flower print; light green base surrounded with flowers	
	2. Yellow dress; white underskirt with pink pattern; yellow apron; white base surrounded by flowers	
Issued:	1941-by c.1960	
Series:	The Four Seasons, Series One	

B/S:	**Puce**	**Black**
U.S.	$650.00	500.00
Can.	$775.00	600.00
U.K.	£350.00	275.00

RW3340
WINTER
Style One
Modeller: Gwendolen Parnell
Height: 4 ¾", 12.1 cm
Colour: 1. Red hooded cloak and shoes; pink skirt with red flowers;
                white apron; green bag
            2. White cloak and apron trimmed in blue; pink skirt; brown
                bag
Issued: 1941-by c.1960
Series: The Four Seasons, Series One

B/S:	Puce	Black
U.S.	$600.00	450.00
Can.	$725.00	550.00
U.K.	£325.00	250.00

RW3341
AUTUMN
Style One
Modeller: Gwendolen Parnell
Height: 4 ¾", 12.1 cm
Colour: 1. White skirt with red design; mauve apron; red shoes;
                green foliage; orange apples
            2. Yellow and white dotted dress; blue shoes; green foliage;
                orange apples
Issued: 1941-by c.1960
Series: The Four Seasons, Series One

B/S:	Puce	Black
U.S.	$775.00	650.00
Can.	$925.00	775.00
U.K.	£425.00	350.00

RW3342
SPRING
Style Two
Modeller: Gwendolen Parnell
Height: 4 ¾", 12.1 cm
Colour: 1. Blue dress; yellow overskirt; white sleeves and apron;
                straw hat with lilac ribbon; green surround with pink
                flowers
            2. Pink dress with white and red patterned top; white apron;
                red shoes; yellow hat
Issued: 1941-by c.1960
Series: The Four Seasons, Series One

B/S:	Puce	Black
U.S.	$650.00	500.00
Can.	$775.00	600.00
U.K.	£350.00	275.00

RW3346
THE RESCUE
Modeller: Eileen Soper
Height: 4 ½", 10.8 cm
Colour: 1. Pink dress; blue coat; blonde hair; brown shoes;
                black kitten
            2. White
Issued: 1941-by 1943
Series: Wartime

	Coloured	White
U.S.	$2,000.00	650.00
Can.	$2,400.00	775.00
U.K.	£1,750.00	350.00

RW3347
EVACUEES
Modeller: Eileen Soper
Height: 4 ½", 11.9 cm
Colour: 1. Jenny: Blue coat; pink kerchief; grey shoes
Tommy: Orange jersey; blue scarf; grey shorts; light brown shoes
2. White
Issued: 1941
Series: Wartime

	Coloured	White
U.S.	$3,400.00	700.00
Can.	$4,000.00	850.00
U.K.	£1,850.00	375.00

RW3348
CHINOISERIE GIRL (Head down)
Modeller: Gwendolen Parnell
Height: 6 ¼", 15.9 cm
Colour: Black, turquoise and white robes with Chinese red details; grey squirrel
Issued: 1941
Series: Chinoiserie Children

U.S.	$450.00
Can.	$550.00
U.K.	£250.00

Photograph not
available
at press time

RW3349
BOY AND DOLPHIN
Modeller: Frederick M. Gertner
Height: Unknown
Colour: Unknown
Issued: 1941

U.S.	
Can.	Extremely rare
U.K.	

RW3350
CAIRN TERRIER "RATS"
Modeller: Aline Ellis
Height: 3 ¼", 8.3 cm
Colour: Light beige terrier; green base "Rats"
Issued: 1941
Comm. by: Alex Dickens U.S.A.

U.S.	$650.00
Can.	$775.00
U.K.	£350.00

Note: Made exclusively for the U.S.A. market.

RW3351
TAKE COVER
Modeller: Eileen Soper
Height: 4 ½", 11.9 cm
Colour: 1. Boy: Blue shirt; grey shorts; brown shoes and hair; brown and white puppy
Girl: Yellow dress; white and yellow dotted sleeves and collar; blonde hair
2. White
Issued: 1941
Series: Wartime

	Coloured	White
U.S.	$3,400.00	650.00
Can.	$4,000.00	775.00
U.K.	£1,850.00	350.00

RW3352
SPITFIRE
Modeller: Eileen Soper
Height: 6 ½", 16.5 cm
Colour: 1. Older boy: Blue vest and cap; paler blue checkered shirt; light brown trousers; brown shoes
Younger boy: Red jersey; pale grey trousers; light brown shoes
2. White
Issued: 1941
Series: Wartime

	Coloured	White
U.S.	$3,250.00	650.00
Can.	$3,900.00	775.00
U.K.	£1,750.00	350.00

RW3353
SEAWEED
Modeller: Frederick M. Gertner
Height: 7", 17.8 cm
Colour: Unknown
Issued: 1941-by 1953
U.S.
Can. Extremely rare
U.K.

RW3354
CHINOISERIE BOY
Modeller: Gwendolen Parnell
Height: 5", 12.7 cm
Colour: Black trousers and hair; turquoise jacket; grey shirt
Issued: 1941
Series: Chinoiserie Children
U.S. $325.00
Can. $400.00
U.K. £175.00

RW3355
WEST HIGHLAND TERRIER "MACK"
Modeller: Aline Ellis
Height: 3", 7.6 cm
Colour: Creamy brown terrier; green base
Issued: 1941
Comm. by: Alex Dickens U.S.A.
U.S. $500.00
Can. $600.00
U.K. £275.00

Note: Made exclusively for the U.S.A. market.

RW3356
HOUND "RANTER"
Modeller: Aline Ellis
Height: 4", 10.1 cm
Colour: White with red-brown, brown and black patches; green-brown base "Ranter"
Issued: 1941
Comm. by: Alex Dickens U.S.A.
U.S. $500.00
Can. $600.00
U.K. £275.00

Note: Made exclusively for the U.S.A. market.

RW3357
APPLE BLOSSOM SPRAY AND ONE BEE
Modeller: Dorothy Doughty
Height: 6 ½", 16.5 cm
Colour: Pink and white flowers; green leaves; one bee
Plinth: Wooden
Issued: 1941 in a limited edition of 250
U.S. $650.00
Can. $775.00
U.K. £350.00

Note: Missing plinth.

RW3358
APPLE BLOSSOM SPRAY AND TWO BEES
Modeller: Dorothy Doughty
Height: 4", 10.4 cm
Colour: Pink and white flowers; green leaves; two bees
Plinth: Wooden
Issued: 1941 in a limited edition of 250
U.S. $650.00
Can. $775.00
U.K. £350.00

Note: Missing plinth.

RW3359
BOW (The)
Modeller: Freda Doughty
Height: 7 ½", 19.1 cm
Colour: 1.   Creamy-white suite with white and grey collar and cuffs;
                    burgundy sash; brown hair; green and cream base
              2.   Turquoise suit with white collar and cuffs; burgundy sash;
                    yellow hair; brown shoes; cream base
Issued: 1941-1974
Varieties: Also called "Masquerade Boy"

U.S. $325.00
Can. $400.00
U.K.   £175.00

RW3360
CURTSEY (The)
Style One
Modeller: Freda Doughty
Height: 6 ¼", 15.9 cm
Colour: 1.   Cream dress edged with blue dots; cream bows;
                    silver shoe; yellow hair
              2.   Pink dress with green bows; green shoe; brown hair
              3.   Turquoise dress; brown hair and shoe
Issued: 1941-1974
Varieties: Also called "Masquerade," Style One

U.S. $500.00
Can. $600.00
U.K.   £275.00

RW3361
SPANIEL PUPPY "TONY"
Modeller: Aline Ellis
Height: 3", 7.6 cm
Colour: Brown and white;
              green base "Tony"
Issued: 1941
Comm. by: Alex Dickens U.S.A.

U.S. $500.00
Can. $600.00
U.K.   £275.00

Note: Made exclusively for the
U.S.A. market.

RW3362
CHINOISERIE GIRL (Head up)
Modeller: Gwendolen Parnell
Height: 5", 12.7cm
Colour: Black, turquoise and
              white robe; Chinese
              red slippers
Issued: 1941-by 1952
Series: Chinoiserie Children

U.S. $325.00
Can. $400.00
U.K.   £175.00

RW3363
PIED WOODPECKERS (On stump)
Modeller: Eva Soper
Height: 4 ¾", 12.1 cm
Colour: Grey, white and black
Issued: 1942-1986
Series: Double Birds on Tree
              Stumps

U.S. $275.00
Can. $325.00
U.K.   £150.00

RW3364
CHAFFINCHES (On stump)
Modeller: Eva Soper
Height: 5", 12.7 cm
Colour: Browns, blue and white
Issued: 1942-1986
Series: Double Birds on Tree
              Stumps

U.S. $275.00
Can. $325.00
U.K.   £150.00

RW3365
LINNETS (On stump)

Modeller:	Eva Soper
Height:	4 ¾", 12.1 cm
Colour:	Reddish-brown, grey and yellow
Issued:	1942-1986
Series:	Double Birds on Tree Stumps
U.S.	$275.00
Can.	$325.00
U.K.	£150.00

RW3366
WELSH CORGI "TAFFY"

Modeller:	Aline Ellis
Height:	3", 7.6 cm
Colour:	Reddish-brown and white; green base "Taffy"
Issued:	1941
Comm. by:	Alex Dickens U.S.A.
U.S.	$600.00
Can.	$725.00
U.K.	£325.00

Note: Made exclusively for the U.S.A. market.

RW3367
INDIGO BUNTING AND BLACKBERRY (Cock)
(Passerina Cyanea)

Modeller:	Dorothy Doughty
Height:	8 ½", 21.6 cm
Colour:	Blue bird; red berries; white flowers; green leaves; brown branch
Plinth:	Wooden
Issued:	1941 in a limited edition of 500
Series:	Doughty American Birds
Comm. by:	Alex Dickens U.S.A.
U.S.	$1,000.00
Can.	$1,200.00
U.K.	£ 550.00

Note: Missing plinth.

RW3368
INDIGO BUNTING AND BLACKBERRY (Hen)
(Passerina Cyanea)

Modeller:	Dorothy Doughty
Height:	8 ½", 21.6 cm
Colour:	Brown bird with red breast; dark blue blackberries; green leaves; brown branch
Plinth:	Wooden
Issued:	1941 in a limited edition of 500
Series:	Doughty American Birds
Comm. by:	Alex Dickens U.S.A.
U.S.	$1,000.00
Can.	$1,200.00
U.K.	£ 550.00

Note: Missing plinth.

RW3369
STOWAWAY

Modeller:	Eileen Soper
Height:	4 ½", 11.9 cm
Colour:	1. Blue dress; white pinafore edged with blue; red beret and scarf
	2. Mauve dress; cream pinafore edged with green; pink beret and scarf
	3. White
Issued:	1941-by 1942
Series:	Wartime

	Coloured	White
U.S.	$3,250.00	650.00
Can.	$3,900.00	775.00
U.K.	£1,750.00	350.00

RW3370
SALVAGE
Modeller: Eileen Soper
Height: 5 ½", 14.0 cm
Colour:
1. White shirt; blue dungarees; red, brown and green toys; brown and white dog; white sign
2. White
Issued: 1941-by 1942
Series: Wartime

	Coloured	White
U.S.	$3,750.00	650.00
Can.	$4,500.00	775.00
U.K.	£2,000.00	350.00

RW3373
NUDE BOY WITH CORNUCOPIA
Modeller: Frederick M. Gertner
Height: 7 ¾", 19.7 cm
Colour: Unknown
Issued: 1942-by 1953

U.S.
Can. Extremely rare
U.K.

RW3374
NUDE GIRL WITH CORNUCOPIA
Modeller: Frederick M. Gertner
Height: 7 ¾", 19.7 cm
Colour: Unknown
Issued: 1942-by 1953

U.S.
Can. Extremely rare
U.K.

RW3375
BLUE TITS (On stump)
Modeller: Eva Soper
Height: 4 ¾", 12.1 cm
Colour: Blue and yellow
Issued: 1942-1986
Series: Double Birds on Tree Stumps

U.S. $275.00
Can. $325.00
U.K. £150.00

RW3376
COLE TITS (On stump)
Modeller: Eva Soper
Height: 4 ¾", 12.1 cm
Colour: Light browns, yellow and black
Issued: 1942-1986
Series: Double Birds on Tree Stumps

U.S. $275.00
Can. $325.00
U.K. £150.00

RW3377
YELLOWHAMMERS (On stump)
Modeller: Eva Soper
Height: 4 ¾", 12.1 cm
Colour: Yellow and light browns
Issued: 1942-1986
Series: Double Birds on Tree Stumps

U.S. $275.00
Can. $325.00
U.K. £150.00

RW3378
ORANGE BLOSSOM SPRAY AND BUTTERFLY
Modeller: Dorothy Doughty
Height: 7 ¼", 18.4 cm
Colour: White flowers with yellow centres; green leaves; brown and gold butterfly
Plinth: Wooden
Issued: 1947 in a limited edition of 175

U.S. $750.00
Can. $900.00
U.K. £400.00

RW3379
ORANGE BLOSSOM SPRAY
Modeller: Dorothy Doughty
Height: 7 ¼", 18.4 cm
Colour: White flowers with yellow centres; green leaves
Plinth: Wooden
Issued: 1947 in a limited edition of 175

U.S.	$750.00
Can.	$900.00
U.K.	£400.00

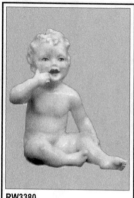

RW3380
CHILD (Seated)
Modeller: Freda Doughty
Height: 4 ¼", 10.8 cm
Colour: Fleshtones; yellow hair
Issued: 1942-1955

U.S.	$1,100.00
Can.	$1,300.00
U.K.	£ 600.00

RW3381
CHILD (Crawling)
Modeller: Freda Doughty
Height: 3 ½", 8.9 cm
Colour: Fleshtones; yellow hair
Issued: 1942-1955

U.S.	$1,100.00
Can.	$1,300.00
U.K.	£ 600.00

RW3382
THE LETTER
Modeller: Eileen Soper
Height: 4 ½", 11.9 cm
Colour: 1. Mother: Blue skirt; red top; white apron with red trim; brown hair
Child: White dress with blue dots; yellow hair
2. White
Issued: 1941-by 1953
Series: Wartime

	Coloured	White
U.S.	$4,500.00	650.00
Can.	$5,500.00	775.00
U.K.	£2,500.00	350.00

RW3385
FOXHOUND (Standing)
Style One
Modeller: Aline Ellis
Height: 7", 17.8 cm
Colour: White with red-brown patches; matt
Issued: 1942
Comm. by: Alex Dickens U.S.A.

U.S.	$700.00
Can.	$850.00
U.K.	£375.00

Note: Made exclusively for the U.S.A. market.

Photograph not available at press time

R3386
FOXHOUND (Standing)
Style Two
Modeller: Aline Ellis
Height: 7", 17.8 cm
Colour: White with red-brown patches; green base
Issued: 1942

U.S.	$700.00
Can.	$850.00
U.K.	£375.00

RW3387
FOX
Style One
Modeller: Aline Ellis
Height: 5", 12.7 cm
Colour: Red-brown; black paws, and markings; light green base
Issued: 1942-by 1948

U.S. $650.00
Can. $775.00
U.K. £350.00

Photograph not
available
at press time

RW3388
SOUTHWIND
Modeller: Agnes Pinder-Davis
Height: 7 ¼", 18.4 cm
Colour: Unknown
Issued: 1942

U.S.
Can. Extremely rare
U.K.

Photograph not
available
at press time

RW3396
WESTWIND
Modeller: Agnes Pinder-Davis
Height: 7", 17.8 cm
Colour: Unknown
Issued: 1944

U.S.
Can. Extremely rare
U.K.

RW3397
CHINOISERIE FIGURE (Male, kneeling) / THE GREETING
Modeller: Agnes Pinder-Davis
Height: 6", 15.0 cm
Colour: **Chinoiserie Figure (Male, kneeling)**
1. Black and green tunic; white base
2. Blue and pink tunic, yellow pants; white base
The Greeting
White; gold lined base
Issued: **Chinoiserie Figure (Male, kneeling):** 1944
The Greeting: 1982-1985
Series: **Chinoiserie Figure (Male, kneeling):**
Chinoiserie Figures
The Greeting: Art Deco

Name:	Chinoiserie	Greeting
U.S.	$550.00	200.00
Can.	$675.00	250.00
U.K.	£300.00	110.00

RW3398
CHINOISERIE FIGURE (Female, kneeling) / THE FAN
Modeller:	Agnes Pinder-Davis
Height:	5 ¼", 13.3 cm
Colour:	**Chinoiserie Figure (Female kneeling)**
	1. Black and green tunic; white base
	2. Blue and pink tunic; yellow pants; white base
	The Fan
	White; gold lined base
Issued:	**Chinoiserie Figure (Female, kneeling):** 1944
	The Fan: 1982-1985
Series:	**Chinoiserie Figure (Female, kneeling):**
	Chinoiserie Figures
	The Fan: Art Deco

Name:	Chinoiserie	The Fan
U.S.	$550.00	200.00
Can.	$675.00	250.00
U.K.	£300.00	100.00

RW3399
CHINOISERIE FIGURE
(Male, standing)
Modeller:	Agnes Pinder-Davis
Height:	8 ½", 21.6 cm
Colour:	1. Black, green and purple; white base
	2. Blue tunic; pink pants; white base
Issued:	1944-by 1958
Series:	Chinoiserie Figures

U.S.	$1,100.00
Can.	$1,300.00
U.K.	£ 600.00

RW3400
CHINOISERIE FIGURE
(Female, standing)
Modeller:	Agnes Pinder-Davis
Height:	7 ½", 19.1 cm
Colour:	1. Green tunic; black skirt; white base
	2. Pink tunic; yellow skirt; white base
Issued:	1944
Series:	Chinoiserie Figures

U.S.	$1,100.00
Can.	$1,300.00
U.K.	£ 600.00

RW3402
WATTEAU FIGURE
(Male, standing)
Modeller:	Agnes Pinder-Davis
Height:	8", 20.3 cm
Colour:	Sage green vest; grey sleeves; yellow collar; pink pants; white hat with blue band
Issued:	1946-1953
Series:	Watteau Figures

U.S.	$1,200.00
Can.	$1,450.00
U.K.	£ 650.00

RW3403
WATTEAU FIGURE
(Female, standing)
Modeller:	Agnes Pinder-Davis
Height:	7 ½", 19.1 cm
Colour:	Grey, pink and turquoise dress; brown basket of yellow flowers
Issued:	1946-1953
Series:	Watteau Figures

U.S.	$1,400.00
Can.	$1,675.00
U.K.	£ 750.00

RW3404
WATTEAU FIGURE (Male, seated)
Modeller:	Agnes Pinder-Davis
Height:	6", 15.0 cm
Colour:	Grey shirt; pink vest; turquoise pants; yellow collar and bow; tan hat; white and brown dog
Issued:	1946-1953
Series:	Watteau Figures

U.S.	$1,400.00
Can.	$1,675.00
U.K.	£ 750.00

RW3405
WATTEAU FIGURE
(Female, seated)
Modeller:	Agnes Pinder-Davis
Height:	6", 15.0 cm
Colour:	Grey, turquoise and pink dress; brown basket of apples
Issued:	1946-1953
Series:	Watteau Figures
U.S.	$1,000.00
Can.	$1,200.00
U.K.	£ 550.00

RW3414
REGENCY LADY
Modeller:	Agnes Pinder-Davis	
Height:	10", 25.4 cm	
Colour:	1.	Pink dress with blue and green; blue belt/edging; green shawl
	2.	White dress; light blue belt/ edging; light blue shawl
Issued:	1947-by 1953	
U.S.	$1,200.00	
Can.	$1,450.00	
U.K.	£ 650.00	

RW3415
REGENCY LADY WITH SHAWL IN HAND
Modeller:	Agnes Pinder-Davis	
Height:	10", 25.4 cm	
Colour:	1.	Turquoise dress with red flowers; green ribbons; yellow shawl
	2.	White dress; light blue ribbons and shawl; white and blue base
	3.	Pink flower springs and yellow shawl
Issued:	1947-by 1953	
U.S.	$1,200.00	
Can.	$1,450.00	
U.K.	£ 650.00	

RW3416
APRIL
Modeller:	Freda Doughty
Height:	6", 15.0 cm
Colour:	Yellow bodice, white skirt with yellow and lavender stripes; white lamb with brown markings; green base with yellow and white flowers
Issued:	1947-1985
Series:	Months of the Year
U.S.	$375.00
Can.	$450.00
U.K.	£200.00

Note: See also miniature version RW4168 Springtime.

RW3417
OCTOBER
Modeller:	Freda Doughty
Height:	8", 20.3 cm
Colour:	Yellow sweater with blue bands; blue shorts; brown hair; brown squirrels; green base
Issued:	1951-1985
Series:	Months of the Year
U.S.	$375.00
Can.	$450.00
U.K.	£200.00

Note: See also miniature version RW4157 Woodland Walk.

RW3418
NOVEMBER
Modeller:	Freda Doughty
Height:	7 ½", 19.1 cm
Colour:	Lavender coat with cream highlights; orange hat and leggings; four white doves
Issued:	c.1950-1985
Varieties:	Fantails RW3760
Series:	Months of the Year

U.S.	$375.00
Can.	$450.00
U.K.	£200.00

Note: See also miniature version RW4167 Peace.

RW3419
CHINESE FIGURE WITH SHORT TUNIC (Female)
Modeller:	Agnes Pinder-Davis
Height:	11", 27.9 cm
Colour:	1. Biscuit
	2. Bronze tunic with gilt leaves; claret lining, flower and scarf
	3. Green and black
	4. Green, yellow and pink
	5. Shaded grey robe; cream cuffs; apricot skirt; yellow scarf
Issued:	1947

B/S:	Gold	Black
U.S.	$785.00	700.00
Can.	$940.00	830.00
U.K.	£425.00	375.00

RW3420
CHINESE FIGURE WITH LONG TUNIC (Female)
Modeller:	Agnes Pinder-Davis
Height:	11", 27.9 cm
Colour:	1. Biscuit
	2. Bronze tunic with gilt leaves; claret lining, flower and scarf
	3. Green and black
	4. Green, yellow and pink
	5. Shaded grey robe; cream cuffs; apricot skirt; yellow scarf
Issued:	1947

B/S:	Gold	Black
U.S.	$785.00	700.00
Can.	$940.00	830.00
U.K.	£425.00	375.00

Photograph not
available
at press time

RW3421
WOOD PIGEON
Style One
Modeller:	Doris Lindner
Height:	7", 17.8 cm
Colour:	Naturalistically coloured
Issued:	1947

U.S.	$ 925.00
Can.	$1,100.00
U.K.	£ 500.00

Photograph not
available
at press time

RW3422
WOOD PIGEON
Style Two
Modeller:	Doris Lindner
Height:	7", 17.8 cm
Colour:	Naturalistically coloured
Issued:	1947

U.S.	$ 925.00
Can.	$1,100.00
U.K.	£ 500.00

RW3425
AFGHANISTAN HOUND

Modeller:	Doris Lindner	
Height:	8", 20.3 cm	
Colour:	1. Naturalistically coloured	
	2. White	
Issued:	1947-c.1958	
Series:	Large Dogs	

	Natural	**White**
U.S.	$1,100.00	550.00
Can.	$1,325.00	675.00
U.K.	£ 600.00	300.00

RW3426
BORZOI
Style One

Modeller:	Doris Lindner	
Height:	8", 20.3 cm	
Colour:	1. Naturalistically coloured	
	2. White	
Issued:	1947-c.1958	
Series:	Large Dogs	

	Natural	**White**
U.S.	$1,000.00	550.00
Can.	$1,200.00	675.00
U.K.	£ 550.00	300.00

RW3429
MAGNOLIA WABLER AND MAGNOLIA (Hen)
(Dendroica Magnolia)

Modeller:	Dorothy Doughty
Height:	14 ¾", 37.5 cm
Colour:	Green, yellow and brown bird; white flower; green leaves
Plinth:	Wooden
Issued:	1950 in a limited edition of 150
Series:	Doughty American Birds

U.S.	$1,475.00
Can.	$1,775.00
U.K.	£ 800.00

Note: Missing plinth.

RW3430
MAGNALIA WABLER AND MAGNOLIA (Cock)
(Dendroica Magnolia)

Modeller:	Dorothy Doughty
Height:	14 ¾", 37.5 cm
Colour:	Dark grey and yellow bird; white flower; green leaves
Plinth:	Wooden
Issued:	1950 in a limited edition of 150
Series:	Doughty American Birds

U.S.	$1,475.00
Can.	$1,775.00
U.K.	£ 800.00

Note: Missing plinth.

RW3431
MEXICAN FEIJOA AND LADYBIRD
Style One

Modeller:	Dorothy Doughty
Height:	10 ¾", 27.8 cm
Colour:	Rose-pink and pale pink flowers; green leaves; grey branch; red ladybird
Plinth:	Wooden
Issued:	1950 in a limited edition of 125

U.S.	$1,475.00
Can.	$1,775.00
U.K.	£ 800.00

RW3432
MEXICAN FEIJOA AND LADYBIRD
Style Two

Modeller:	Dorothy Doughty
Height"	10 ¾", 27.8 cm
Colour:	Rose-pink and pale pink flowers; green leaves; grey branch; red ladybird
Plinth:	Wooden
Issued:	1950 in a limited edition of 125

U.S.	$1,475.00
Can.	$1,775.00
U.K.	£ 800.00

RW3433
JOHNNIE / FARMER'S BOY
Modeller:	Freda Doughty
Height:	6 ½", 16.5 cm
Colour:	**Johnnie**
	White shirt; green shorts; dark brown hair; five yellow ducklings
	Farmer's Boy
	White shirt; blue shorts; brown hair; five white ducklings
Issued:	**Johnnie:** 1947-1955
	Farmer's Boy: 1947-1983
Varieties:	Also called "Young Farmer"

Name:	Johnnie	Farmer's Boy	Young Farmer
U.S.	$475.00	425.00	425.00
Can.	$575.00	500.00	500.00
U.K.	£250.00	225.00	225.00

RW3434
H.R.H. PRINCESS ELIZABETH ON "TOMMY"
Modeller:	Doris Lindner
Height:	With plinth:
	15", 38.1 cm
Colour:	1. Navy blue uniform; chestnut horse
	2. White (Classic)
Issued:	1948 in a limited edition of 100

	Coloured	White
U.S.	$6,500.00	
Can.	$7,750.00	Very
U.K.	£3,500.00	rare

RW3435
HAPPY DAYS
Modeller:	Freda Doughty
Height:	7 ½", 19.1 cm
Colour:	Light green shirt; blue-grey trousers; yellow hair; cream and brown pony; cream base
Issued:	1948-by 1955
U.S.	$1,850.00
Can.	$2,250.00
U.K.	£1,000.00

RW3438
RUBY-THROATED HUMMINGBIRD AND FUCHSIA (Cock)
(Archilochus Colubris)
Modeller:	Dorothy Doughty
Height:	9 ¼", 23.5 cm
Colour:	Green, yellow and grey bird; pink and blue fuchsia; green leaves
Plinth:	Wooden
Issued:	1950 in a limited edition of 500
Series:	Doughty American Birds
U.S.	$1,300.00
Can.	$1,550.00
U.K.	£ 700.00

Note: Missing plinth.

RW3439
RUBY-THROATED HUMMINGBIRD AND FUCHSIA (Hen)
(Archilochus Colubris)
Modeller:	Dorothy Doughty
Height:	9 ¼", 23.5 cm
Colour:	Green, yellow and grey bird; brown nest with eggs; pink and blue fuchsia; green leaves
Plinth:	Wooden
Issued:	1950 in a limited edition of 500
Series:	Doughty American Birds
U.S.	$1,300.00
Can.	$1,550.00
U.K.	£ 700.00

Note: Missing plinth.

DAVID FRYER

RW4284
Golden Eagle (Aquila Chrysaetos)

The largest model ever produced by Royal Worcester.

DAVID FRYER
American Birds of Prey on Bronze
Large Size

Peregrine Falcon

American Birds on Bronze was a series of eight American wildlife birds sculpted by David Fryer. The eight models were to be issued in a limited edition of 9,800 each, however, due to the manufacturing and shipping problems that arose, the edition sizes was not completed, and all were discontinued prematurely.

The models were produced in small and large sizes (the large size being illustrated here), and do not carry RW numbers on the base. Thus, the figures are illustrated here but are not incorporated into the text.
We would appreciate hearing from anyone who can supply further information on this series. Valuations for individual models are in the £200. / U.S. $400. range

Screech Owl

Sharp-Shinned Hawk

DAVID FRYER
American Birds of Prey on Bronze

Bald Eagle

Red-Tailed Hawk

Great Horned Owl

Grey Falcon

American Kestrel

DORIS LINDNER
Cattle and Horses

RW3746
British Friesian Bull
"Terling Trusty"

RW3781
Dairy Shorthorn Bull
"Royal Event"

RW3871
Prince's Grace and Foal

RW3922
Galloping Dartmoor Ponies

DORIS LINDNER
Horses

RW3759
Shire Stallion "Manor Premier King"

RW3944
Clydesdale Stallion

RW3882
Palomino "Yellow Straw"

RW4106
Thoroughbred Foal

BERNARD WINSKILL
Military Commanders

RW3956
Alexander (The Great)

RW3870
The Duke of Wellington

RW4034
Richard Coeur De Lion

RW3860
Napoleon Bonaparte

MOUNTED RIDERS

RW3952
Cheltenham

RW3434
H.R.H Princess Elizabeth on "Tommy"

RW3623
Officer of the Blues

CATS

RW4027
Persian Kitten (Seated)

RW4318
Cat (Seated)

RW4007
Kitten (Seated)

TROPICAL FISH

RW3602
Red Hind Fish
(Style Two)

RW3575
Sergeant-Major Fish

RW3603
Blue Angel Fish
(Style Two)

RW3440
JULY
Modeller:	Freda Doughty
Height:	7", 17.8 cm
Colour:	Pink bathing suit; brown hair; blue and white base
Issued:	c.1950-1985
Series:	Months of the Year
U.S.	$375.00
Can.	$450.00
U.K.	£200.00

Note: See also miniature version RW4190 At The Seaside.

RW3441
AUGUST
Modeller:	Freda Doughty
Height:	5", 12.7 cm
Colour:	Fleshtones; brown hair; blue base with white highlights; multicoloured fish
Issued:	c.1950-1985
Series:	Months of the Year
U.S.	$375.00
Can.	$450.00
U.K.	£200.00

Note: See also miniature version RW4191 Little Mermaid.

RW3446
CHINOISERIE FIGURE HOLDING BIRD (Female)
Modeller:	Agnes Pinder-Davis
Height:	13", 33.0 cm
Colour:	1. Bronze coat; fawn-pink sleeves; darker bronze and salmon dress; salmon hat; bronze bird
	2. Shot gold on black coat; purple dress with gold trim; turquoise hat and bird
	3. White glazed
Issued:	1949-c.1960
Series:	Chinoiserie Figures

	Coloured	White
U.S.	$1,400.00	425.00
Can.	$1,650.00	500.00
U.K.	£ 750.00	225.00

RW3447
CHINOISERIE FIGURE HOLDING BIRD (Male)
Modeller:	Agnes Pinder-Davis
Height:	13", 33.0 cm
Colour:	1. Bronze coat, hat and bird; pink sleeves; yellow pantaloons
	2. Shot gold on black, purple and white; white and green hat; green bird
	3. White glazed
Issued:	1949-c.1960
Series:	Chinoiserie Figures

	Coloured	White
U.S.	$1,400.00	425.00
Can.	$1,650.00	500.00
U.K.	£ 750.00	225.00

RW3452
JANUARY
Modeller:	Freda Doughty
Height:	6", 15.0 cm
Colour:	Burgundy coat; beige leggings; brown shoes; green scarf; yellow hair
Issued:	c.1950-1985
Series:	Months of the Year
U.S.	$375.00
Can.	$450.00
U.K.	£200.00

Note: See also miniature version RW4189 The Slide.

RW3453
FEBRUARY
Modeller: Freda Doughty
Height: 6 ¼", 15.9 cm
Colour: 1. Blue raincoat; black hat and wellingtons; brown and white base
2. Green raincoat; black hat and wellingtons; brown and white base
Issued: c.1950-1985
Series: Months of the Year

U.S. $375.00
Can. $450.00
U.K. £200.00

Note: See also miniature version RW4165 Fisherman.

RW3454
MARCH
Modeller: Freda Doughty
Height: 6", 15.0 cm
Colour: Pink dress; blue hat; yellow hair; yellow shoes; green and beige base
Issued: 1947-1949
Series: Months of the Year

U.S. $375.00
Can. $450.00
U.K. £200.00

Note: See also miniature version RW4202 Windy.

RW3455
MAY
Modeller: Freda Doughty
Height: 5", 12.7 cm
Colour: Blue dress; yellow hair; white daisies on a green base
Issued: c.1950-1985
Series: Months of the Year

U.S. $375.00
Can. $450.00
U.K. £200.00

Note: See also miniature version RW4203 Daisy Chain.

RW3456
JUNE
Style Two
Modeller: Freda Doughty
Height: 6 ½", 16.5 cm
Colour: White shirt; yellow shorts; multicoloured tie and belt; yellow hair; brown dog; grey and green base
Issued: c.1950-1985
Series: Months of the Year

U.S. $375.00
Can. $450.00
U.K. £200.00

Note: See also miniature version RW4204 Musical Moments.

RW3457
SEPTEMBER / SNOWY
Modeller: Freda Doughty
Height: 4 ¾", 12.1 cm
Colour: **September:** White shirt; blue tie, shorts, shoes and hat; white cat; green and beige base
Snowy: White shirt; brown tie and shorts; red shoes; white hat with red band; white cat
Issued: **September:** c.1950-1985
Snowy: c.1950-1983
Series: **September:** Months of the Year

Name:	September	Snowy
U.S.	$550.00	550.00
Can.	$675.00	675.00
U.K.	£300.00	300.00

Note: See also miniature version RW4156 Christopher.

RW3458
DECEMBER
Modeller: Freda Doughty
Height: 6 ½", 16.5 cm
Colour: Creamy yellow coat and hat trimmed with burgundy; burgundy mittens and shoes
Issued: c.1950-1985
Series: Months of the Year

U.S. $375.00
Can. $450.00
U.K. £200.00

Note: See also miniature version RW4166 Snowball.

RW3462
ALSATIAN
Style Two
Modeller: Doris Lindner
Height: 9 ¾" x 11 ½",
24.7 x 29.2 cm
Colour: 1. Brown with black
shading
2. White
Issued: 1950-c.1958
Series: Large Dogs

	Coloured	**White**
U.S.	$ 825.00	275.00
Can.	$1,000.00	325.00
U.K.	£ 450.00	150.00

RW3463
ENGLISH SETTER / IRISH SETTER
(Without Base)
Modeller: Doris Lindner
Height: 8", 20.3 cm
Colour: 1. English Setter:
White and black
2. Irish Setter:
Reddish-brown
Issued: 1950
Series: Large Dogs
U.S. $ 825.00
Can. $1,000.00
U.K. £ 450.00

RW3464
YELLOW-HEADED BLACKBIRD AND SPIDERWORT (Cock)
(Xanthocephalus Xanthocephalus)
Modeller: Dorothy Doughty
Height: 11" 27.9 cm
Colour: Yellow and black bird; purple-blue flowers; green foliage;
green-brown base
Plinth: Wooden
Issued: 1952 in a limited edition of 350
Series: Doughty American Birds

U.S. $1,475.00
Can. $1,775.00
U.K. £ 800.00

Note: Missing plinth.

RW3465
YELLOW HEADED BLACKBIRD AND SPIDERWORT (Hen)
(Xanthocephalus Xanthocephalus)
Modeller: Dorothy Doughty
Height: 11", 27.9 cm
Colour: Purple, brown and yellow bird; deep blue flowers; green
foliage; green-brown base
Plinth: Wooden
Issued: 1952 in a limited edition of 350
Series: Doughty American Birds

U.S. $1,475.00
Can. $1,775.00
U.K. £ 800.00

Note: Missing plinth.

RW3466
WILD HORSES
Modeller: Doris Lindner
Height: 16 ¼", 41.2 cm
Colour: 1. Grey
2. White
Plinth: Wooden, large oval
Issued: 1950-c.1970s
Varieties: Also called Galloping in Winter RW3958

U.S. Very few pieces of this early version were produced
Can. Extremely rare
U.K.

Note: In 1974 the central support was eliminated, and the model was produced
in colour as a limited edition of 250 and entitled "Galloping in Winter."

RW3467
GOLDEN-CROWNED KINGLET AND NOBLE PINE (Cock)
(Regulus Satrapa)
Modeller:	Dorothy Doughty
Height:	7 ¾", 19.7 cm
Colour:	Blue-grey, green, brown, yellow and grey bird; green foliage; brown branch
Plinth:	Wooden
Issued:	1952 in a limited edition of 500
Series:	Doughty American Birds
U.S.	$1,000.00
Can.	$1,200.00
U.K.	£ 550.00

Note: Missing plinth.

RW3468
GOLDEN CROWNED KINGLET AND NOBLE PINE (Double)
(Regulus Satrapa)
Modeller:	Dorothy Doughty
Height:	7 ¾", 19.7 cm
Colour:	Green, blue-grey, brown, yellow and grey birds; green foliage; brown branch
Plinth:	Wooden
Issued:	1952 in a limited edition of 500
Series:	Doughty American Birds
U.S.	$1,000.00
Can.	$1,200.00
U.K.	£ 550.00

Note: Missing plinth.

RW3469
RED-EYED VIREO AND SWAMP AZALEA (Cock)
(Vireo Olivaceus)
Modeller:	Dorothy Doughty
Height:	7 ¾", 19.7 cm
Colour:	Blue-grey, green and grey bird; pink and white blossom; grey-green branch
Plinth:	Wooden
Issued:	1952 in a limited edition of 500
Series:	Doughty American Birds
U.S.	$1,000.00
Can.	$1,200.00
U.K.	£ 550.00

RW3470
RED-EYED VIREO AND SWAMP AZALEA (Hen)
(Vireo Olivaceus)
Modeller:	Dorothy Doughty
Height:	7 ¾", 19.7 cm
Colour:	Blue-grey, green and grey bird; pink and white blossom; grey-green branch
Plinth:	Wooden
Issued:	1952 in a limited edition of 500
Series:	Doughty American Birds
U.S.	$1,000.00
Can.	$1,200.00
U.K.	£ 550.00

RW3471
BATTLEDORE
Modeller: Freda Doughty
Height: 9 ¾", 24.7 cm
Colour: Red frock coat, yellow waistcoat and breeches black buckled shoes
Issued: 1951-1951
U.S.
Can. Extremely rare
U.K.

RW3472
SHUTTLECOCK
Modeller: Freda Doughty
Height: Unknown
Colour: Unknown
Issued: 1951-1951
U.S.
Can. Extremely rare
U.K.

RW3473
BALINESE DANCER
Style One
Modeller: Agnes Pinder-Davis
Height: 17", 43.2 cm
Colour: Unknown
Issued: 1951 in a limited edition of 25
U.S. $2,775.00
Can. $3,350.00
U.K. £1,500.00

RW3474
SIAMESE DANCER
Style One
Modeller: Agnes Pinder-Davis
Height: 21", 53.3 cm
Colour: Gold
Issued: 1951 in a limited edition of 25
U.S. $2,775.00
Can. $3,350.00
U.K. £1,500.00

RW3476
CHAFFINCH (Hen)
Modeller: Dorothy Doughty
Height: Unknown
Colour: Grey and reddish-brown; white flowers; wooden base
Issued: 1951
U.S.
Can. Extremely rare
U.K.

Note: Not put into full production, only a few examples known.

RW3479
PAUL
Modeller: Freda Doughty
Height: Unknown
Colour: Unknown
Issued: 1952-1952
U.S.
Can. Extremely rare
U.K.

RW3480
PRISCILLA
Modeller: Freda Doughty
Height: Unknown
Colour: Pink dress, blonde hair and black shoes
Issued: 1952-1952
U.S.
Can. Extremely rare
U.K.

RW3481
CHINESE GODDESS
(Arms crossed)
Modeller: Agnes Pinder-Davis
Height: 12 ¼", 31.1 cm
Colour: Gold lustre
Issued: 1952
U.S.
Can. Extremely rare
U.K.

RW3482
CHINESE GODDESS (With flower)
Modeller:	Agnes Pinder-Davis
Height:	12 ¼", 31.1 cm
Colour:	Burnished gilt robe; green dress; red necklace; grey base
Issued:	1952
U.S.	
Can.	Extremely rare
U.K.	

RW3483
JESTER
Style Two
Modeller:	Miss M. J. Stevens
Height:	8 ¾", 22.2 cm
Colour:	Yellow tunic with white and red frills; black hair and blue shoes
Issued:	1952-by 1955
Varieties:	Also known as "Cha-U-Kao" RW4216
U.S.	$1,650.00
Can.	$2,150.00
U.K.	£ 950.00

RW3488
PUNCH
Modeller:	Freda Doughty
Height:	5 ½", 14.0 cm
Colour:	Yellow shirt; white collar; blue shorts; pink belt; ginger hair
Issued:	1952-1959
U.S.	$800.00
Can.	$950.00
U.K.	£425.00

RW3489
JUDY
Modeller:	Freda Doughty
Height:	6", 15.0 cm
Colour:	Blue dress with white frills and purple highlights; yellow hair
Issued:	1952-1959
U.S.	$1,100.00
Can.	$1,325.00
U.K.	£ 600.00

RW3491
SEA SCOUT
Modeller:	Agnes Pinder-Davis
Height:	5 ½", 14.0 cm
Colour:	1. Green seahorse; yellow vest; blonde hair
	2. White seahorse with blue trim; blue vest; brown hair
Issued:	1953-by 1957
Series:	Chinoiserie Sayings
U.S.	$750.00
Can.	$900.00
U.K.	£400.00

RW3492
LUCKY SPIDER
Modeller:	Agnes Pinder-Davis
Height:	5 ½", 14.0 cm
Colour:	1. Black and white
	2. Cream dress; green jacket; brown hair; brown spider
	3. White glazed
Issued:	1953-by 1957
Series:	Chinoiserie Sayings

	Coloured	White
U.S.	$750.00	175.00
Can.	$900.00	200.00
U.K.	£400.00	100.00

RW3493
FUNNY FISH
Modeller:	Agnes Pinder-Davis
Height:	5 ½", 14.0 cm
Colour:	1. Black and white
	2. Blue and white suit; red shoes; white fish with blue highlights; white and blue rock
	3. White glazed
Issued:	1953-by 1957
Series:	Chinoiserie Sayings

	Coloured	White
U.S.	$750.00	175.00
Can.	$900.00	200.00
U.K.	£400.00	100.00

RW3494
DON'T LET THE CAT OUT OF THE BAG
Modeller:	Agnes Pinder-Davis
Height:	5 ½", 14.0 cm
Colour:	1. Black and white
	2. Bright colours
	3. White glazed
Issued:	1953-by 1957
Series:	Chinoiserie Sayings

	Coloured	White
U.S.	$700.00	175.00
Can.	$850.00	200.00
U.K.	£375.00	100.00

RW3495
SLOW COACH
Modeller:	Agnes Pinder-Davis
Height:	5 ½," 14.0 cm
Colour:	1. Black and white
	2. Green trousers; red vest; pink shoes; brown turtle
	3. White glazed
Issued:	1953-by 1957
Series:	Chinoiserie Sayings

	Coloured	White
U.S.	$800.00	175.00
Can.	$950.00	200.00
U.K.	£425.00	100.00

RW3496
JOY RIDE
Modeller:	Agnes Pinder-Davis
Height:	5 ½", 14.0 cm
Colour:	1. Beige fish; flesh coloured child; green base
	2. Black and white
	3. Blue fish; flesh coloured child; blue and white base
	4. White glazed
Issued:	1953-by 1957
Series:	Chinoiserie Sayings

	Coloured	White
U.S.	$ 875.00	175.00
Can.	$1,050.00	200.00
U.K.	£ 475.00	100.00

RW3497
APPLE OF YOUR EYE
Modeller:	Agnes Pinder-Davis
Height:	5 ½", 14.0 cm
Colour:	1. Black and white
	2. Blue top edged with white; yellow trousers; red apples and shoes
	3. White glazed
Issued:	1953-by 1957
Series:	Chinoiserie Sayings

	Coloured	White
U.S.	$700.00	175.00
Can.	$850.00	200.00
U.K.	£375.00	100.00

RW3498
EARLY BIRD
Modeller:	Agnes Pinder-Davis
Height:	5 ½", 14.0 cm
Colour:	1. Black and white
	2. Green trousers; white blouse with blue trim; yellow hair; red shoes; brown bird
	3. White glazed
Issued:	1953-by 1957
Series:	Chinoiserie Sayings

	Coloured	White
U.S.	$700.00	175.00
Can.	$850.00	200.00
U.K.	£375.00	100.00

RW3499
TWO'S COMPANY, THREE'S NONE

Modeller:	Agnes Pinder-Davis
Height:	5", 12.7 cm
Colour:	1. Black and white
	2. Green tunic; light pink trousers; red slippers; yellow hat
	3. White tunic with blue flowers; blue trousers; red slippers
Issued:	1953-by 1957
Series:	Chinoiserie Sayings

U.S.	$750.00
Can.	$900.00
U.K.	£400.00

RW3500
WISE AS AN OWL

Modeller:	Agnes Pinder-Davis
Height:	5 ½", 14.0 cm
Colour:	1. Black and white
	2. Dark blue dress; white skirt with blue flowers; blue owl
	3 Green dress with white collar; cream trousers; red shoes; blonde hair; taupe owl
	4. White glazed
Issued:	1953-by 1957
Series:	Chinoiserie Sayings

	Coloured	White
U.S.	$750.00	200.00
Can.	$900.00	250.00
U.K.	£400.00	100.00

RW3501
HEN PARTY

Modeller:	Agnes Pinder-Davis
Height:	5 ½", 14.0 cm
Colour:	1. Black and white
	2. Turquoise top with white collar; light blue trousers; red shoes; white hen with brown highlights
	3. White glazed
Issued:	1953-by 1957
Series:	Chinoiserie Sayings

	Coloured	White
U.S.	$750.00	200.00
Can.	$900.00	250.00
U.K.	£400.00	100.00

RW3502
MAD AS A HATTER

Modeller:	Agnes Pinder-Davis
Height:	5 ½", 14.0 cm
Colour:	1. Black and white
	2. Blue trousers; white and blue top; blue hat; red shoes white hare with blue flecks
	3. White glazed
Issued:	1953-by 1957
Varieties:	Also called "Mad as a March Hare"
Series:	Chinoiserie Sayings

	Coloured	White
U.S.	$750.00	200.00
Can.	$900.00	250.00
U.K.	£400.00	100.00

RW3503
THE QUEEN'S BEASTS

Two models make up this style number, one of a dog holding a shield emblazoned with the Tudor rose, the other a horse with a shield with quartered royal arms, both on circular bases. Eleven pairs of these animals were intended to be mounted onto the Queen's Coronation Vase, but a few extra models were produced. They were painted by Harry Davis.

Modeller:	Frederick M. Gertner	
Height:	5 ½", 14.0 cm	
Colour:	1. Dog: White	
	2. Horse: White horse holds Royal Standard	
Issued:	1953	

	Dog	Horse
U.S.	$275.00	275.00
Can.	$325.00	325.00
U.K.	£150.00	150.00

RW3506
BLUE-GREY GNATCATCHER AND DOGWOOD (Single)
(Polioptila Caerulea)

Modeller:	Dorothy Doughty
Height:	11 ½", 29.2 cm
Colour:	Blue-grey and white bird; white flowers; green leaves
Plinth:	Wooden
Issued:	1955 in a limited edition of 500
Series:	Doughty American Birds
U.S.	$1,100.00
Can.	$1,300.00
U.K.	£ 600.00

RW3507
BLUE-GREY GNATCATCHER AND DOGWOOD (Double)
(Polioptila Caerulea)

Modeller:	Dorothy Doughty
Height:	11 ½", 29.2 cm
Colour:	Blue-grey and white birds; white flowers; green leaves
Plinth:	Wooden
Issued:	1955 in a limited edition of 500
Series:	Doughty American Birds
U.S.	$1,100.00
Can.	$1,300.00
U.K.	£ 600.00

RW3508
MYRTLE WARBLER AND WEEPING CHERRY (Cock)
(Dendroica Coronata)

Modeller:	Dorothy Doughty
Height:	9 ½", 24.0 cm
Colour:	Blue, grey, orange and black bird; pink and white blossom; grey-green branch
Plinth:	Wooden
Issued:	1955 in a limited edition of 500
Series:	Doughty American Birds
U.S.	$1,100.00
Can.	$1,300.00
U.K.	£ 600.00

RW3509
MYRTLE WARBLER AND WEEPING CHERRY (Hen)
(Dendroica Coronata)
Modeller: Dorothy Doughty
Height: 9 ½", 24.0 cm
Colour: Grey, yellow and black bird; pink and white blossom;
               grey-green branch
Plinth: Wooden
Issued: 1955 in a limited edition of 500
Series: Doughty American Birds

U.S. $1,000.00
Can. $1,200.00
U.K.   £ 600.00

Photograph not
available
at press time

RW3510
RED RIDING HOOD
Modeller: Miss M. J. Stevens
Height: 8", 20.3 cm
Colour: Patterned dress
Issued: 1954

U.S.
Can.   Extremely rare
U.K.

RW3511
WOLF
Modeller: Miss M. J. Stevens
Height: 8", 20.3 cm
Colour: Brown wolf; greenish-
               yellow dress; mauve
               shawl; white base
Issued: 1954

U.S.
Can.   Extremely rare
U.K.

RW3512
BEWICK'S WREN AND YELLOW JASMINE (Cock)
(Thryomanes Bewickii)
Modeller: Dorothy Doughty
Height: 10", 25.4 cm
Colour: Brown with cream breast; yellow flowers; green leaves;
               green-brown branch
Plinth: Wooden
Issued: 1956 in a limited edition of 500
Series: Doughty American Birds

U.S. $1,000.00
Can. $1,200.00
U.K.   £ 600.00

RW3513
BEWICK'S WREN AND YELLOW JASMINE (Hen)
(Thryomanes Bewickii)
Modeller: Dorothy Doughty
Height: 10", 25.4 cm
Colour: Brown with cream breast; yellow flowers; green leaves;
               green-brown branch
Plinth: Wooden
Issued: 1956 in a limited edition of 500
Series: Doughty American Birds

U.S. $1,000.00
Can. $1,200.00
U.K.   £ 600.00

RW3514
FOALS (Without base)
Modeller: Doris Lindner
Height: 5", 12.7 cm
Colour: Light tan; dark tan;
light green base
Issued: 1954
Varieties: Foals (With base)
RW3152

U.S. $ 925.00
Can. $1,100.00
U.K. £ 500.00

RW3515
CALVES (Without base)
Modeller: Doris Lindner
Height: 3 ½", 8.9 cm
Colour: White and red-brown
Issued: 1954
Varieties: Calves (With base)
RW3146

U.S. $650.00
Can. $775.00
U.K. £350.00

RW3516
MAYTIME (Without base)
Modeller: Doris Lindner
Height: 3", 7.6 cm
Colour: Creamy white
Issued: 1954
Varieties: Maytime (With base)
RW3123

U.S. $550.00
Can. $650.00
U.K. £300.00

RW3517
KIDS AT PLAY (Without base)
Modeller: Doris Lindner
Height: 4 ¼", 10.8 cm
Colour: Grey-blue and white
Issued: 1954
Varieties: Kids at Play (With
base) RW3153
Series: Goats

U.S. $550.00
Can. $650.00
U.K. £300.00

RW3518
SUNDAY'S CHILD (Girl)
Modeller: Freda Doughty
Height: 7", 17.75 cm
Colour: Blue bodice; white skirt with red dots and hem;
turquoise hat; blue shoes; yellow hair; green
and white base
Issued: 1938-1984
Reissued: 1996-2002
Series: The Days of the Week

B/S:	Blue	Black	Black, circle	Black, diamond
U.S.	$475.00	325.00	275.00	250.00
Can.	$575.00	400.00	325.00	300.00
U.K.	£250.00	175.00	150.00	125.00

Note: Earlier models of Sunday's Child held a porcelain windmill.
See also miniature version RW4161 Let's Run.

RW3519
MONDAY'S CHILD (Boy) / ALL MINE

Modeller:	Freda Doughty
Height:	7 ¼", 19.1 cm
Colour:	**Monday's Child**
	Blue shirt, shorts, shoes; blonde hair; white and brown puppies
	All Mine
	Yellow shirt; green shorts; white shoes; white and brown puppies
Issued:	**Monday's Child:** 1938-1984
	All Mine: 1982-1983
Reissued:	**Monday's Child:** 1996-2002
Series:	**Monday's Child:** The Days of the Week

MONDAY'S CHILD

B/S:	Blue	Black	Black, circle	Black, diamond
U.S.	$475.00	325.00	275.00	250.00
Can.	$575.00	400.00	325.00	300.00
U.K.	£250.00	175.00	150.00	125.00

ALL MINE

	Black, circle
	Very rare

Note: See also miniature version RW4158 Three's Company.

RW3521
WEDNESDAY'S CHILD (Boy)

Modeller:	Freda Doughty
Height:	7", 17.8 cm
Colour:	Green top; orange shorts; red hair; grey teddy bear; orange and white base
Issued:	1938-1984
Reissued:	1996-2002
Series:	The Days of the Week

B/S:	Blue	Black	Black, circle	Black, diamond
U.S.	$375.00	375.00	325.00	275.00
Can.	$450.00	450.00	400.00	325.00
U.K.	£200.00	200.00	175.00	150.00

Note: See also miniature version RW4195 Poor Teddy.

RW3522
THURSDAY'S CHILD (Girl)

Modeller:	Freda Doughty
Height:	7", 17.8 cm
Colour:	Turquoise dress with white collar and cuffs; pink belt; turquoise and pink hat; brown shoes; green, beige and white bases
Issued:	1938-1984
Reissued:	1996-2002
Series:	The Days of the Week

B/S:	Blue	Black	Black, circle	Black, diamond
U.S.	$375.00	375.00	325.00	275.00
Can.	$450.00	450.00	400.00	325.00
U.K.	£200.00	200.00	175.00	150.00

Note: See also miniature version RW4159 Hometime.

RW3523
FRIDAY'S CHILD (Girl)
Modeller: Freda Doughty
Height: 6", 15.0 cm
Colour: Yellow dungarees; brown bird; green base
Issued: 1938-1984
Reissued: 1996-2002
Series: The Days of the Week

B/S:	Blue	Black	Black, circle	Black, diamond
U.S.	$375.00	375.00	325.00	275.00
Can.	$450.00	450.00	400.00	325.00
U.K.	£200.00	200.00	175.00	150.00

Note: See also miniature version RW4160 Teatime.

RW3524
SATURDAY'S CHILD (Boy)
Modeller: Freda Doughty
Height: 6", 15.0 cm
Colour: Blue overalls; white shirt and hat; brown and grey spade; brown and green base
Issued: 1938-1984
Reissued: 1996-2002
Series: The Days of the Week

B/S:	Blue	Black	Black circle	Black, diamond
U.S.	$375.00	375.00	325.00	275.00
Can.	$450.00	450.00	400.00	325.00
U.K.	£200.00	200.00	175.00	150.00

Note: See also miniature version RW4192 Gardener.

RW3525
SCARLET TANAGER AND WHITE OAK (Cock)
(Piranga Olivacea)
Modeller: Dorothy Doughty
Height: 11", 27.9 cm
Colour: Scarlet and black bird; green foliage; brown branch
Plinth: Wooden
Issued: 1956 in a limited edition of 500
Series: Doughty American Birds

U.S.	$1,000.00
Can.	$1,200.00
U.K.	£ 600.00

RW3526
SCARLET TANAGER AND WHITE OAK (Hen)
(Piranga Olivacea)
Modeller: Dorothy Doughty
Height: 11", 27.9 cm
Colour: Yellow bird, orange beak; green foliage; brown-grey branch
Plinth: Wooden
Issued: 1956 in a limited edition of 500
Series: Doughty American Birds

U.S.	$1,000.00
Can.	$1,200.00
U.K.	£ 600.00

RW3527
FOX (Lying, without base)
Modeller:	Doris Lindner
Length:	4", 10.1 cm
Colour:	Chestnut red fox
Issued:	1954
Varieties:	Fox (Lying on curved base) RW2950; Fox Ashtray RW2873; Fox Tobacco Jar RW2925
U.S.	$325.00
Can.	$400.00
U.K.	£175.00

RW3528
HOUND (Lying, straight without base)
Style One
Modeller:	Doris Lindner
Length:	4", 10.1 cm
Colour:	White with chestnut brown and black spots
Issued:	1954
U.S.	$325.00
Can.	$400.00
U.K.	£175.00

RW3529
FAWNS, YOUNG SPOTTED DEER (Without base)
Modeller:	Doris Lindner
Height:	3 ½", 8.9 cm
Colour:	Brown with white markings
Issued:	1952
Varieties:	Fawns, Young Spotted Deer (With rectangular base); RW3266 Fawns, Young Spotted Deer (With oval base) RW3316
Series:	Zoo Babies
U.S.	$ 925.00
Can.	$1,100.00
U.K.	£ 500.00

RW3530
GOAT (Head raised, without base)
Modeller:	Henri Bargas
Height:	5", 12.7 cm
Colour:	White with black markings
Issued:	1954
Varieties:	Goat (Head raised, with base) RW3125
Series:	Goats
U.S.	$600.00
Can.	$725.00
U.K.	£325.00

RW3531
GOAT (Licking hind leg, without base)
Modeller:	Henri Bargas
Height:	4 ½", 11.9 cm
Colour:	White with black markings
Issued:	1954
Varieties:	Goat (Licking hind leg, with base) RW3124
Series:	Goats
U.S.	$600.00
Can.	$725.00
U.K.	£325.00

RW3532
OVENBIRD WITH LADY'S SLIPPER (Cock)
(Seiurus Aurocapillus)
Modeller:	Dorothy Doughty
Height:	11", 27.9 cm
Colour:	Green-brown, blue, grey and black bird; blue lady's slipper flowers; green and brown leaves
Plinth:	Wooden
Issued:	1957 in a limited edition of 250
Series:	Doughty American Birds
U.S.	$1,300.00
Can.	$1,550.00
U.K.	£ 700.00

Note: Missing plinth.

RW3533
OVENBIRD WITH CRESTED IRIS (Hen)
(Seiurus Aurocapillus)
Modeller: Dorothy Doughty
Height: 11", 27.9 cm
Colour: Green-brown, blue, grey and black bird; mauve iris;
              green and brown leaves
Plinth: Wooden
Issued: 1957 in a limited edition of 250
Series: Doughty American Birds

U.S. $1,300.00
Can. $1,550.00
U.K.   £ 700.00

Note: Missing plinth.

RW3534
TUESDAY'S CHILD (Boy)
Modeller: Freda Doughty
Height: 6", 15.0 cm
Colour: Yellow sweater and hat with red stripes; blue trousers;
              brown skates; pale blue and white base
Issued: 1938-1984
Reissued: 1996-2002
Series: The Days of the Week

B/S: Blue	Black	Black,	Black, circle	diamond
U.S.	$375.00	375.00	325.00	275.00
Can.	$450.00	450.00	400.00	325.00
U.K.	£200.00	200.00	175.00	150.00

Note: See also miniature version RW4199 Skating.

RW3535
OFFICER OF THE 29TH FOOT (WORCESTERSHIRE REGIMENT) 1812
Modeller: Frederick M. Gertner
Height: 12", 30.5 cm
Colour: Red military jacket; white trousers; black boots, hat and base
Issued: 1954-c.1975
Series: Historical Military Figures

U.S. $1,000.00
Can. $1,200.00
U.K.   £ 550.00

RW3536
PARULA WARBLER AND SWEET BAY (Cock)
(Parula Americana)
Modeller: Dorothy Doughty
Height: 9", 22.9 cm
Colour: Grey-green, yellow and white bird; white flower and bud;
              green leaves; grey-brown branch
Plinth: Wooden
Issued: 1957 in a limited edition of 500
Series: Doughty American Birds

U.S. $1,000.00
Can. $1,200.00
U.K.   £ 600.00

Note: Missing plinth.

RW3537
PARULA WARBLER AND SWEET BAY (Hen)
(Parula Americana)
Modeller: Dorothy Doughty
Height: 9", 22.9 cm
Colour: Blue, yellow and white bird; white flower and bud;
               green leaves; green-brown branch
Plinth: Wooden
Issued: 1957 in a limited edition of 500
Series: Doughty American Birds

U.S. $1,000.00
Can. $1,200.00
U.K.   £ 600.00

Note: Missing plinth.

Possibly not
put into
production

RW3538
ISABELLA
Style One
Modeller: Miss Mitchell-Smith
Height: Unknown
Colour: Unknown
Issued: 1955

U.S.
Can.   Extremely rare
U.K.

RW3539
YELLOW-THROAT AND WATER HYACINTH (Cock)
(Geothlypis Trichas)
Modeller: Dorothy Doughty
Height: 11", 27.9 cm
Colour: Greenish-purple and yellow bird; lilac, blue and yellow flowers;
               greenish-yellow leaves
Plinth: Wooden
Issued: 1958 in a limited edition of 350
Series: Doughty American Birds

U.S. $1,475.00
Can. $1,775.00
U.K.   £ 800.00

Note: Missing plinth.

RW3540
YELLOW-THROAT AND WATER HYACINTH (Hen)
(Geothlypis Trichas)
Modeller: Dorothy Doughty
Height: 11", 27.9 cm
Colour: Greenish-purple, yellow and black bird; lilac,
               yellow and blue flowers; greenish-white leaves
Plinth: Wooden
Issued: 1958 in a limited edition of 350
Series: Doughty American Birds

U.S. $1,475.00
Can. $1,775.00
U.K.   £ 800.00

Note: Missing plinth.

RW3541
ROSE
Style Two
Modeller: Agnes Pinder-Davis
Height: Unknown
Colour: Unknown
Issued: 1955
Series: The Cries of London

U.S.
Can.   Extremely rare
U.K.

RW3542
VIOLET
Modeller: Agnes Pinder-Davis
Height: Unknown
Colour: Unknown
Issued: 1955
Series: The Cries of London

U.S.
Can.   Extremely rare
U.K.

RW3543
HEATHER
Modeller: Agnes Pinder-Davis
Height: Unknown
Colour: Unknown
Issued: 1955
Series: The Cries of London

U.S.
Can.   Extremely rare
U.K.

RW3546
SPRING MORNING / SPRING MORN / RACHEL (Style One)
First Version-6"
Modeller: Freda Doughty
Height: 6", 15.0 cm
Colour: **Spring Morning**
1. Green dress with white collar and cuffs; pink sash; dark green hat; yellow flowers in light brown basket
2. Red dress with white collar and cuffs; turquoise sash; blue hat
Spring Morn: Green dress; white apron with yellow flowered design; yellow hat
Rachel (Style One): Peach dress; white collar, cuffs and apron; straw basket of yellow flowers
Issued: **Spring Morning:** 1955-1962
Spring Morn: 1982-c.1985
Rachel (Style One): 1988-1991
Series: **Spring Morn:** Age of Romance, Series One
Rachel: Age of Romance, Series One

Name:	Spring Morn	Spring Morning	Rachel
U.S.	$375.00	375.00	425.00
Can.	$450.00	450.00	500.00
U.K.	£200.00	200.00	225.00

SPRING MORNING
Second Version-9"
Modeller: Freda Doughty
Height: 9", 22.5 cm
Colour: Orange dress with white collar and cuffs; green sash; green hat; yellow daffodils; brown basket
Issued: 1955-1962

U.S. $450.00
Can. $550.00
U.K.   £250.00

RW3547
SUMMER DAY / SUMMER'S DAY / SARAH (Style One)
First Version-7½"

Modeller:	Freda Doughty
Height:	7 ½", 19.1 cm
Colour:	**Summer Day:** Red dress; white collar and underskirt; blue ribbon; straw basket of flowers
	Summer's Day: Blue bodice and underskirt; white overskirt with pink flowers; blue ribbon; straw basket of lowers
	Sarah (Style One): Pink dress; white overskirt with pink flowers; pink ribbon; straw basket of flowers
Issued:	**Summer Day:** 1955-1958
	Summer's Day: 1982-c.1985
	Sarah (Style One): 1988-1991
Series:	**Summer's Day:** Age of Romance, Series One
	Sarah: Age of Romance, Series One

Name:	Summer Day	Summer's Day	Sarah (Style One)
U.S.	$425.00	425.00	425.00
Can.	$500.00	500.00	500.00
U.K.	£225.00	225.00	225.00

SUMMER DAY
Second Version-9½"

Modeller:	Freda Doughty
Height:	9 ½", 24.1 cm
Colour:	1. Red dress with white collar and underdress; blue sash; blue hat with yellow band; yellow shoe
	2. Rose-pink dress with white collar, cuffs and underdress; green sash and shoes
Issued:	1955-1958

U.S.	$650.00
Can.	$775.00
U.K.	£350.00

RW3548
PHOEBE AND FLAME VINE (Cock)
(Sayornis Phoebe)

Modeller:	Dorothy Doughty
Height:	9 ¾", 24.7 cm
Colour:	Blue-grey, green and yellowish-grey bird; orange flowers; green leaves; green-brown branch
Plinth:	Wooden
Issued:	1958 in a limited edition of 500
Series:	Doughty American Birds

U.S.	$1,100.00
Can.	$1,325.00
U.K.	£ 600.00

RW3549
PHOEBE AND FLAME VINE (Hen)
(Sayornis Phoebe)

Modeller:	Dorothy Doughty
Height:	9 ¾", 24.7 cm
Colour:	Brown and grey bird; orange flowers; green leaves; grey-green branch
Plinth:	Wooden
Issued:	1958 in a limited edition of 500
Series:	Doughty American Birds

U.S.	$1,100.00
Can.	$1,325.00
U.K.	£ 600.00

RW3550
BALINESE DANCER
Style Two
Modeller: Agnes Pinder-Davis
Height: 6", 15.0 cm
Colour: 1. Coloured
          2. Gold
Issued: 1955

	Coloured	Gold
U.S.		$1,750.00
Can.	Extremely	$1,500.00
U.K.	Rare	£ 875.00

Note: RW3550 was available with or without a base.

RW3551
SIAMESE DANCER
Style Two
Modeller: Agnes Pinder-Davis
Height: 6", 15.0 cm
Colour: 1. Coloured
          2. Gold
Issued: 1955

	Coloured	Gold
U.S.		$1,750.00
Can.	Extremely	$1,500.00
U.K.	Rare	£ 875.00

Note: RW3551 was available with or without a base.

Possibly not
put into
production

RW3557
PHILLIP
Modeller: Miss Mitchell-Smith
Height: Unknown
Colour: Unknown
Issued: 1955

U.S.
Can. Extremely rare
U.K.

RW3558
WHITE BOY
Modeller: Unknown
Height: Unknown
Colour: Unknown
Issued: 1955

U.S.
Can. Extremely rare
U.K.

RW3559
PICKANINNY
Modeller: Unknown
Height: Unknown
Colour: Unknown
Issued: 1955

U.S.
Can. Extremely rare
U.K.

Possibly not
put into
production

RW3560
DAISY
Style One
Modeller: Agnes Pinder-Davis
Height: Unknown
Colour: Unknown
Issued: 1955
Series: The Cries of London

U.S.
Can. Extremely rare
U.K.

RW3561
CHANTICLEER (Cockerel)
Modeller: Doris Lindner
Height: 11", 27.9 cm
Colour: 1. Unglazed biscuit
          2. White with green
             and mauve
             highlights; red
             comb; yellow beak
Issued: 1955

	Biscuit	Coloured
U.S.	$250.00	700.00
Can.	$300.00	850.00
U.K.	£135.00	375.00

RW3562
GAMECOCK
Modeller: Doris Lindner
Height: 13", 33.0 cm
Colour: 1. Unglazed biscuit
          2. White with green
             and gold highlights;
             red head
Issued: 1955

	Biscuit	Coloured
U.S.	$250.00	700.00
Can.	$300.00	850.00
U.K.	£135.00	375.00

RW3569
THE SEAMSTRESS
First Version-6"
Modeller: Freda Doughty
Height: 6", 15.0 cm
Colour: 1. Lemon dress; cream patterned fabrics
         2. Red dress; multicoloured fabrics
         3. Turquoise dress; blue and rose fabrics
Issued: 1956-1959

U.S.	$550.00
Can.	$675.00
U.K.	£300.00

Second Version-9"
Modeller: Freda Doughty
Height: 9", 22.9 cm
Colour: 1. Red
         2. Mauve
Issued: 1956-1959

U.S.	$700.00
Can.	$850.00
U.K.	£375.00

See page 50 for this model with a base.

RW3570
FOX (Lying straight, without base)
Modeller: Doris Lindner
Height: 4 ½", 11.9 cm
Colour: Reddish-brown
Issued: 1956
Varieties: Fox (Lying straight, on base) RW2997

U.S.	$325.00
Can.	$400.00
U.K.	£175.00

RW3571
HOUND
(Lying straight, without base)
Style Two
Modeller: Doris Lindner
Size: 1 ¼" x 5", 3.2 x 12.7 cm
Colour: White with dark brown and black patches
Issued: 1956
Varieties: Hound (Lying straight, on base) RW2998

U.S.	$325.00
Can.	$400.00
U.K.	£175.00

RW3572
RED HIND FISH
Style One
Modeller: Ronald Van Ruyckevelt
Height: 5 ½", 14.0 cm
Colour: 1. Cream with red spots; black-edged fins; orange mouth; mauve rocks
         2. White
Issued: 1956-c.1975
Series: Tropical Fish (Small size)

	Coloured	White
U.S.	$275.00	175.00
Can.	$325.00	200.00
U.K.	£150.00	95.00

RW3573
FOUR-EYED BUTTERFLY FISH
Modeller: Ronald Van Ruyckevelt
Height: 5 ½", 14.0 cm
Colour: 1. Pink-brown with yellow and black stripes
         2. White
Issued: 1956-c.1975
Series: Tropical Fish (Small size)

	Coloured	White
U.S.	$275.00	175.00
Can.	$325.00	200.00
U.K.	£150.00	95.00

RW3574
BLUE ANGEL FISH
Style One
Modeller: Ronald Van Ruyckevelt
Height: 5 ½", 14.0 cm
Colour: 1.   Pink, blue and
                       yellow fish; pink
                       and brown coral
                  2.   White
Issued: 1956-c.1975
Series: Tropical Fish
                    (Small size)

	Coloured	White
U.S.	$275.00	175.00
Can.	$325.00	200.00
U.K.	£150.00	95.00

RW3575
SERGEANT-MAJOR FISH
Modeller: Ronald Van Ruyckevelt
Height: 5 ½", 14.0 cm
Colour: 1.   Bluish-green;
                       yellow shading;
                       black stripes
                  2.   White
Issued: 1956-c.1975
Series: Tropical Fish
                    (Small size)

	Coloured	White
U.S.	$275.00	175.00
Can.	$325.00	200.00
U.K.	£150.00	95.00

RW3576
YELLOW GRUNT FISH
Modeller: Ronald Van Ruyckevelt
Height: 5 ½", 14.0 cm
Colour: 1.   Yellow-orange with dark blue stripes; green-mauve coral
                  2.   White
Issued: 1956-c.1975
Series: Tropical Fish (Small size)

	Coloured	White
U.S.	$275.00	175.00
Can.	$325.00	200.00
U.K.	£150.00	95.00

RW3577
FOUR-EYED FISH AND BANDED BUTTERFLY
Modeller: Ronald Van Ruyckevelt
Height: 12", 30.5 cm
Colour: Upper fish: Black and pale blue
                  Lower fish: Grey, yellow, black and blue
                  Coral: Pink, yellow and blue
Plinth: Wooden
Issued: 1957 in a limited edition of 500
Series: Tropical Fish (Large size)

U.S.	$ 825.00
Can.	$1,000.00
U.K.	£ 450.00

RW3578
SPANISH HOG AND SERGEANT-MAJOR FISH
Modeller: Ronald Van Ruyckevelt
Height: 12", 30.5 cm
Colour: Upper fish: Purple, blue and yellow
                  Lower fish: Blue, yellow and black
                  Coral: Purple, green, blue and yellow
Plinth: Wooden
Issued: 1956 in a limited edition of 500
Series: Tropical Fish (Large size)

U.S.	$ 825.00
Can.	$1,000.00
U.K.	£ 450.00

130

RW3579
SPADE FISH

Modeller:	Ronald Van Ruyckevelt
Height:	5 ½", 14.0 cm
Colour:	1. Pearly grey and black stripes; green and pink coral
	2. White
Issued:	1956-c.1975
Series:	Tropical Fish (Small size)

	Coloured	White
U.S.	$275.00	175.00
Can.	$325.00	200.00
U.K.	£150.00	95.00

RW3580
TROOPER OF THE SWISS GUARD OF HIS HOLINESS THE POPE

Modeller:	Frederick M. Gertner
Height:	15", 38.1 cm
Colour:	Orange, blue and red striped uniform; platinum and red helmet; brown and platinum staff
Issued:	1956 in a limited edition of 150
Series:	Papal Guard

U.S.	$ 925.00
Can.	$1,100.00
U.K.	£ 500.00

Note: Each model is numbered and comes with a certificate of authenticity.

RW3581
LISERION (Bird)

Modeller:	A. Azori
Height:	9", 22.9 cm
Colour:	1. Naturalistically coloured
	2. White biscuit porcelain
Issued:	1956

	Natural	White
U.S.	$650.00	275.00
Can.	$775.00	325.00
U.K.	£350.00	150.00

RW3582
MARGUERITE (Cockerel)

Modeller:	A. Azori
Height:	9", 22.9 cm
Colour:	1. Naturalistically coloured
	2. White biscuit porcelain
Issued:	1956

	Natural	White
U.S.	$650.00	275.00
Can.	$775.00	325.00
U.K.	£350.00	150.00

RW3583
COQUELICOT (Bird)

Modeller:	A. Azori
Height:	9", 22.9 cm
Colour:	1. Naturalistically coloured
	2. White biscuit porcelain
Issued:	1956

	Natural	White
U.S.	$650.00	275.00
Can.	$775.00	325.00
U.K.	£350.00	150.00

RW3584
ANEMONE (Bird)

Modeller:	A. Azori
Height:	9", 22.9 cm
Colour:	1. Naturalistically coloured
	2. White biscuit porcelain
Issued:	1956

	Natural	White
U.S.	$650.00	275.00
Can.	$775.00	325.00
U.K.	£350.00	150.00

RW3585
LE PANIER

Modeller:	A. Azori
Height:	11 ¼", 28.5 cm
Colour:	1. Glazed cream (Wallbody)
	2. Glazed white (Bone china)
Issued:	1956
Series:	Bisque Figures

	Cream	White
U.S.	$500.00	175.00
Can.	$600.00	200.00
U.K.	£275.00	100.00

RW3586
LA FLEUR

Modeller:	A. Azori	
Height:	11 ¼", 28.5 cm	
Colour:	1. Glazed cream (Wallbody)	
	2. Glazed white (Bone china)	
Issued:	1956	
Series:	Bisque Figures	

	Cream	White
U.S.	$450.00	175.00
Can.	$550.00	200.00
U.K.	£250.00	100.00

RW3587
L'OISEAU

Modeller:	A. Azori	
Height:	11 ¼", 28.5 cm	
Colour:	1. Glazed cream (Wallbody)	
	2. Glazed white (Bone china)	
Issued:	1956	
Series:	Bisque Figures	

	Cream	White
U.S.	$450.00	175.00
Can.	$550.00	200.00
U.K.	£250.00	100.00

RW3588
LA MIROIR

Modeller:	A. Azori	
Height:	11 ¼", 28.5 cm	
Colour:	1. Glazed cream (Wallbody)	
	2. Glazed white (Bone china)	
Issued:	1956	
Series:	Bisque Figures	

	Cream	White
U.S.	$450.00	175.00
Can.	$550.00	200.00
U.K.	£250.00	100.00

RW3589
PRIVY CHAMBERLAIN OF THE SWORD AND CAPE TO THE POPE IN THE SPANISH COSTUME

Modeller:	Frederick M. Gertner
Height:	11", 27.9 cm
Colour:	Charcoal, black, scarlet and white
Issued:	1956 in a limited edition of 150
Series:	Papal Guard

U.S.	$ 925.00
Can.	$1,100.00
U.K.	£ 500.00

RW3590
HOODED WARBLER AND CHEROKEE ROSE (Cock)
(Wilsonia Critina)

Modeller:	Dorothy Doughty
Height:	10 ½", 26.0 cm
Colour:	Yellow, green and black bird; white flower and bud; green foliage; grey-green base
Plinth:	Wooden
Issued:	1961 in a limited edition of 500
Series:	Doughty American Birds

U.S.	$1,000.00
Can.	$1,200.00
U.K.	£ 550.00

Note: Missing plinth.

RW3591
HOODED WARBLER AND CHEROKEE ROSE (Hen)
(Wilsonia Critina)

Modeller:	Dorothy Doughty
Height:	10 ½", 26.0 cm
Colour:	Yellow and mauve bird; white flowers and bud; green foliage; green-brown base
Plinth:	Wooden
Issued:	1961 in a limited edition of 500
Series:	Doughty American Birds

U.S.	$1,000.00
Can.	$1,200.00
U.K.	£ 550.00

Note: Missing plinth.

132

RW3592
DOWNY WOODPECKER AND PECAN (Cock)
(Dendrocopus Pubescens)
Modeller: Dorothy Doughty
Height: 10", 25.4 cm
Colour: 1. Dark grey, white and red bird; green leaves; brown-green
                 branch
             2. White
Plinth: Wooden
Issued: 1. Coloured: 1967 in a limited edition of 500
             2. White: 1967 in a limited edition of 75
Series: Doughty American Birds

	Coloured	**White**
U.S.	$1,000.00	375.00
Can.	$1,200.00	450.00
U.K.	£ 550.00	200.00

RW3593
DOWNY WOODPECKER AND PECAN (Hen)
(Dendrocopus Pubescens)
Modeller: Dorothy Doughty
Height: 10", 25.4 cm
Colour: 1. Brown, dark grey and white bird; green leaves;
                 brown-grey branch
             2. White
Plinth: Wooden
Issued: 1. Coloured: 1967 in a limited edition of 500
             2. White: 1967 in a limited edition of 75
Series: Doughty American Birds

	Coloured	**White**
U.S.	$1,000.00	375.00
Can.	$1,200.00	450.00
U.K.	£ 550.00	200.00

RW3594
COLONEL OF THE NOBLE GUARD
IN GALA UNIFORM
Modeller: Neal French
Height: 12", 30.5 cm
Colour: Red jacket with gold
             decoration; white
             trousers; long black
             boots
Issued: 1956 in a limited edition
             of 150
Series: Papal Guard

U.S.	$ 925.00
Can.	$1,100.00
U.K.	£ 500.00

RW3595
AN OFFICER OF THE PALATINE GUARD
Modeller: Neal French
Height: 12", 30.5 cm
Colour: Black jacket with gold trim; blue trousers; black shoes;
             black and gold hat with white plume
Issued: 1956 in a limited edition of 150
Series   Papal Guard

U.S.	$ 925.00
Can.	$1,100.00
U.K.	£ 500.00

RW3596
PAPAL GENDARME
Modeller: Neal French
Height: 12", 30.5 cm
Colour: Indigo tunic; white
             trousers; black helmet
             with red plume; black
             boots
Issued: 1956 in a limited edition
             of 150
Series: Papal Guard

U.S.	$ 925.00
Can.	$1,100.00
U.K.	£ 500.00

Note: Each model is numbered and comes with a certificate of authenticity.

RW3602
RED HIND FISH
Style Two
Modeller:	Ronald Van Ruyckevelt
Height:	12 ¾", 32.4 cm
Colour:	White with pink dots and stripes; yellow and black fins
Plinth:	Wooden
Issued:	1956 in a limited edition of 500
Series:	Tropical Fish (Large size)
U.S.	$ 825.00
Can.	$1,000.00
U.K.	£ 450.00

RW3603
BLUE ANGEL FISH
Style Two
Modeller:	Ronald Van Ruyckevelt
Height:	12", 30.5 cm
Colour:	Blue, green and yellow
Plinth:	Wooden
Issued:	1956 in a limited edition of 500
Series:	Tropical Fish (Large size)
U.S.	$ 825.00
Can.	$1,000.00
U.K.	£ 450.00

Note: Missing plinth.

RW3604
SQUIRREL FISH
Modeller:	Ronald Van Ruyckevelt
Height:	10 ½", 26.7 cm
Colour:	Pink, yellow, aqua, black and purple
Plinth:	Wooden
Issued:	1956 in a limited edition of 500
Series:	Tropical Fish (Large size)
U.S.	$ 825.00
Can.	$1,000.00
U.K.	£ 450.00

RW3605
ROCK BEAUTY FISH
Modeller:	Ronald Van Ruyckevelt
Height:	10", 30.5 cm
Colour:	Black, green and yellow
Plinth:	Wooden
Issued:	1956 in a limited edition of 500
Series:	Tropical Fish (Large size)
U.S.	$ 825.00
Can.	$1,000.00
U.K.	£ 450.00

RW3606
RAINBOW PARROT FISH
Modeller:	Ronald Van Ruyckevelt
Height:	12", 30.5 cm
Colour:	Unknown
Plinth:	Wooden
Issued:	1956 in a limited edition of 500
Series:	Tropical Fish (Large size)
U.S.	$ 825.00
Can.	$1,000.00
U.K.	£ 450.00

RW3607
CLARISSA
Modeller:	Neal French
Height:	7", 17.8 cm
Colour:	Light green dress with leaf pattern; apricot underskirt, bustle; black, white and gold base
Issued:	1956-by 1959
U.S.	$500.00
Can.	$600.00
U.K.	£275.00

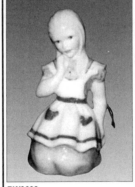

RW3608
ALICE
Style One
Modeller:	Freda Doughty
Height:	4", 10.1 cm
Colour:	Pale blue dress; white apron edged with pink; yellow hair
Issued:	1957-1959
Series:	Alice in Wonderland
U.S.	$ 825.00
Can.	$1,000.00
U.K.	£ 450.00

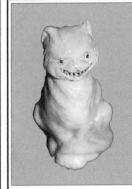

RW3609
CHESHIRE CAT
Modeller:	Freda Doughty
Height:	4", 10.1 cm
Colour:	Grey with white markings
Issued:	1957-1959
Series:	Alice in Wonderland
U.S.	$ 925.00
Can.	$1,100.00
U.K.	£ 500.00

RW3610
MOCK TURTLE
Modeller: Freda Doughty
Height: 3 ¼", 8.3 cm
Colour: Brown head; green flippers; yellow shell
Issued: 1957-1959
Series: Alice in Wonderland

U.S. $ 825.00
Can. $1,000.00
U.K. £ 450.00

Note: The Mock Turtle is a hollow-based figure and not a candle-snuffer.

RW3611
WHITE RABBIT
Modeller: Freda Doughty
Height: 4", 10.1 cm
Colour: Red coat; yellow waistcoat; black buttons and bow-tie; white gloves
Issued: 1957-1959
Series: Alice in Wonderland

U.S. $ 925.00
Can. $1,100.00
U.K. £ 500.00

RW3612
THE DUCHESS
Modeller: Freda Doughty
Height: 4", 10.1 cm
Colour: Purple robe edged in yellow; yellow dress; purple headdress; white veil
Issued: 1957-1959
Series: Alice in Wonderland

U.S. $ 825.00
Can. $1,000.00
U.K. £ 450.00

RW3613
DODO (The)
Modeller: Freda Doughty
Height: 4", 10.1 cm
Colour: 1. Brown back; yellow breast; cream and yellow face; red eyes, beak and feet; brown cane
2. Pale brown back; yellow breast; pale green and yellow face; blue cuffs; pink eyes, beak and feet; pale brown cane
Issued: 1957-1959
Series: Alice in Wonderland

U.S. $ 825.00
Can. $1,000.00
U.K. £ 450.00

Note: The Dodo is a hollow-based figure and not a candle-snuffer.

RW3614
OLD FATHER WILLIAM
Modeller: Freda Doughty
Height: 3 ¼", 8.3 cm
Colour: Blue coat; yellow waistcoat with blue buttons; brown trousers; red cravat; white hair and pipe
Issued: 1957-1959
Series: Alice in Wonderland

U.S. $ 925.00
Can. $1,100.00
U.K. £ 500.00

Note: Old Father William is a hollow-based figure and not a candle-snuffer.

RW3615
LONG-HAIRED CAT
Modeller:	Freda Doughty
Height:	4", 10.1 cm
Colour:	1. Ginger and white
	2. Grey and white
Issued:	1957
U.S.	$225.00
Can.	$275.00
U.K.	£125.00

RW3616
SHORT-HAIRED CAT
Modeller:	Freda Doughty
Height:	3", 7.5 cm
Colour:	1. White with brown markings
	2. Tortoiseshell (white, black and ginger)
Issued:	1957
U.S.	$225.00
Can.	$275.00
U.K.	£125.00

RW3617
ELF OWL AND SAGUARO
(Micropallas Whitneyi Whitneyi)
Modeller:	Dorothy Doughty
Height:	11", 27.9 cm
Colour:	Grey and white bird; white flowers with yellow centres; green foliage base
Plinth:	Wooden
Issued:	1958 in a limited edition of 500
Series:	Doughty American Birds
U.S.	$1,100.00
Can.	$1,325.00
U.K.	£ 600.00

Note: Missing plinth.

RW3618
CACTUS WREN AND PRICKLY PEAR (Cock)
(Heleodytis Brunneicapillus Couesi)
Modeller:	Dorothy Doughty
Height:	10 ½", 26.7 cm
Colour:	Black, yellow and white bird; yellow flowers; mauve and green cactus; red, yellow and black snake; green-brown base
Plinth:	Wooden
Issued:	1959 in a limited edition of 500
Series:	Doughty American Birds
U.S.	$1,100.00
Can.	$1,325.00
U.K.	£ 600.00

Note: Missing plinth.

RW3619
CACTUS WREN AND PRICKLY PEAR (Hen)
(Heleodytis Brunneicapillus Couesi)
Modeller:	Dorothy Doughty
Height:	10 ½", 26.7 cm
Colour:	Browns, black and white bird; yellow flowers; mauve and green cactus; brown base
Plinth:	Wooden
Issued:	1959 in a limited edition of 500
Series:	Doughty American Birds
U.S.	$1,100.00
Can.	$1,325.00
U.K.	£ 600.00

Note: Missing plinth.

136

RW3620
AMANDA
Style One
Modeller: Neal French
Height: 7", 17.8 cm
Colour: 1. Beige overdress; blue underskirt; green edging
2. Light blue overdress; cream underskirt; green and white base
3. White dress with claret rose pattern; claret and white striped bodice; black, white and gold base
Issued: 1957-by 1959

U.S. $500.00
Can. $600.00
U.K. £275.00

RW3622
OFFICER OF THE LIFE GUARDS
Modeller: Doris Lindner
Heights: 9", 22.9 cm
Colour: Red, white and black
Plinth: Wooden
Issued: 1957 in a limited edition of 150

U.S. $1,850.00
Can. $2,200.00
U.K. £1,000.00

RW3623
OFFICER OF THE BLUES
Modeller: Doris Lindner
Heights: 9", 22.9 cm
Colour: Blue, white and black
Plinth: Wooden
Issued: 1957 in a limited edition of 150

U.S. $1,850.00
Can. $2,200.00
U.K. £1,000.00

RW3627
SCISSOR-TAILED FLYCATCHERS (Wall hanging)
(Muscivora Forficata)
Modeller: Dorothy Doughty
Length: 24", 61.0 cm
Colour: 1. Blue, green-brown and orange
2. White
Issued: 1. Coloured: 1957 in a limited edition of 250
2. White: 1957 in a limited edition of 75
Series: Doughty American Birds

	Coloured	White
U.S.	$ 925.00	275.00
Can.	$1,100.00	325.00
U.K.	£ 500.00	150.00

RW3629
FIRST DANCE
Style One
Modeller: Freda Doughty
Height: 7", 17.8 cm
Colour: 1. Cream dress; burgundy stole with black fringe
2. Green dress with yellow highlights; yellow stole with gold fringe
3. Mauve dress; pink stole with yellow and blue edging and black fringe
Issued: 1957-1983
Reissued: 1990-1996

U.S. $275.00
Can. $325.00
U.K. £150.00

RW3630
SWEET ANNE
Modeller:	Freda Doughty
Height:	7", 17.8 cm
Colour:	1. Blue dress with white cuffs and underskirt; light brown hair; green fan (gloss)
	2. Mottled green and lilac dress (gloss)
	3. Pale green dress with white cuffs and underskirt; multicouloured fan; light brown hair (matt)
Issued:	1957-1983

U.S.	$275.00
Can.	$325.00
U.K.	£150.00

RW3632
EXTINCT CAROLINA PAROQUETS (Wall hanging)
(Conuropsis Carolinensis)
Modeller:	Dorothy Doughty
Length:	15", 38.1 cm
Colour:	1. Green, blue, yellow and red
	2. White
Issued:	1. Coloured: 1957 in a limited edition of 250
	2. White: 1957 in a limited edition of 75
Series:	Doughty American Birds

	Coloured	White
U.S.	$ 925.00	275.00
Can.	$1,100.00	325.00
U.K.	£ 500.00	150.00

RW3639
CANYON WREN AND WILD LUPIN (Cock)
(Catherpes Mexicanus)
Modeller:	Dorothy Doughty
Height:	8", 20.3 cm
Colour:	Brown-green and grey bird; mauve-blue flowers; green leaves; brown base
Plinth:	Wooden
Issued:	1961 in a limited edition of 500
Series:	Doughty American Birds

U.S.	$1,000.00
Can.	$1,200.00
U.K.	£ 550.00

Note: Missing plinth.

RW3640
CANYON WREN AND WILD LUPIN (Hen)
(Catherpes Mexicanus)
Modeller:	Dorothy Doughty
Height:	8", 20.3 cm
Colour:	Brown-green, grey and russet bird; mauve-blue flowers; green leaves; brown base
Plinth:	Wooden
Issued:	1961 in a limited edition of 500
Series:	Doughty American Birds

U.S.	$1,000.00
Can.	$1,200.00
U.K.	£ 550.00

Note: Missing plinth.

RW3642
LISETTE
Modeller:	Ruth Van Ruyckevelt
Height:	6 ½", 16.5 cm
Colour:	Turquoise jacket and muff edged with white; yellow and white skirt; lavender underskirt with ruffled edges; pink shoe
Issued:	1958 in a limited edition of 500
Series:	Victorian Ladies
U.S.	$675.00
Can.	$825.00
U.K.	£375.00

RW3643
PENELOPE
Style One
Modeller:	Ruth Van Ruyckevelt
Height:	6 ½", 16.5 cm
Colour:	Pale orange dress; yellow overskirt trimmed with white; brown hair; green shoe; yellow and white bouquet
Issued:	1958 in a limited edition of 500
Series:	Victorian Ladies
U.S.	$675.00
Can.	$825.00
U.K.	£375.00

RW3645
CARDINAL
Modeller:	Ronald Van Ruyckevelt
Height:	3 ¼", 8.3 cm
Colour:	Red with black highlights
Issued:	1958-1977
Series:	Small American Birds
U.S.	$ 90.00
Can.	$110.00
U.K.	£ 50.00

RW3646
BLUE JAY (American Version)
Modeller:	Ronald Van Ruyckevelt
Height:	3 ¼", 8.3 cm
Colour:	Light brown, light blue and grey
Issued:	1958-1977
Series:	Small American Birds
U.S.	$ 90.00
Can.	$110.00
U.K.	£ 50.00

RW3647
AMERICAN ROBIN
Modeller:	Ronald Van Ruyckevelt
Height:	4", 10.1 cm
Colour:	Brown with black head and wing feathers; yellow beak
Issued:	1958-1977
Series:	Small American Birds
U.S.	$ 90.00
Can.	$110.00
U.K.	£ 50.00

RW3648
WAX WING
Modeller:	Ronald Van Ruyckevelt
Height:	3", 7.6 cm
Colour:	Orange and black
Issued:	1958-1977
Series:	Small American Birds
U.S.	$ 90.00
Can.	$110.00
U.K.	£ 50.00

RW3649
BLUEBIRD
Modeller: Ronald Van Ruyckevelt
Height: 3", 7.6 cm
Colour: Light blue and orange
Issued: 1958-1977
Series: Small American Birds

U.S. $ 90.00
Can. $110.00
U.K. £ 50.00

RW3650
WESTERN TANAGER
Modeller: Ronald Van Ruyckevelt
Height: 2 ½", 5.7 cm
Colour: Yellow; red head, black and yellow wings
Issued: 1958-1977
Series: Small American Birds

U.S. $ 90.00
Can. $110.00
U.K. £ 50.00

RW3651
LAZULI BUNTING AND CHOKE CHERRY (Cock)
(Passerina Amoena)
Modeller: Dorothy Doughty
Height: 10", 25.4 cm
Colour: 1. Blue, white and russet bird; white blossom; green leaves; grey-brown branch
2. White
Plinth: Wooden
Issued: 1. Coloured: 1958 in a limited edition of 500
2. White: 1958 in a limited edition of 250
Series: Doughty American Birds

	Coloured	White
U.S.	$1,100.00	375.00
Can.	$1,325.00	450.00
U.K.	£ 600.00	200.00

RW3652
LAZULI BUNTING AND CHOKE CHERRY (Hen)
(Passerina Amoena)
Modeller: Dorothy Doughty
Height: 10", 25.4 cm
Colour: 1. Mauve, blue and brown bird; white blossom; green leaves; grey-brown branch
2. White
Plinth: Wooden
Issued: 1. Coloured: 1958 in a limited edition of 500
2. White: 1958 in a limited edition of 250
Series: American Birds

	Coloured	White
U.S.	$1,100.00	375.00
Can.	$1,325.00	450.00
U.K.	£ 600.00	200.00

RW3655
SURPRISE
Modeller: Freda Doughty
Height: 7 ½", 19.1 cm
Colour: Yellow dress; pink and green sash; brown hair
Issued: 1958-1958

U.S. $1,100.00
Can. $1,325.00
U.K. £ 600.00

RW3656
MAYFLOWER
First Version (Hat and telescope on base)
Modeller: Freda Doughty
Height: 7 ½", 19.1 cm
Colour: 1. Blue jacket; yellow epaulettes and buttons; cream
                  waistcoat; light brown breeches; brown bow, shoes and
                  hat; dark brown ship with cream sails
              2. Red jacket; yellow waistcoat, epaulettes and buttons;
                  pale green breeches; black bow, shoes and hat; light
                  brown ship with yellow sails
Issued: 1958-1958
Varieties: RW3761

U.S. $ 925.00
Can. $1,100.00
U.K.   £ 500.00

RW3657
VERMILION FLYCATCHER AND PUSSY WILLOW (Cock)
(Pyrocephalus Rubinus Mexicanus)
Modeller: Dorothy Doughty
Height: 9 ¼", 23.5 cm
Colour: Red and brown bird; yellow pussy willow; green-brown
              base and stem
Plinth: Wooden
Issued: 1962 in a limited edition of 500
Series: Doughty American Birds

U.S. $ 925.00
Can. $1,100.00
U.K.   £ 500.00

Note: Missing plinth.

RW3658
VERMILION FLYCATCHER AND PUSSY WILLOW (Hen)
(Pyrocephalus Rubinus Mexicanus)
Modeller: Dorothy Doughty
Height: 9 ¼", 23.5 cm
Colour: Green-brown and dull yellow bird; yellow flowers;
              green-brown base and stem
Plinth: Wooden
Issued: 1962 in a limited edition of 500
Series: Doughty American Birds

U.S. $ 925.00
Can. $1,100.00
U.K.   £ 500.00

Note: Missing plinth.

RW3659
CERULEAN WARBLER AND RED MAPLE (Cock)
(Dendroica Cerulea)
Modeller: Dorothy Doughty
Height: 8 ½", 21.6 cm
Colour: Blue, black and white bird; green and red foliage;
              green-grey base
Plinth: Wooden
Issued: 1965 in a limited edition of 500
Series: Doughty American Birds

U.S. $ 925.00
Can. $1,100.00
U.K.   £ 500.00

Note: Missing plinth.

RW3660
CERULEAN WARBLER AND RED MAPLE (Hen)
(Dendroica Cerulea)
Modeller: Dorothy Doughty
Height: 8 ½", 21.6 cm
Colour: Blue-grey and creamy yellow bird; green and red foliage;
              green-grey base
Plinth: Wooden
Issued: 1965 in a limited edition of 500
Series: Doughty American Birds

U.S. $ 925.00
Can. $1,100.00
U.K.   £ 500.00

Note: Missing plinth.

RW3662
SISTER, THE LONDON HOSPITAL
Modeller: Ruth Van Ruyckevelt
Height: 6 ¾", 17.2 cm
Colour: Blue uniform with white cuffs, buttons, collar and cap;
              brown shoes; white and blue patterned chair with wooden
              frame; white and gold base
Issued: 1958 in a limited edition of 500
Series: Nursing Sisters

U.S. $ 925.00
Can. $1,100.00
U.K.   £ 500.00

RW3663
SISTER, NIGHTINGALE TRAINING SCHOOL
ST. THOMAS' HOSPITAL (LONDON)
Modeller: Ruth Van Ruyckevelt
Height: 7", 17.8 cm
Colour: Dark blue uniform with white cuffs; white apron and cap;
              black shoes; white and mauve striped chair; white and gold
              base
Issued: 1958 in a limited edition of 500
Series: Nursing Sisters

U.S. $ 925.00
Can. $1,100.00
U.K.   £ 500.00

RW3665
MOUNTAIN BLUEBIRD AND SPLEENWORT NIGER (Cock)
(Sialia Currucoides)
Modeller: Dorothy Doughty
Height: 9 ½", 24.1 cm
Colour: Blue and white bird; green foliage; green-grey base
Plinth: Wooden
Issued: 1964 in a limited edition of 500
Series: Doughty American Birds

U.S. $650.00
Can. $775.00
U.K.   £350.00

Note: Missing plinth.

RW3666
MOUNTAIN BLUEBIRD AND SPLEENWORT NIGER (Hen)
(Sialia Currucoides)
Modeller:	Dorothy Doughty
Height:	9 ½", 24.1 cm
Colour:	Blue and white bird; green foliage; green-grey base
Plinth:	Wooden
Issued:	1964 in a limited edition of 500
Series:	Doughty American Birds
U.S.	$650.00
Can.	$775.00
U.K.	£350.00

Note: Missing plinth.

RW3667
THE WINNER WITH JOCKEY AND STABLE BOY
Modeller:	Doris Lindner
Height:	11 ¼", 28.5 cm
Colour:	1. Grey
	2. Brown
Issued:	1959-1959
U.S.	
Can.	Extremely rare
U.K.	

Note: To make production more practical, the stable boy was eliminated from model RW3667 and the plinth was shortened slightly. Although the jockey came painted in the Queen's racing colours, for an extra fee, the colours could be customised.

RW3668
HEREFORD BULL "VERN INSPIRATION"
Modeller:	Doris Lindner
Height:	7", 17.8 cm
Colour:	Reddish-brown and white
Plinth:	Wooden
Issued:	1959 in a limited edition of 1,000
Series:	Prize Cattle
U.S.	$ 925.00
Can.	$1,100.00
U.K.	£ 500.00

RW3669
AUDUBON WARBLER AND PALO VERDI (Cock)
(Dendroica Auduboni)
Modeller:	Dorothy Doughty
Height:	7 ½", 19.1 cm
Colour:	Brownish-grey, yellow and white bird; yellow flowers; green stem; brown-grey base
Plinth:	Wooden
Issued:	1963 in a limited edition of 500
Series:	Doughty American Birds
U.S.	$ 875.00
Can.	$1,050.00
U.K.	£ 475.00

Note: Missing plinth.

RW3670
AUDUBON WARBLER AND PALO VERDI (Female)
(Dendroica Auduboni)
Modeller: Dorothy Doughty
Height: 7 ½", 19.1 cm
Colour: Brownish-grey, yellow and white bird; yellow flowers;
green stem; brown-grey base
Plinth: Wooden
Issued: 1963 in a limited edition of 500
Series: Doughty American Birds

U.S. $ 875.00
Can. $1,050.00
U.K. £ 475.00

Note: Missing plinth.

RW3671
THE WINNER
Modeller: Doris Lindner
Height: 11 ¼", 28.5 cm
Colour: Rider: Red and purple silks; white jodhpurs; black hat and
boots
Horse: Bay or grey
Plinth: Wooden
Issued: 1959-by 1980

U.S. $1,850.00
Can. $2,250.00
U.K. £1,000.00

Note: This is model RW3667 with the stable boy eliminated, and the plinth
shortened. Although the jockey came painted in the Queen's racing
colours, for an extra fee, the colours could be customised.

Photograph not
available
at press time

RW3675
OFFICER OF THE COLDSTREAM GUARDS 1815
Third Version
Modeller: Frederick M. Gertner
Height: 11 ¾", 29.8 cm
Colour: Red tunic; white trousers; black hat and boots; gold
decoration
Issued: 1959-c.1979
Variations: RW2635 (First Version), RW2676 (Second Version)
Series: Historical Military Figures
Comm. by: Aspreys, London, England

U.S. $ 825.00
Can. $1,050.00
U.K. £ 475.00

Photograph not
available
at press time

RW3677
OFFICER OF THE SCOTS GUARDS
Modeller: Frederick M. Gertner
Height: 11 ¼", 28.5 cm
Colour: Red jacket with gold epaulettes; green, blue and turquoise
kilt; black bearskin
Issued: 1959-c.1979
Varieties: Also called RW2657 "Seaforth Highlander Officer"
Series: Historical Military Figures
Comm. by: Aspreys, London, England,

U.S. $ 825.00
Can. $1,050.00
U.K. £ 475.00

144

RW3678
FOXHUNTER AND LIEUT.-COL. H.M. LLEWELLYN, C.B.E.

Modeller:	Doris Lindner
Height:	12", 30.5 cm
Colour:	Rider: Red jacket; white jodhpurs; black boots and hat
	Horse: Bay with black lower legs and tail
Issued:	1959 in a limited edition of 500

U.S.	$1,850.00
Can.	$2,250.00
U.K.	£1,000.00

Note: There are 100 signed and 400 unsigned pieces.

RW3679
MERLIN

Modeller:	Freda Doughty
Height:	7", 17.8 cm
Colour:	Cream shirt; beige and maroon doublet; brown shoes; dark brown and golden merlin
Issued:	1959-1959
Varieties:	Also called "The Falconer"

U.S.	$1,300.00
Can.	$1,550.00
U.K.	£ 700.00

RW3681
BEATRICE

Modeller:	Ruth Van Ruyckevelt
Height:	7 ½", 19.1 cm
Colour:	Lavender
Issued:	1959 in a limited edition of 500
Series:	Victorian Ladies

U.S.	$750.00
Can.	$900.00
U.K.	£400.00

RW3682
CAROLINE
Style One

Modeller:	Ruth Van Ruyckevelt
Height:	7 ½", 19.1 cm
Colour:	Light blue skirt with white flowers and trim; red striped bodice; white fan; black gloves; brown hair
Issued:	1959 in a limited edition of 500
Series:	Victorian Ladies

U.S.	$750.00
Can.	$900.00
U.K.	£400.00

RW3686
LARK SPARROW WITH TWIN POD AND RED GILA
(Chondestes Grammacus Striciatus)

Modeller:	Dorothy Doughty
Height:	4 ½", 11.4 cm
Colour:	Cream and brown bird; yellow and coral flowers; green leaves; dark grey-green base
Plinth:	Wooden
Issued:	1966 in a limited edition of 500
Series:	Doughty American Birds

U.S.	$600.00
Can.	$725.00
U.K.	£375.00

RW3687
REBECCA
Style One
Modeller: Ruth Van Ruyckevelt
Height: 8 ¼", 21.0 cm
Colour: 1. Green bodice; multicoloured ruffled skirt;
            black and purple bow; cream and yellow lattice chair
         2. Pink and blue crinoline
Issued: 1959 in a limited edition of 500
Series: Victorian Ladies

U.S. $ 825.00
Can. $1,000.00
U.K. £ 450.00

RW3688
LOUISA
Modeller: Ruth Van Ruyckevelt
Height: 7 ¾", 19.7 cm
Colour: White, pink and lavender
Issued: 1959 in a limited edition of 500
Series: Victorian Ladies

U.S. $750.00
Can. $900.00
U.K. £400.00

RW3689
JERSEY COW "BRAMLEY ZENORA"
Modeller: Doris Lindner
Height: 7 ¼", 18.4 cm
Colour: Light brown with black
Plinth: Wooden
Issued: 1959 in a limited edition of 500
Series: Prize Cattle

U.S. $1,100.00
Can. $1,325.00
U.K. £ 600.00

RW3690
GREY WAGTAIL AND CELANDINE
(Cock) (Motacilla Melanope)
Modeller: Dorothy Doughty
Height: 6 ½", 16.5 cm
Colour: Light grey with yellow breast; green leaves; yellow flower
Plinth: Wooden
Issued: 1968 in a limited edition of 500
Series: Doughty British Birds

U.S. $ 875.00
Can. $1,050.00
U.K. £ 475.00

Note: Missing plinth.

RW3692
ENGLISH REDSTART ON GORSE IN SPRING (Cock)
(Ruticilla Phoenicurus)
Modeller: Dorothy Doughty
Height: 11 ¼", 28.5 cm
Colour: Grey with orange bird; yellow flowers; grey-green gorse
Plinth: Wooden
Issued: 1968 in a limited edition of 500
Series: Doughty British Birds

U.S. $ 875.00
Can. $1,050.00
U.K. £ 475.00

RW3693
ENGLISH REDSTART ON GORSE
(Hen) (Ruticilla Phoenicurus)
Modeller: Dorothy Doughty
Height: 7 ¾", 19.7 cm
Colour: Brown bird with red breast; green gorse; yellow flowers
Plinth: Wooden
Issued: 1968 in a limited edition of 500
Series: Doughty British Birds

U.S. $ 875.00
Can. $1,050.00
U.K. £ 475.00

RW3694
LESSER WHITETHROAT ON WILD
ROSE (Cock)
(Sylvia Curruca)
Modeller:	Dorothy Doughty
Height:	10 ¼", 26.0 cm
Colour:	Unknown
Plinth:	Wooden
Issued:	1966 in a limited edition of 500
Series:	Doughty British Birds
U.S.	$ 925.00
Can.	$1,100.00
U.K.	£ 500.00

RW3695
LESSER WHITETHROAT ON WILD
ROSE (Hen)
(Sylvia Curruca)
Modeller:	Dorothy Doughty
Height:	10 ½", 26.7 cm
Colour:	Unknown
Plinth:	Wooden
Issued:	1966 in a limited edition of 500
Series:	Doughty British Birds
U.S.	$ 925.00
Can.	$1,100.00
U.K.	£ 500.00

RW3696
WREN AND BURNET ROSE (Cock)
(Troglodytes Parvulus)
Modeller:	Dorothy Doughty
Height:	5 ¾", 14.6 cm
Colour:	Unknown
Plinth:	Wooden
Issued:	1966 in a limited edition of 500
Series:	Doughty British Birds
U.S.	$ 925.00
Can.	$1,100.00
U.K.	£ 500.00

RW3697
ABERDEEN ANGUS BULL
"NEWHOUSE JEWLIAN ERIC"
Modeller:	Doris Lindner
Height:	7 ½", 19.1 cm
Colour:	Black
Plinth:	Wooden
Issued:	1959 in a limited edition of 500
Series:	Prized Cattle
U.S.	$1,100.00
Can.	$1,325.00
U.K.	£ 600.00

RW3698
INVITATION
Style One
Modeller:	Freda Doughty
Height:	8 ¾", 22.2 cm
Colour:	1. Pale green-yellow dress; red and green neck bow; yellow hair
	2. Yellow spotted dress; with black bows and trim
Issued:	1960
U.S.	$1,575.00
Can.	$1,900.00
U.K.	£ 850.00

RW3699
RED RIBBONS
Style One
Modeller:	Freda Doughty
Height:	8", 20.3 cm
Colour:	Multicoloured
Issued:	1960-1960
U.S.	$1,575.00
Can.	$1,900.00
U.K.	£ 850.00

RW3700
THE TEA PARTY
Modeller:	Ruth Van Ruyckevelt
Height:	8", 20.3 cm
Colour:	Standing lady: Mustard dress, white trim; pink feather in brown hat
	Seated lady: Light blue-grey dress with white trim; purple hat, with lilac feather and purple parasol
	Girl: Light blue and white patterned dress; straw hat
	Dog: White and brown
Issued:	1960 in a limited edition of 250
Series:	Victorian Figures
U.S.	$3,000.00
Can.	$2,500.00
U.K.	£1,350.00

RW3701
NIGHTINGALE AND HONEYSUCKLE
(Daulias Luscinia)

Modeller:	Dorothy Doughty
Height:	10 ¼", 26.0 cm
Colour:	Russet brown and white bird; brown branch, pink flowers and green-grey leaves
Plinth:	Wooden
Issued:	1971 in a limited edition of 500
Series:	Doughty British Birds
U.S.	$ 875.00
Can.	$1,050.00
U.K.	£ 475.00

RW3702
SANTA GERTRUDIS BULL
"PRINCE"

Modeller:	Doris Lindner
Height:	8 ¼", 20.9 cm
Colour:	Dark brown
Plinth:	Wooden
Issued:	1960 in a limited edition of 500
Series:	Prize Cattle
U.S.	$1,100.00
Can.	$1,325.00
U.K.	£ 600.00

RW3703
GOLDCREST AND LARCH (Cock)
(Regulus Cristatus)

Modeller:	Dorothy Doughty
Height:	10 ¼", 26.0 cm
Colour:	Unknown
Plinth:	Wooden
Issued:	1973 in a limited edition of 500
Series:	Doughty British Birds
U.S.	$ 875.00
Can.	$1,050.00
U.K.	£ 475.00

Note: Missing plinth.

RW3704
GOLDCREST AND LARCH (Hen)
(Regulus Cristatus)

Modeller:	Dorothy Doughty
Height:	10 ½", 26.6 cm
Colour:	Unknown
Plinth:	Wooden
Issued:	1973 in a limited edition of 500
Series:	Doughty British Birds
U.S.	$ 875.00
Can.	$1,050.00
U.K.	£ 475.00

Note: Missing plinth.

RW3707
ROBIN IN AUTUMN WOODS
(Erythacus Rebecula)

Modeller:	Dorothy Doughty
Height:	7 ¼", 18.1 cm
Colour:	Orange, browns and light blue; yellow mushrooms; green branches; brown rocks
Plinth:	Wooden
Issued:	1966 in a limited edition of 500
Series:	Doughty British Birds
U.S.	$ 925.00
Can.	$1,100.00
U.K.	£ 500.00

RW3708
BLUE-TIT AND PUSSY WILLOW IN SPRING (Cock)
(Parus Coeruleus)

Modeller:	Dorothy Doughty
Height:	7 ¾", 19.7 cm
Colour:	Unknown
Plinth:	Wooden
Issued:	1966 in a limited edition of 500
Series:	Doughty British Birds
U.S.	$ 925.00
Can.	$1,100.00
U.K.	£ 500.00

RW3709
BLUE-TIT BATHING IN AN OLD WILLOW STUMP (Hen)
Modeller:	Dorothy Doughty
Height:	6 ¾", 17.1 cm
Colour:	Unknown
Plinth:	Wooden
Issued:	1966 in a limited edition of 500
Series:	Doughty British Birds
U.S.	$ 925.00
Can.	$1,100.00
U.K.	£ 500.00

RW3712
BULLFINCH AND BLACKTHORNE
(Pyrrhula Europoea)
Modeller:	Dorothy Doughty
Height:	Unknown
Colour:	Orange, black and grey bird; white flowers
Plinth:	Wooden
Issued:	1962 in a limited edition of 500
Series:	Doughty British Birds
U.S.	$ 925.00
Can.	$1,100.00
U.K.	£ 500.00

RW3713
MEADOW PIPIT AND SILVERWEED
(Cock) (Anthus Pratensis)
Modeller:	Dorothy Doughty
Height:	6", 15.0 cm
Colour:	Yellow and light brown bird; yellow flowers; green fern leaves
Plinth:	Wooden
Issued:	1975 in a limited edition of 500
Series:	Doughty British Birds
U.S.	$750.00
Can.	$900.00
U.K.	£400.00

Note: Missing plinth.

RW3719
ARAB STALLION "INDIAN MAGIC"
Modeller:	Doris Lindner
Height:	10", 25.4 cm
Colour:	1. Dappled
	2. White
Plinth:	Wooden
Issued:	1961 in a limited edition of 500

	Coloured	White
U.S.	$1,400.00	275.00
Can.	$1,675.00	325.00
U.K.	£ 750.00	150.00

RW3720
WILL YOU, WON'T YOU?
Modeller:	Freda Doughty
Height:	8 ½", 21.6 cm
Colour:	Cream dress with pink rose buds; red hair
Issued:	1961-1961
U.S.	
Can.	Extremely rare
U.K.	

RW3721
SAIL FISH
Modeller:	Ronald Van Ruyckevelt
Height:	8 ½", 21.6 cm
Colour:	Blue and white
Plinth:	Wooden
Issued:	1961 in a limited edition of 500
Series:	Sporting Fish
U.S.	$750.00
Can.	$900.00
U.K.	£400.00

Note: Missing plinth.

RW3722
FLYING FISH
Modeller:	Ronald Van Ruyckevelt
Height:	8 ½", 21.6 cm
Colour:	Blue, green and white
Plinth:	Wooden
Issued:	1961 in a limited edition of 500
Series:	Sporting Fish
U.S.	$750.00
Can.	$900.00
U.K.	£400.00

RW3723
CHIFFCHAFF ON HOGWEED
(Phylloscopus Rufus)
Modeller:	Dorothy Doughty
Height:	17 ¾", 45.1 cm
Colour:	Yellow bird, green foliage
Plinth:	Wooden
Issued:	1966 in a limited edition of 500
Series:	Doughty British Birds
U.S.	$ 925.00
Can.	$1,100.00
U.K.	£ 500.00

RW3726
MOORHEN CHICK ON WATERLILY
PADS (Gallinula Chloropus)

Modeller:	Dorothy Doughty
Height:	3 ¾", 9.5 cm
Colour:	Black bird with yellow beak; white lily; green leaves
Issued:	1970 in a limited edition of 500
Series:	Doughty British Birds
U.S.	$750.00
Can.	$900.00
U.K.	£400.00

RW3727
WREN ON BURNET ROSE (Hen)
(Troglodytes Parvulus)

Modeller:	Dorothy Doughty
Height:	7 ¼", 19.7 cm
Colour:	Unknown
Plinth:	Wooden
Issued:	1966 in a limited edition of 500
Series:	Doughty British Birds
U.S.	$ 875.00
Can.	$1,100.00
U.K.	£ 500.00

Photograph not
available
at press time

RW3731
RED ADMIRAL BUTTERFLY ON
CLEMATIS

Modeller:	Peter Ewence
Height:	Unknown
Colour:	Unknown
Issued:	1962
U.S.	
Can.	Extremely rare
U.K.	

RW3733
AMERICAN QUARTER HORSE
"POCO STAMPEDE"

Modeller:	Doris Lindner
Height:	9 ½", 24.0 cm
Colour:	Light chestnut with black tail and lower legs
Plinth:	Wooden
Issued:	1962 in a limited edition of 500
U.S.	$1,400.00
Can.	$1,672.00
U.K.	£ 750.00

RW3734
KINGFISHER AND AUTUMN
BEECH (Cock)
(Alcedo Ispida)

Modeller:	Dorothy Doughty
Height:	12 ¼", 31.1 cm
Colour:	Blue, green and brown; gold leaves
Plinth:	Wooden
Issued:	1966 in a limited edition of 500
Series:	Doughty British Birds
U.S.	$ 925.00
Can.	$1,100.00
U.K.	£ 500.00

RW3735
LONG-TAILED TITS ON
FLOWERING LARCH
(Acredula Caudata)

Modeller:	Dorothy Doughty
Height:	Unknown
Colour:	Unknown
Issued:	1962 in a limited edition of 500
Series:	Doughty British Birds
U.S.	Not put
Can.	into full
U.K.	production

RW3745
CAPTAIN RAIMONDO D'INZEO ON
MERANO

Modeller:	Doris Lindner
Height:	11", 27.9 cm
Colour:	Rider: Olive jacket and cap; white jodhpurs; black boots Horse: Chestnut
Plinth:	Wooden
Issued:	1962 in a limited edition of 500
U.S.	$1,750.00
Can.	$2,100.00
U.K.	£ 950.00

RW3746
BRITISH FRIESIAN BULL
"TERLING TRUSTY"

Modeller:	Doris Lindner
Height:	8 ½", 21.6 cm
Colour:	Black and white
Plinth:	Wooden
Issued:	1962 in a limited edition of 500
Series:	Prize Cattle
U.S.	$1,300.00
Can.	$1,550.00
U.K.	£ 700.00

RW3747
YOUNG ENGLAND
Modeller:	Neal French
Height:	5", 12.7 cm
Colour:	Dark green jersey; white shorts; brown ball and football(soccer) boots; light brown sandals
Issued:	1962
Series:	Playtime Series
U.S.	$700.00
Can.	$850.00
U.K.	£375.00

RW3748
TREASURE TROVE
Modeller:	Neal French
Height:	5", 12.7cm
Colour:	Light green dress; pink headband; brown hair; beige box with red lining
Issued:	1962
Series:	Playtime Series
U.S.	$700.00
Can.	$850.00
U.K.	£375.00

RW3749
MELANIE
Style One
Modeller:	Ruth Van Ruyckevelt
Height:	8 ¼", 21.0 cm
Colour:	Unknown
Issued:	1962 in a limited edition of 500
Series:	Victorian Ladies
U.S.	$750.00
Can.	$900.00
U.K.	£400.00

RW3750
ROSALIND
Style One
Modeller:	Ruth Van Ruyckevelt
Height:	8", 20.3 cm
Colour:	Cream dress with pink trim; light grey dotted skirt; black neck bow; black hair
Issued:	1962 in a limited edition of 500
Series:	Victorian Ladies
U.S.	$750.00
Can.	$900.00
U.K.	£400.00

RW3751
TARPON
Modeller:	Ronald Van Ruyckevelt
Height:	12", 30.5 cm
Colour:	White, grey and black
Plinth:	Wooden
Issued:	1962 in a limited edition of 500
Series:	Sporting Fish
U.S.	$750.00
Can.	$900.00
U.K.	£400.00

RW3753
DOLPHIN
Modeller:	Ronald Van Ruyckevelt
Height:	10 ½", 26.7 cm
Colour:	Turquoise and cream
Plinth:	Wooden
Issued:	1962 in a limited edition of 500
Series:	Sporting Fish
U.S.	$750.00
Can.	$900.00
U.K.	£400.00

RW3754
POUPÉE
Modeller:	Neal French
Height:	5", 12.7 cm
Colour:	Dark blue bodice; white collar, cuffs and skirt; red belt and shoes; blonde hair; doll dressed in red
Issued:	1962
Series:	Playtime Series
U.S.	$700.00
Can.	$850.00
U.K.	£375.00

RW3755
MASTER MARINER
Modeller:	Neal French
Height:	5", 12.7 cm
Colour:	Cream T-shirt; blue trousers; green boat with white sails
Issued:	1962
Series:	Playtime Series
U.S.	$700.00
Can.	$850.00
U.K.	£375.00

RW3756
FIRST AID

Modeller:	Neal French
Height:	5", 12.7 cm
Colour:	Blue and white uniform; white cap with red cross; black shoes; golden bear
Issued:	1962
Series:	Playtime Series
U.S.	$700.00
Can.	$850.00
U.K.	£375.00

RW3757
SHERIFF

Modeller:	Neal French
Height:	5", 12.7 cm
Colour:	Light blue jersey; light brown shorts; black cowboy boots; dark brown hat
Issued:	1962
Series:	Playtime Series
U.S.	$700.00
Can.	$850.00
U.K.	£375.00

RW3758
HYPERION

Modeller:	Doris Lindner
Height:	10", 25.4 cm
Colour:	Brown with white socks
Plinth:	Wooden
Issued:	1963 in a limited edition of 500
U.S.	$1,400.00
Can.	$1,675.00
U.K.	£ 750.00

RW3759
SHIRE STALLION "MANOR PREMIER KING"

Modeller:	Doris Lindner
Height:	10 ½", 26.7 cm
Colour:	Brown with black and white socks
Plinth:	Wooden
Issued:	1963 in a limited edition of 500
Series:	Heavy Horses
U.S.	$1,400.00
Can.	$1,675.00
U.K.	£ 750.00

RW3760
FANTAILS

Modeller:	Freda Doughty
Height:	7 ¼", 18.4 cm
Colour:	White coat with lilac highlights; blue leggings; blue cap trimmed with white; three white doves
Issued:	1962-c.1982
Varieties:	Also called November RW3418
U.S.	$325.00
Can.	$400.00
U.K.	£175.00

RW3761
MAYFLOWER
Second Version (Without hat and telescope)

Modeller:	Freda Doughty
Height:	7 ½", 19.0 cm
Colour:	Blue, yellow, beige, black, brown and white
Issued:	1963-1963
Varieties:	RW3656
U.S.	$1,000.00
Can.	$1,200.00
U.K.	£ 550.00

RW3771
SISTER, THE UNIVERSITY COLLEGE HOSPITAL, LONDON

Modeller:	Ruth Van Ruyckevelt
Height:	9", 22.9 cm
Colour:	Black and white uniform; grey cap; black shoes; grey clipboard
Issued:	1964 in a limited edition of 500
Series:	Nursing Sisters
U.S.	$550.00
Can.	$675.00
U.K.	£300.00

RW3774
ELIZABETH
Style One

Modeller:	Ruth Van Ruyckevelt
Height:	8 ½", 21.6 cm
Colour:	Grey-black bodice; white skirt and sleeves with black dots; scarlet umbrella
Issued:	1964 in a limited edition of 500
Series:	Victorian Ladies
U.S.	$750.00
Can.	$900.00
U.K.	£400.00

RW3775
MADELAINE
Modeller:	Ruth Van Ruyckevelt
Height:	8 ½", 21.6 cm
Colour:	Ivory dress; lilac bow and plume in hair
Issued:	1964 in a limited edition of 500
Series:	Victorian Ladies
U.S.	$750.00
Can.	$900.00
U.K.	£400.00

RW3776A
JERSEY BULL
"LEEBARN CARLISLE II"
First Version (Tail up)
Modeller:	Doris Lindner
Height:	7 ¼", 18.4 cm
Colour:	Light brown and black
Plinth:	Wooden
Issued:	1964 in a limited edition of 500
Series:	Prize Cattle
U.S.	$1,100.00
Can.	$1,3025.00
U.K.	£ 600.00

RW3776B
JERSEY BULL
"LEEBARN CARLISLE II"
Second Version (Tail down)
Modeller:	Doris Lindner
Height:	7 ¼", 18.4 cm
Colour:	Light brown and black
Plinth:	Wooden
Issued:	1964 in a limited edition of 500
Series:	Prize Cattle
U.S.	$1,100.00
Can.	$1,325.00
U.K.	£ 600.00

RW3778
BLUE MARLIN
Modeller:	Ronald Van Ruyckevelt
Height:	11 ½", 29.2 cm
Colour:	Blue and white
Plinth:	Wooden
Issued:	1964 in a limited edition of 500
Series:	Sporting Fish
U.S.	$750.00
Can.	$900.00
U.K.	£400.00

RW3781
DAIRY SHORTHORN BULL
"ROYAL EVENT"
Modeller:	Doris Lindner
Height:	8", 20.3 cm
Colour:	Browns and white
Plinth:	Wooden
Issued:	1964 in a limited edition of 500
Series:	Prize Cattle
U.S.	$1,200.00
Can.	$1,450.00
U.K.	£ 650.00

RW3786
PERCHERON STALLION
"SALTMARSH SILVER CREST"
Modeller:	Doris Lindner
Height:	10", 25.4 cm
Colour:	Iron grey
Plinth:	Wooden
Issued:	1965 in a limited edition of 500
Series:	Heavy Horses
U.S.	$1,400.00
Can.	$1,675.00
U.K.	£ 750.00

RW3787
BLUE-FIN TUNA
Modeller:	Ronald Van Ruyckevelt
Height:	11 ½", 29.2 cm
Colour:	Blue
Plinth:	Wooden
Issued:	1965 in a limited edition of 500
Series:	Sporting Fish
U.S.	$750.00
Can.	$900.00
U.K.	£400.00

RW3788
SWORDFISH
Modeller:	Ronald Van Ruyckevelt
Height:	14 ½", 36.8 cm
Colour:	Unknown
Plinth:	Wooden
Issued:	1965 in a limited edition of 500
Series:	Sporting Fish
U.S.	$750.00
Can.	$900.00
U.K.	£400.00

RW3789
AMERICAN SALMON
Modeller: Ronald Van Ruyckevelt
Height: Unknown
Colour: Unknown
Issued: 1965

U.S.   Not put
Can.   into full
U.K.   production

RW3790
AMERICAN TROUT
Modeller: Ronald Van Ruyckevelt
Height: Unknown
Colour: Unknown
Issued: 1965

U.S.   Not put
Can.   into full
U.K.   production

RW3802
WELSH MOUNTAIN PONY "COED COCH PLANED"
Modeller: Doris Lindner
Height: 8", 20.3 cm
Colour: White
Plinth: Wooden
Issued: 1965 in a limited
         edition of 500

U.S. $1,300.00
Can. $1,550.00
U.K.   £ 700.00

RW3803
MARION
Modeller: Ruth Van Ruyckevelt
Height: 7 ½", 19.1 cm
Colour: Navy skirt with white
        trim; light blue and
        white blouse; red and
        white striped tie and
        hat band; straw hat
Issued: 1965 in a limited
        edition of 500
Series: Victorian Ladies

U.S. $750.00
Can. $900.00
U.K.   £400.00

RW3804
CHARLOTTE AND JANE
Modeller: Ruth Van Ruyckevelt
Height: 6 ½", 16.5 cm
Colour: Lady: Green dress with white ruffles; green hat with white
        and yellow flowers; dark red handbag
        Girl: Lilac and white dress; white stockings; black shoes;
        red hair
Issued: 1965 in a limited edition of 500
Series: Victorian Ladies

U.S. $1,100.00
Can. $1,325.00
U.K.   £ 600.00

RW3805
ROYAL CANADIAN MOUNTED POLICE
Modeller: Doris Lindner
Height: 12 ¼", 31.1 cm
Colour: Red, black and brown
Plinth: Wooden
Issued: 1967 in a limited
        edition of 500

U.S. $1,850.00
Can. $2,200.00
U.K.   £1,000.00

Note: The first 100 models issued
         bore the Canadian Centennial
         Symbol for 1967.

RW3808
ARAB STALLION'S HEAD
Modeller: Raoh Schorr
Height: 12 ¼", 31.1 cm
Colour: White porcelain
Issued: 1966

U.S.   Trial
Can.   models
U.K.   only

RW3809
BOY WITH HAT (ANTHONY)
Modeller:	Ronald Van Ruyckevelt
Height:	Unknown
Colour:	Unknown
Issued:	1966

U.S.	
Can.	Extremely rare
U.K.	

Photograph not available at press time

RW3810
GIRL WITH HAT (SARAH JANE)
Modeller:	Ronald Van Ruyckevelt
Height:	Unknown
Colour:	Unknown
Issued:	1966

U.S.	
Can.	Extremely rare
U.K.	

RW3811
FAWN'S HEAD (Vase)
Modeller:	Raoh Schorr
Height:	12", 30.5 cm
Colour:	White porcelain
Issued:	1966

U.S.	$450.00
Can.	$550.00
U.K.	£250.00

Photograph not available at press time

RW3812
HORSE'S HEAD (Vase)
Modeller:	Raoh Schorr
Height:	12", 30.5 cm
Colour:	White porcelain
Issued:	1966

U.S.	$450.00
Can.	$550.00
U.K.	£250.00

RW3813
MALLARD (Drake)
Modeller:	Ronald Van Ruyckevelt
Height:	12", 30.5 cm
Colour:	White, brown and green
Plinth:	Wooden
Issued:	1966 in a limited edition of 500
Series:	Game Birds

U.S.	$ 925.00
Can.	$1,100.00
U.K.	£ 500.00

RW3814
MALLARD (Hen)
Modeller:	Ronald Van Ruyckevelt
Height:	13 ½", 34.3 cm
Colour:	Browns and green
Plinth:	Wooden
Issued:	1966 in a limited edition of 500
Series:	Game Birds

U.S.	$ 925.00
Can.	$1,100.00
U.K.	£ 500.00

Note: Missing plinth.

RW3815
MONKEY (Two feet on ground)
Modeller:	Raoh Schorr
Height:	Unknown
Colour:	White porcelain
Issued:	1966

U.S.	Trial
Can.	models
U.K.	only

RW3816
MONKEY (Four feet on ground)
Modeller:	Raoh Schorr
Height:	Unknown
Colour:	White porcelain
Issued:	1966

U.S.	Trial
Can.	models
U.K.	only

RW3817
ARKLE
Modeller:	Doris Lindner
Height:	10 ¼", 26.0 cm
Colour:	Chestnut and black
Plinth:	Wooden
Issued:	1966 in a limited edition of 500
Series:	Race Horses
U.S.	$1,500.00
Can.	$1,775.00
U.K.	£ 800.00

RW3818
RING-NECKED PHEASANT (Cock)
Modeller:	Ronald Van Ruyckevelt
Height:	13 ¾", 34.9 cm
Colour:	Black head with red eye patch; reddish-brown and yellow body; white stripe around neck
Plinth:	Wooden
Issued:	1966 in a limited edition of 500
Series:	Game Birds
U.S.	$ 925.00
Can.	$1,100.00
U.K.	£ 500.00

RW3819
RING-NECKED PHEASANT (Hen)
Modeller:	Ronald Van Ruyckevelt
Height:	12 ¾", 32.4 cm
Colour:	Browns and green
Plinth:	Wooden
Issued:	1966 in a limited edition of 500
Series:	Game Birds
U.S.	$ 925.00
Can.	$1,100.00
U.K.	£ 500.00

RW3821
BRAHMAN BULL
"J. D. H. DE ELLARY MANSO"
Modeller:	Doris Lindner
Height:	8 ¾", 22.2 cm
Colour:	White and black
Plinth:	Wooden
Issued:	1967 in a limited edition of 500
Series:	Prize Cattle
U.S.	$1,100.00
Can.	$1,325.00
U.K.	£ 600.00

RW3822
BULLDOG "MACK"
Modeller:	Doris Lindner
Height:	8 ½", 21.6 cm
Colour:	Brown and white
Plinth:	Wooden
Issued:	1967 in a limited edition of 500
Comm. by:	Mack Trucks Inc., U.S.A.
U.S.	$ 825.00
Can.	$1,000.00
U.K.	£ 450.00

RW3824
CHAROLOIS BULL "VAILLANT"
Modeller:	Doris Lindner
Height:	8", 20.3 cm
Colour:	Cream
Plinth:	Wooden
Issued:	1967 in a limited edition of 500
Series:	Prize Cattle
U.S.	$1,100.00
Can.	$1,325.00
U.K.	£ 600.00

RW3825
SUFFOLK PUNCH
"BECCLES WARRENDER"
Modeller:	Doris Lindner
Height:	9 ¼", 23.5 cm
Colour:	Chestnut
Plinth:	Wooden
Issued:	1967 in a limited edition of 500
Series:	Heavy Horses
U.S.	$1,675.00
Can.	$2,000.00
U.K.	£ 900.00

RW3827
BOB-WHITE QUAIL (Cock)
Style Two
Modeller:	Ronald Van Ruyckevelt
Height:	9 ¼", 23.5 cm
Colour:	Dark brown, cream and green
Plinth:	Wooden
Issued:	1967 in a limited edition of 500
Series:	Game Birds
U.S.	$ 925.00
Can.	$1,100.00
U.K.	£ 500.00

RW3828
BOB-WHITE QUAIL (Hen)
Style Two
Modeller:	Ronald Van Ruyckevelt
Height:	7", 17.8 cm
Colour:	Browns, black, white and green
Plinth:	Wooden
Issued:	1967 in a limited edition of 500
Series:	Game Birds
U.S.	$ 925.00
Can.	$1,100.00
U.K.	£ 500.00

RW3831
CANVASBACK DUCK
Modeller:	Ronald Van Ruyckevelt
Height:	16 ½" 41.9 cm
Colour:	Black, brown, grey and green
Plinth:	Wooden
Issued:	1967 in a limited edition of 500
Series:	Game Birds
U.S.	$ 925.00
Can.	$1,100.00
U.K.	£ 500.00

Note: Missing plinth.

RW3833
PINTAIL (Drake)
Modeller:	Ronald Van Ruyckevelt
Height:	7 ½", 19.1 cm
Colour:	Grey, green, brown and white
Plinth:	Wooden
Issued:	1967 in a limited edition of 500
Series:	Game Birds
U.S.	$ 925.00
Can.	$1,100.00
U.K.	£ 500.00

Note: Missing plinth.

RW3834
PINTAIL (Hen)
Modeller:	Ronald Van Ruyckevelt
Height:	13 ½", 34.3 cm
Colour:	Cream and light green
Plinth:	Wooden
Issued:	1967 in a limited edition of 500
Series:	Game Birds
U.S.	$ 925.00
Can.	$1,100.00
U.K.	£ 500.00

RW3836
GREEN-WINGED TEAL
Modeller:	Ronald Van Ruyckevelt
Height:	8 ¾", 22.2 cm
Colour:	Grey, white and yellow
Plinth:	Wooden
Issued:	1967 in a limited edition of 500
Series:	Game Birds
U.S.	$ 925.00
Can.	$1,100.00
U.K.	£ 500.00

Note: Missing plinth.

RW3840
MOURNING DOVES
Modeller:	Ronald Van Ruyckevelt
Height:	17 ¾", 45.1 cm
Colour:	Browns
Plinth:	Wooden, tall
Issued:	1967 in a limited edition of 500
Series:	Game Birds
U.S.	$ 925.00
Can.	$1,100.00
U.K.	£ 500.00

Note: Missing plinth.

RW3841
EMILY
Style One
Modeller:	Ruth Van Ruyckevelt
Height:	7 ¾", 19.7 cm
Colour:	White skirt; red jacket trimmed with black; black hat; brown and cream muff
Issued:	1967 in a limited edition of 500
Series:	Victorian Ladies
U.S.	$750.00
Can.	$900.00
U.K.	£400.00

RW3842
BRIDGET
Modeller:	Ruth Van Ruyckevelt
Height:	7 ½", 19.1 cm
Colour:	White dress; yellow hat with blue trim; red ball
Issued:	1967 in a limited edition of 500
Series:	Victorian Ladies
U.S.	$750.00
Can.	$900.00
U.K.	£400.00

RW3844
PUFFIN
Modeller:	Raoh Schorr
Height:	Unknown
Colour:	White, black and orange (porcelain)
Issued:	1967
U.S.	$750.00
Can.	$900.00
U.K.	£400.00

RW3845
FULMAR
Modeller:	Raoh Schorr
Height:	Unknown
Colour:	Grey and white; yellow beak (porcelain)
Issued:	1967
U.S.	$750.00
Can.	$900.00
U.K.	£400.00

RW3846
H.R.H. THE DUKE OF EDINBURGH ON HIS POLO PONY
Modeller:	Doris Lindner
Height:	15 ¾" 40.0 cm
Colour:	Dark grey shirt; white jodhpurs; black hat; bay horse
Issued:	1968 in a limited edition of 750
U.S.	$1,850.00
Can.	$2,250.00
U.K.	£1,000.00

RW3860
NAPOLEON BONAPARTE
Modeller:	Bernard Winskill
Height:	16 ¼", 41.2 cm
Colour:	1. Bone china: Red cape; dark blue coat, hat, boots and saddlecloth; cream breeches and gloves; white horse; gold reins
	2. Bronze metal
Plinth:	Wooden
Issued:	1. Bone china: 1969 in a limited edition of 750
	2. Bronze metal: 1969 in a limited edition of 15
Series:	Military Commanders

	Bone China	Bronze Metal
U.S.	$2,775.00	5,500.00
Can.	$3,350.00	6,500.00
U.K.	£1,500.00	3,000.00

RW3861
BRITISH RED CROSS
V.A.D. MEMBER
Modeller:	Ruth Van Ruyckevelt
Height:	8 ½", 21.6 cm
Colour:	Blue uniform; white apron with red cross on bib; white cap; black bag
Issued:	1968 in a limited edition of 750
U.S.	$650.00
Can.	$775.00
U.K.	£350.00

RW3864
19TH CENTURY CIGAR STORE INDIAN
Modeller:	Peter Ewence
Height:	9", 22.9 cm
Colour:	Green wrap; red-brown headdress; dark brown leggings; black hair
Issued:	1968 in a limited edition of 500
Comm. by:	Rothmans of Pall Mall
U.S.	$ 925.00
Can.	$1,100.00
U.K.	£ 500.00

RW3869
APPALOOSA "IMBODEN'S DRIFTWOOD BOB"
Modeller:	Doris Lindner
Height:	9 ¾", 24.7 cm
Colour:	White and brown
Plinth:	Wooden
Issued:	1968 in a limited edition of 750

U.S.	$1,400.00
Can.	$1,675.00
U.K.	£ 750.00

RW3870
THE DUKE OF WELLINGTON
Modeller:	Bernard Winskill
Height:	16", 40.6 cm
Colour:	1. Bone china: Rider: Red jacket with blue sash; white jodhpurs; black boots
	Horse: Brown
	2. Bronze metal
Plinth:	Wooden
Issued:	1. Bone china: 1968 in a limited edition of 750
	2. Bronze metal: 1968 in a limited edition of 15
Series:	Military Commanders

	Bone China	Bronze Metal
U.S.	$2,800.00	6,700.00
Can.	$3,350.00	5,600.00
U.K.	£1,500.00	3,000.00

RW3871
PRINCE'S GRACE AND FOAL
Modeller:	Doris Lindner
Height:	8 ¼", 21.0 cm
Colour:	1. Coloured (with wooden plinth)
	2. White (Classic, without plinth)
Issued:	1. Coloured: 1968 in a limited edition of 750
	2. White: 1968 in a limited edition of 250

	Coloured	White
U.S.	$1,850.00	925.00
Can.	$2,250.00	1,100.00
U.K.	£1,000.00	500.00

RW3872
STROLLER AND MARION COAKES
Modeller:	Doris Lindner
Height:	11 ¼", 28.5 cm
Colour:	Rider: Black jacket and boots; white jodhpurs
	Horse: Light brown
Plinth:	Wooden
Issued:	1968 in a limited edition of 750

U.S.	$1,850.00
Can.	$2,250.00
U.K.	£1,000.00

Note: Only trial pieces are known for the following models:
RW3873 Baltimore Oriole; RW3874 Purple Thrush;
RW3875 American Goldfinch; RW3876 Nashville Warbler.

RW3877
ELAINE
Modeller:	Ruth Van Ruyckevelt
Height:	5 ¾", 14.6 cm
Colour:	Orange patterned dress with white upper bodice; black hair; brown guitar
Issued:	1971 in a limited edition of 750
Series:	Victorian Ladies
U.S.	$550.00
Can.	$675.00
U.K.	£300.00

RW3878
FELICITY
Style One
Modeller:	Ruth Van Ruyckevelt
Height:	6 ¾", 17.2 cm
Colour:	White dress with blue design; blue hat; golden brown retriever
Issued:	1971 in a limited edition of 750
Series:	Victorian Ladies
U.S.	$650.00
Can.	$775.00
U.K.	£350.00

RW3880
AMERICAN SADDLE HORSE
Modeller:	Doris Lindner
Height:	10 ¼", 26.0 cm
Colour:	Brown
Plinth:	Wooden
Issued:	1971 in a limited edition of 500
U.S.	$1,575.00
Can.	$1,900.00
U.K.	£ 850.00

RW3881
THE PICNIC
Modeller:	Ruth Van Ruyckevelt
Height:	6 ½", 16.5 cm
Colour:	Lady Kneeling: Green dress with white trim; straw hat Lady seated: White dress with pink flowers
Issued:	1969 in a limited edition of 250
Series:	Victorian Ladies
U.S.	$2,500.00
Can.	$3,000.00
U.K.	£1,350.00

RW3882
PALOMINO "YELLOW STRAW"
Modeller:	Doris Lindner
Height:	10 ¼", 26.0 cm
Colour:	Palomino
Plinth:	Wooden
Issued:	1971 in a limited edition of 750
U.S.	$1,575.00
Can.	$1,900.00
U.K.	£ 850.00

Note: Only trial pieces are known for the following models:
RW3885 Chickadee;
RW3886 Wren.

RW3887
ALICE
Style Two
Modeller:	Ruth Van Ruyckevelt
Height:	8 ½", 21.6 cm
Colour:	Blue dress; white underskirt; black hat with pink roses
Issued:	1969 in a limited edition of 750
Series:	Victorian Ladies
U.S.	$650.00
Can.	$775.00
U.K.	£350.00

RW3892
CECILIA
Modeller:	Ruth Van Ruyckevelt
Height:	7 ½", 19.1 cm
Colour:	Royal blue dress with white trim
Issued:	1969 in a limited edition of 750
Series:	Victorian Ladies
U.S.	$650.00
Can.	$775.00
U.K.	£350.00

RW3893
NIJINSKY
Modeller:	Doris Lindner
Height:	10 ¼", 26.0 cm
Colour:	Tawny
Plinth:	Wooden
Issued:	1971 in a limited edition of 500
Series:	Race Horses
U.S.	$1,575.00
Can.	$1,900.00
U.K.	£ 850.00

RW3894
SPARROWHAWK AND BULLFINCH

Modeller:	James Alder
Height:	1. Bone china: 22", 55.9 cm
	2. Bronze: 25 ½", 64.8 cm
Colour:	1A Bone china: White
	1B Bone china: Yellow and grey; grey and brown
	2. Bronze
Issued:	1A. White: 1969 in a limited edition of 150
	1B. Coloured: 1969 in a limited edition of 250
	2. Bronze: 1969 in a limited edition of 25

	White	Coloured	Bronze
U.S.	$375.00	1,100.00	2,800.00
Can.	$450.00	1,325.00	3,350.00
U.K.	£200.00	600.00	1,500.00

RW3897
WASHINGTON (George)

Modeller:	Bernard Winskill
Height:	18", 45.7 cm
Colour:	1. Bone china: Navy jacket with gold trim; black boots; white jodhpurs; grey horse
	2. Bronze metal
Plinth:	Wooden
Issued:	1. Bone china: 1972 in a limited edition of 750
	2. Bronze metal: 1975 in a limited edition of 15
Series:	Military Commanders

	Bone China	Bronze
U.S.	$2,800.00	6,700.00
Can.	$3,350.00	5,600.00
U.K.	£1,500.00	3,000.00

Note: Missing plinth.

RW3898
KINGFISHER ON BRONZE
Style One

Modeller:	David Fryer
Height:	7", 17.8 cm
Colour:	Blue and orange bird; yellow flower; bronze foliage and base
Issued:	1984-1988
Series:	British Birds on Bronze (Small size)

U.S.	$150.00
Can.	$175.00
U.K.	£ 85.00

RW3899
SWALLOW ON BRONZE

Modeller:	David Fryer
Height:	5 ½", 14.0 cm
Colour:	Blue, white and red bird, pink flowers; bronze foliage and base
Issued:	1984-1988
Series:	British Birds on Bronze (Small size)

U.S.	$150.00
Can.	$175.00
U.K.	£ 85.00

RW3900
WREN ON BRONZE
Style One

Modeller:	David Fryer
Height:	4 ½", 11.9 cm
Colour:	Brown bird, pink flowers; bronze foliage and base
Issued:	1984-1988
Series:	British Birds on Bronze (Small size)

U.S.	$150.00
Can.	$175.00
U.K.	£ 85.00

RW3901
ROBIN ON BRONZE
Style One

Modeller:	David Fryer
Height:	6 ¾", 17.2 cm
Colour:	Red and brown bird, white and yellow flowers; bronze foliage and base
Issued:	1984-1988
Series:	British Birds on Bronze (Small size)

U.S.	$150.00
Can.	$175.00
U.K.	£ 85.00

RW3902
GOLDCREST ON BRONZE
Style Two
Modeller: David Fryer
Height: 4", 10.1 cm
Colour: Yellow, green and
             brown bird; brown
             acorns; bronze foliage
             and base
Issued: 1984-1988
Series: British Birds on Bronze
             (Small size)

U.S. $150.00
Can. $175.00
U.K.   £ 85.00

RW3903
BLUE TIT ON BRONZE
Style Two
Modeller: David Fryer
Height: 5", 12.7 cm
Colour: Blue, green and white
             bird, yellow flowers;
             bronze foliage and
             base
Issued: 1984-1988
Series: British Birds on Bronze
             (Small size)

U.S. $150.00
Can. $175.00
U.K.   £ 85.00

Photograph not
available
at press time

RW3904
KINGFISHER ON BRONZE (Domed)
Style Two
Modeller: David Fryer
Height: 3", 7.6 cm
Colour: Blue and orange bird;
             bronze foliage
Issued: 1984
Series: British Birds on Bronze
             (Miniature)

U.S. $125.00
Can. $150.00
U.K.   £ 65.00

Note: Model RW3904 was issued
           with a wooden plinth and
           glass dome (4").

Photograph not
available
at press time

RW3905
ROBIN ON BRONZE (Domed)
Style Two
Modeller: David Fryer
Height: 3", 7.6 cm
Colour: Brown and red bird;
             bronze foliage
Issued: 1984
Series: British Birds on Bronze
             (Miniature)

U.S. $125.00
Can. $150.00
U.K.   £ 65.00

Note: Model RW3905 was issued
           with a wooden plinth and
           glass dome (4").

Photograph not
available
at press time

RW3907
NUTHATCH ON BRONZE (Domed)
Modeller: David Fryer
Height: 3", 7.6 cm
Colour: Unknown
Issued: 1984
Series: British Birds on Bronze
             (Miniature)

U.S. $125.00
Can. $150.00
U.K.   £ 65.00

Note: Model RW3907 was issued
           with a wooden plinth and glass
           dome (4").

Photograph not
available
at press time

RW3908
BLUE TIT ON BRONZE (Domed)
Style Three
Modeller: David Fryer
Height: 3", 7.6 cm
Colour: Blue bird; bronze
             foliage and base
Issued: 1984
Series: British Birds on Bronze
             (Miniature)

U.S. $125.00
Can. $150.00
U.K.   £ 65.00

Note: Model RW3908 was issued
           with a wooden plinth and glass
           dome (4").

Photograph not
available
at press time

RW3909
GOLDCREST ON BRONZE (Domed)
Style Three
Modeller: David Fryer
Height: 3", 7.6 cm
Colour: Unknown
Issued: 1984
Series: British Birds on Bronze
             (Miniature)

U.S. $125.00
Can. $150.00
U.K.   £ 65.00

Note: Model RW3909 was issued
           with a wooden plinth and glass
           dome (4").

Photograph not
available
at press time

RW3910
WREN ON BRONZE (Domed)
Style Two
Modeller: David Fryer
Height: 3", 7.6 cm
Colour: Brown bird; bronze
             foliage and base
Issued: 1984
Series: British Birds on Bronze
             (Miniature)

U.S. $125.00
Can. $150.00
U.K.   £ 65.00

Note: Model RW3910 was issued
           with a wooden plinth and glass
           dome (4").

Photograph not
available
at press time

RW3911
MERLIN HAWK ON BRONZE

Modeller:	David Fryer
Height:	Unknown
Colour:	Unknown
Issued:	1984
Series:	British Birds on Bronze (Large size)
U.S.	
Can.	Extremely rare
U.K.	

RW3912
H.R.H. PRINCESS ANNE AND DOUBLET

Modeller:	Doris Lindner
Height:	13", 33.0 cm
Colour:	Rider: Blue jersey; cream jodhpurs; black hat
	Horse: Brown
Issued:	1972 in a limited edition of 750
U.S.	$1,850.00
Can.	$2,250.00
U.K.	£1,000.00

Note: Missing plinth.

RW3913
WHITE DOVES

Modeller:	Ronald Van Ruyckevelt
Height:	18", 45.7 cm
Colour:	White
Plinth:	Wooden
Issued:	1972 in a limited edition of 25
U.S.	$1,575.00
Can.	$1,900.00
U.K.	£ 850.00

Note: White Doves, model RW3913 was issued to commemorate the Silver Wedding Anniversary of HM Queen Elizabeth II and the Duke of Edinburgh. Missing plinth.

RW3914
THE DUKE OF MARLBOROUGH

Modeller:	Bernard Winskill
Height:	18", 45.7 cm
Colour:	1. Bone china: Red jacket; blue sash and trim; grey horse
	2. Bronze metal
Plinth:	Wooden
Issued:	1. Bone china: 1973 in a limited edition of 350
	2. Bronze metal: 1973 in a limited edition of 15
Series:	Military Commanders

	Bone China	Bronze
U.S.	$2,800.00	6,700.00
Can.	$3,350.00	5,600.00
U.K.	£1,500.00	3,000.00

Note: Missing plinth.

RW3921
RAINBOW LORIKEET ON RED FLOWERED GUM

Modeller:	James Alder
Height:	20 ½", 52.1 cm
Colour:	Red, yellow, blue and green bird; green leaves; brown eucalyptus branch with green leaves
Plinth:	Wooden
Issued:	1972 in a limited edition of 50
U.S.	$1,400.00
Can.	$1,675.00
U.K.	£ 750.00

RW3922
GALLOPING DARTMOOR PONIES
Modeller:	Doris Lindner
Height:	8 ¾", 22.2 cm
Colour:	1. Brown and black
	2. White
Plinth:	Wooden
Issued:	1. Coloured: 1972 in a limited edition of 500
	2. White: 1972 in a limited edition of 250

	Brown/black	White
U.S.	$2,800.00	1,100.00
Can.	$3,350.00	1,325.00
U.K.	£1,500.00	600.00

RW3934
MAN AND WOMAN
Modeller:	Cecil Michaelis
Height:	12", 30.5 cm
Colour:	1. Bronze metal
	2. Glazed bone china
Issued:	1. Bronze metal: 1973 in a limited edition of 15
	2. Glazed Bone China: 1973 in a limited edition of 100
Series:	Sur La Plage

	Bone China	Bronze
U.S.	550.00	$1,850.00
Can.	675.00	$2,200.00
U.K.	300.00	£1,000.00

RW3935
HACKNEY STALLION
Modeller:	Doris Lindner
Height:	11", 27.9 cm
Colour:	Brown with black shading
Plinth:	Wooden
Issued:	1973 in a limited edition of 500

U.S.	$1,575.00
Can.	$1,900.00
U.K.	£ 850.00

RW3936
QUEEN MARY I
Style One
Modeller:	Ronald Van Ruyckevelt
Height:	9", 22.9 cm
Colour:	Dark blue and grey-green
Issued:	1973 in a limited edition of 250
Series:	Queens Regnant

U.S.	$ 875.00
Can.	$1050.00
U.K.	£ 475.00

Note: A base of elm burr with solid rosewood coping and ceramic tile on top accompanied this piece.

RW3937
QUEEN ELIZABETH I
Style Two
Modeller:	Ronald Van Ruyckevelt
Height:	12 ½", 31.7 cm
Colour:	Gold and white dress
Issued:	1973 in a limited edition of 250
Series:	Queens Regnant

U.S.	$1,300.00
Can.	$1,550.00
U.K.	£ 700.00

RW3938
QUEEN ANNE
Style One
Modeller:	Ronald Van Ruyckevelt
Height:	Unknown
Colour:	Yellow dress with light grey highlights
Issued:	1973 in a limited edition of 250
Series:	Queens Regnant

U.S.	$ 875.00
Can.	$1,050.00
U.K.	£ 475.00

RW3939
QUEEN MARY II

Modeller:	Ronald Van Ruyckevelt
Height:	12", 30.5 cm
Colour:	Yellow dress; green and cream cape
Issued:	1973 in a limited edition of 250
Series:	Queens Regnant
U.S.	$ 875.00
Can.	$1,050.00
U.K.	£ 475.00

RW3940
QUEEN VICTORIA
Style One

Modeller:	Ronald Van Ruyckevelt
Height:	9", 22.9 cm
Colour:	Light grey and white skirt edged with white frill; black top and veil
Issued:	1973 in a limited edition of 250
Series:	Queens Regnant
U.S.	$1,200.00
Can.	$1,450.00
U.K.	£ 650.00

RW3941
QUEEN ELIZABETH II
Style One

Modeller:	Ronald Van Ruyckevelt
	Kenneth Potts
Height:	14 ¾", 37.5 cm
Colour:	White dress; royal blue cloak with white lining and bows; royal blue hat with white plume; white gloves; red sash
Issued:	1973 in a limited edition of 250
Series:	Queens Regnant
Comm. by:	Compton & Woodhouse Ltd.
U.S.	$1,000.00
Can.	$1,200.00
U.K.	£ 550.00

RW3942
MILL REEF

Modeller:	Doris Lindner
Height:	11 ½", 29.2 cm
Colour:	Chestnut
Plinth:	Wooden
Issued:	1973 in a limited edition of 500
Series:	Race Horses
U.S.	$1,575.00
Can.	$1,900.00
U.K.	£ 850.00

RW3943
RICHARD MEADE AND LAURISTON

Modeller:	Doris Lindner
Height:	13", 33.0 cm
Colour:	Rider: Cream riding outfit; black hat Horse: Black
Plinth:	Wooden
Issued:	1974 in a limited edition of 500
U.S.	$1,750.00
Can.	$2,100.00
U.K.	£ 950.00

Note: Missing plinth.

RW3944
CLYDESDALE STALLION

Modeller:	Doris Lindner
Height:	10 ¾", 27.3
Colour:	1. Light chestnut with white feathers
	2. Light tan with white feathers
Plinth:	Wooden
Issued:	1975 in a limited edition of 500
Series:	Heavy Horses
U.S.	$1,575.00
Can.	$1,900.00
U.K.	£ 850.00

Note: Missing plinth.

RW3945
PREFERENCE
Modeller:	Cecil Michaelis	
Height:	13 ½", 34.3 cm	
Colour:	1. Bronze metal	
	2. Glazed bone china	
Issued:	1. Bronze metal: 1975 in a limited edition of 15	
	2. Glazed bone china: 1975 in a limited edition of 100	
Series:	Sur la Plage	

	Bronze	Bone China
U.S.	$1,850.00	550.00
Can.	$2,200.00	675.00
U.K.	£1,000.00	300.00

RW3946
PLONGUER
Modeller:	Cecil Michaelis	
Height:	Unknown	
Colour:	1. Bronze metal	
	2. Glazed bone china	
Issued:	1. Bronze metal: 1974 in a limited edition of 15	
	2. Glazed bone china:1974 in a limited edition of 100	
Series:	Sur la Plage	

	Bronze	Bone China
U.S.	$1,850.00	550.00
Can.	$2,200.00	675.00
U.K.	£1,000.00	300.00

Note: Missing plinth.

RW3947
BAIGNEUSE (La Plongee Attendue)
Modeller:	Cecil Michaelis	
Height:	Unknown	
Colour:	1. Bronze metal	
	2. Glazed bone china	
Issued:	1. Bronze metal: 1974 in a limited edition of 15	
	2. Glazed bone china: 1974 in a limited edition of 100	
Series:	Sur la Plage	

	Bronze	Bone China
U.S.	$1,850.00	550.00
Can.	$2,200.00	675.00
U.K.	£1,000.00	300.00

Note: Missing plinth.

RW3948
BY A SHORT HEAD
Modeller:	Bernard Winskill	
Height:	Unknown	
Colour:	1. Bone china: Riders: Yellow and white silks; blue and white silks	
	Horses: Chestnut	
	2. Bronze metal	
Issued:	1. Bone china: 1974 in a limited edition of 100	
	2. Bronze metal: 1974 in a limited edition of 15	
Series:	Racing Studies	

	Bronze	Bone China
U.S.	$7,500.00	4,500.00
Can.	$9,000.00	5,500.00
U.K.	£4,000.00	2,500.00

Note: Missing plinth.

RW3950
JEUX DE PLAGE
Modeller:	Cecil Michaelis	
Height:	14 ¾, 37.5 cm	
Colour:	1. Bronze metal	
	2. Glazed bone china	
Issued:	1. Bronze metal: 1974 in a limited edition of 15	
	2. Glazed bone china: 1974 in a limited edition of 100	
Series:	Sur la Plage	

	Bronze	Bone China
U.S.	$1,850.00	650.00
Can.	$2,200.00	775.00
U.K.	£1,000.00	350.00

RW3951
HOBBY AND SWALLOW
Modeller:	James Alder	
Height:	26 ½", 67.3 cm	
Colour:	1. Greys and green	
	2. White	
Plinth:	Wooden	
Issued:	1. Coloured: 1974 in a limited edition of 250	
	2. White: 1974 in a limited edition of 100	

	Coloured	White
U.S.	$1,575.00	550.00
Can.	$1,900.00	675.00
U.K.	£ 850.00	300.00

Note: Missing plinth.

RW3952
CHELTENHAM
Modeller:	Bernard Winskill	
Height:	Unknown	
Colour:	1. Bone china:	
	Rider One: Green, pink and white silks; black boots	
	Rider Two: Lilac, grey and white silks; black boots	
	Horses: Grey	
	2. Bronze metal	
Plinth:	Wooden	
Issued:	1. Bone china: 1978 in a limited edition of 100	
	2. Bronze metal: 1978 in a limited edition of 15	
Series:	Racing Studies	

	Bronze	Bone China
U.S.	$7,500.00	4,500.00
Can.	$9,000.00	5,500.00
U.K.	£4,000.00	2,500.00

Note: Missing plinth.

RW3953
LIMPETUEUX

Modeller:	Cecil Michaelis
Height:	11 ¾, 29.8 cm
Colour:	1. Bronze metal
	2. Glazed bone china
Issued:	1. Bronze metal: 1974 in a limited edition of 15
	2. Glazed bone china: 1974 in a limited edition of 100
Series:	Sur la Plage

	Bronze	Bone China
U.S.	$1,850.00	550.00
Can.	$2,200.00	675.00
U.K.	£1,000.00	300.00

RW3954
LEÇON À LA MER

Modeller:	Cecil Michaelis
Height:	Unknown
Colour:	1. Bronze metal
	2. Glazed bone china
Issued:	1. Bronze metal: 1974 in a limited edition of 15
	2. Glazed bone china: 1974 in a limited edition of 100
Series:	Sur la Plage

	Bronze	Bone China
U.S.	$1,850.00	550.00
Can.	$2,200.00	675.00
U.K.	£1,000.00	300.00

RW3955
RED RUM

Modeller:	Doris Lindner
Height:	11", 27.9 cm
Colour:	Chestnut
Plinth:	Wooden
Issued:	1975 in a limited edition of 250
Series:	Race Horses

U.S.	$1,575.00
Can.	$1,900.00
U.K.	£ 850.00

RW3956
ALEXANDER (The Great)

Modeller:	Bernard Winskill
Height:	19", 48.3 cm
Colour:	1. Bone china: Fleshtone; white toga; black horse
	2. Bronze metal
Plinth:	Wooden
Issued:	1. Bone china: 1975 in a limited edition of 250
	2. Bronze metal: 1975 in a limited edition of 15
Series:	Military Commanders

	Bronze	Bone China
U.S.	$5,500.00	2,775.00
Can.	$6,500.00	3,350.00
U.K.	£3,000.00	1,500.00

RW3957
NEW BORN

Modeller:	Doris Lindner
Height:	16", 40.6 cm
Colour:	1. Brown
	2. White (Classic)
Plinth:	Wooden
Issued:	1. Coloured: 1975 in a Ltd edition of 500
	2. White: 1975 in a Ltd edition of 150

	Coloured	White
U.S.	$1,675.00	375.00
Can.	$2,000.00	450.00
U.K.	£ 900.00	200.00

RW3958
GALLOPING IN WINTER
Modeller: Doris Lindner
Height: 15 ¾", 40.0 cm
Colour: Grey
Plinth: Wooden, large oval
Issued: 1974 in a limited
edition of 250
Varieties: Also called "Wild
Horses" RW3466

U.S. $2,775.00
Can. $3,350.00
U.K. £1,500.00

Note: Missing plinth.

RW3959A
AT THE START
Style One (No. 4)
Modeller: Bernard Winskill
Height: Unknown
Colour: 1. Bone china: Rider: Gold and black silks; white jodhpurs;
black and gold boots; Horse: Brown
2. Bronze metal
Plinth: Wooden
Issued: 1. Bone china: 1975 in a limited edition of 100
2. Bronze metal: 1975 in a limited edition of 15
Series: Racing Studies

	Bronze	**Bone China**
U.S.	$3,250.00	1,850.00
Can.	$3,900.00	2,250.00
U.K.	£1,750.00	1,000.00

RW3959B
AT THE START
Style Two (No. 6)
Modeller: Bernard Winskill
Height: Unknown
Colour: Rider: Red silks; white
jodhpurs; black boots
Horse: Brown
Plinth: Wooden
Issued: 1975 in a limited
edition of 100
Series: Racing Studies

U.S. $1,850.00
Can. $2,250.00
U.K. £1,000.00

RW3960
DARTFORD WARBLER
Modeller: James Alder
Height: Unknown
Colour: Brown, red and green
Plinth: Wooden
Issued: 1975 in a limited
edition of 500
Series: British Birds,
Series Two

U.S. $550.00
Can. $675.00
U.K. £300.00

Note: Missing plinth.

RW3961
BEARDED REEDLING
Modeller: James Alder
Height: 11", 27.9 cm
Colour: Yellow and green
Plinth: Wooden
Issued: 1975 in a limited
edition of 500
Series: British Birds,
Series Two

U.S. $550.00
Can. $675.00
U.K. £300.00

Note: Missing plinth.

RW3962
SNOW BUNTING
Modeller: James Alder
Height: Unknown
Colour: Grey, white and green
Plinth: Wooden
Issued: 1975 in a limited
edition of 500
Series: British Birds,
Series Two

U.S. $550.00
Can. $675.00
U.K. £300.00

Note: Missing plinth.

RW3963
SHORELARK
Modeller: James Alder
Height: Unknown
Colour: Browns, black and
white
Plinth: Wooden
Issued: 1975 in a limited
edition of 500
Series: British Birds,
Series Two

U.S. $550.00
Can. $675.00
U.K. £300.00

Note: Missing plinth.

RW3964
WALL CREEPER

Modeller:	James Alder
Height:	Unknown
Colour:	Black, red and green
Plinth:	Wooden
Issued:	1975 in a limited edition of 500
Series:	British Birds, Series Two
U.S.	$550.00
Can.	$675.00
U.K.	£300.00

Note: Missing plinth.

RW3965
DIPPERS

Modeller:	James Alder
Height:	Unknown
Colour:	Black, grey and green
Plinth:	Wooden
Issued:	1976 in a limited edition of 500
Series:	British Birds, Series Two
U.S.	$550.00
Can.	$675.00
U.K.	£300.00

Note: Missing plinth.

RW3967
EXMOOR PONY

Modeller:	Bernard Winskill
Height:	8 ¼", 21.0 cm
Colour:	Brown and black
Plinth:	Wooden
Issued:	1975 in a limited edition of 500
U.S.	$1,375.00
Can.	$1,650.00
U.K.	£ 750.00

RW3968
SHETLAND PONY

Modeller:	Bernard Winskill
Height:	9", 22.9 cm
Colour:	Light tan with cream tail and mane
Plinth:	Wooden
Issued:	1976 in a limited edition of 500
U.S.	$1,375.00
Can.	$1,650.00
U.K.	£ 750.00

Note: Missing plinth.

RW3981
KEK (KESTREL)

Modeller:	James Alder
Height:	7 ½", 19.1 cm
Colour:	1. Bone china: Golden and dark brown, beige
	2. Bronze metal
Plinth:	Wooden
Issued:	1. Bone china: 1976 in a limited edition of 250
	2. Bronze: 1975 in a limited edition of 50
Series:	Hawks and Falcons

	Bone China	Bronze
U.S.	$325.00	925.00
Can.	$400.00	1,100.00
U.K.	£175.00	500.00

Note: Missing plinth.

RW3982
GRUNDY WITH PAT EDDERY UP

Modeller:	Doris Lindner
Height:	11 ½", 29.2 cm
Colour:	Jockey: Blue, white and yellow silks
	Horse: Chestnut
Plinth:	Wooden
Issued:	1976 in a limited edition of 500
Series:	Racing Studies
U.S.	$1,850.00
Can.	$2,250.00
U.K.	£1,000.00

RW3984
DELETTANTE

Modeller:	Kenneth Potts
Height:	10", 25.4 cm
Colour:	Green frock coat with gold highlights; brown and white dog
Issued:	1977 in a limited edition of 500
Series:	The Age of Elegance, Series One
U.S.	$500.00
Can.	$600.00
U.K.	£275.00

RW3985
INNOCENCE

Modeller:	Kenneth Potts
Height:	10", 25.4 cm
Colour:	Pink and white dress, parasol and shoes; gold highlights
Issued:	1977 in a limited edition of 500
Series:	The Age of Elegance, Series One
U.S.	$500.00
Can.	$600.00
U.K.	£275.00

RW3986
THE DANDY

Modeller:	Kenneth Potts
Height:	10", 25.4 cm
Colour:	Unknown
Issued:	1977 in a limited edition of 500
Series:	The Age of Elegance, Series One
U.S.	$500.00
Can.	$600.00
U.K.	£275.00

RW3987
THE PARAMOUR

Modeller:	Kenneth Potts
Height:	10", 25.4 cm
Colour:	Unknown
Issued:	1977 in a limited edition of 500
Series:	The Age of Elegance, Series One
U.S.	$550.00
Can.	$675.00
U.K.	£300.00

RW3989A
BORZOI
Style Two

Modeller:	Kenneth Potts
Height:	5 ¼", 13.0 cm
Colour:	1. Bone china: Grey
	2. Bronze metal
Issued:	1. Bone china: 1979-1984
	2. Bronze metal: 1979 in a limited edition of 50

	Bone China	Bronze
U.S.	$325.00	
Can.	$400.00	Rare
U.K.	£175.00	

RW3989B
SPRINGER SPANIEL

Modeller:	Kenneth Potts
Height:	3 ¾", 9.5 cm
Size:	Small
Colour:	1. Bone china: White with light brown patches
	2. Bronze metal
Issued:	1. Bone china: 1979-1984
	2. Bronze metal: 1979 in a limited edition of 50

	Bone China	Bronze
U.S.	$325.00	
Can.	$400.00	Rare
U.K.	£175.00	

RW3992
ROUGH COLLIE WITH PUPS

Modeller:	Kenneth Potts
Height:	5", 12.7 cm
Size:	Small
Colour:	1. Bone china: Golden brown and cream
	2. Bronze metal
Issued:	1. Bone china: 1978-1984
	2. Bronze metal: 1977 in a limited edition of 50

	Bone China	Bronze
U.S.	$325.00	
Can.	$400.00	Rare
U.K.	£175.00	

RW3993
DICKCISSEL AND SUNFLOWER
Modeller:	James Alder
Height:	Unknown
Colour:	Blue-grey, yellow and brown bird; yellow flowers; green stems and leaves
Plinth:	Wooden
Issued:	1977 in a limited edition of 150
Series:	North American Birds
U.S.	$ 925.00
Can.	$1,100.00
U.K.	£ 500.00

RW3994
CAROLINA WREN AND TRUMPET CREEPER
Modeller:	James Alder
Height:	Unknown
Colour:	Orange and green
Plinth:	Wooden
Issued:	1976 in a limited edition of 150
Series:	North American Birds
U.S.	$ 925.00
Can.	$1,100.00
U.K.	£ 500.00

RW3995
CHESTNUT-COLLARED LONGSPUR
Modeller:	James Alder
Height:	Unknown
Colour:	Brown, grey, white, yellow and green
Issued:	1977 in a limited edition of 150
Series:	North American Birds
U.S.	$ 925.00
Can.	$1,100.00
U.K.	£ 500.00

Note: Missing plinth.

RW3996
RUBY CROWNED KINGLET AND CYPRESS
Modeller:	James Alder
Height:	Unknown
Colour:	Green, yellow, cream and brown
Plinth:	Wooden
Issued:	1976 in a limited edition of 150
Series:	North American Birds
U.S.	$ 925.00
Can.	$1,100.00
U.K.	£ 500.00

Note: Missing plinth.

RW3997
RED-BREASTED NUTHATCH AND OAK
Modeller:	James Alder
Height:	Unknown
Colour:	Grey with red-yellow breast; brown-green branch; green leaves
Plinth:	Wooden
Issued:	1976 in a limited edition of 150
Series:	North American Birds
U.S.	$ 925.00
Can.	$1,100.00
U.K.	£ 500.00

Note: Missing plinth.

RW3998
RUFOUS HUMMINGBIRD
Modeller:	James Alder
Height:	Unknown
Colour:	Orange bird; blue flowers; green leaves
Plinth:	Wooden
Issued:	1977 in a limited edition of 150
Series:	North American Birds
U.S.	$ 925.00
Can.	$1,100.00
U.K.	£ 500.00

Note: Missing plinth.

RW3999
HIGHLAND BULL
Designer:	Doris Lindner
Height:	8 ½", 21.4 cm
Colour:	Brown
Plinth:	Wooden
Issued:	1977 in a limited edition of 500
U.S.	$1,475.00
Can.	$1,775.00
U.K.	£ 800.00

Note: Missing plinth.

RW4001
GREAT TIT FLEDGLING
Modeller:	James Alder
Height:	3 ¾", 9.5 cm
Colour:	Yellow, blue-grey and green
Issued:	1977-1980
Series:	Fledglings
U.S.	$120.00
Can.	$135.00
U.K.	£ 65.00

RW4002
WREN FLEDGLING ON LEAVES
Modeller:	James Alder
Height:	3 ¾", 9.5 cm
Colour:	Golden brown with white highlights; green leaves; grey base
Issued:	1977-1980
Series:	Fledglings
U.S.	$120.00
Can.	$135.00
U.K.	£ 65.00

RW4003
ROBIN FLEDGLING ON BRANCH
Modeller:	James Alder
Height:	4 ½", 11.9 cm
Colour:	Browns, white and green
Issued:	1977-1980
Series:	Fledglings
U.S.	$120.00
Can.	$135.00
U.K.	£ 65.00

RW4004
BLUE TIT FLEDGLING AND CLEMATIS
Modeller:	James Alder
Height:	3 ¼", 8.3 cm
Colour:	Yellow and grey bird; lilac flowers; green leaves
Issued:	1977-1980
Series:	Fledglings
U.S.	$140.00
Can.	$165.00
U.K.	£ 75.00

RW4005
BULLFINCH FLEDGLING ON APPLE BLOSSOM
Modeller:	James Alder
Height:	3 ¼", 8.3 cm
Colour:	Golden and dark brown and white bird; white and pink flowers; green leaves; brown branch
Issued:	1977-1980
Series:	Fledglings
U.S.	$140.00
Can.	$165.00
U.K.	£ 75.00

RW4006
GOLDFINCH FLEDGLING AND THISTLE
Modeller:	James Alder
Height:	3 ¼", 8.3 cm
Colour:	Brown, yellow and black bird; mauve and green thistle
Issued:	1977-1980
Series:	Fledglings
U.S.	$140.00
Can.	$165.00
U.K.	£ 75.00

RW4007
KITTEN (Seated)
Modeller:	James Alder
Height:	4", 10.1 cm
Colour:	Ginger with white
Issued:	1979-1983
Series:	Kittens
U.S.	$120.00
Can.	$135.00
U.K.	£ 65.00

RW4008
LIPPIZANNER
Modeller:	Bernard Winskill
Height:	Unknown
Colour:	Bronze metal
Plinth:	Wooden
Issued:	1978 in a limited edition of 15
U.S.	
Can.	Extremely rare
U.K.	

Note: 1. Not produced in bone china.
2. Missing plinth.

Photograph not available at press time

RW4009
SPARROWHAWK
Modeller:	James Alder
Height:	7 ½", 19.1 cm
Colour:	1. Bone china: Coloured
	2. Bronze metal
Plinth:	Wooden
Issued:	1. Bone china: 1978 in a limited edition of 250
	2. Bronze metal: 1978 in a limited edition of 50
Series:	Hawks and Falcons

	Bone China	Bronze
U.S.	$375.00	925.00
Can.	$450.00	1,100.00
U.K.	£200.00	500.00

RW4010
RED SETTER (Lying on base)
Modeller:	Kenneth Potts
Height:	6 ¼", 15.9 cm
Colour:	1. Bone china: Red-brown
	2. Bronze metal
Issued:	1. Bone china: 1979 in a limited edition of 250
	2. Bronze metal: 1979 in a limited edition of 25

	Bone China	Bronze
U.S.	$600.00	
Can.	$725.00	Rare
U.K.	£325.00	

RW4011
GRACE
Style One
Modeller:	Kenneth Potts
Height:	10", 25.4 cm
Colour:	Lemon dress
Issued:	1977 in a limited edition of 500
Series:	The Age of Elegance, Series One

U.S.	$500.00
Can.	$600.00
U.K.	£275.00

RW4012
PHILANDERER
Modeller:	Kenneth Potts
Height:	10", 25.4 cm
Colour:	Black frock coat
Issued:	1977 in a limited edition of 500
Series:	The Age of Elegance, Series One

U.S.	$500.00
Can.	$600.00
U.K.	£275.00

RW4013
GIRL WITH SETTER
Modeller:	Kenneth Potts
Height:	Unknown
Colour:	Unknown
Issued:	1. Bone china: 1977
	2. Bronze metal: 1977 in a limited edition of 25

	Bone China	Bronze
U.S.		
Can.	Extremely rare	
U.K.		

RW4015
MISTRAL AND LESTER PIGGOT
Modeller:	Bernard Winskill
Height:	16", 40.6 cm
Colour:	1. Bone china: Rider: Blue, green and white silks; white jodhpurs; Horse: Chestnut
	2. Bronze metal
Plinth:	Wooden
Issued:	1. Bone china: 1978 in a limited edition of 150
	2. Bronze metal: 1978 in a limited edition of 25
Series:	Racing Studies

	Bone China	Bronze
U.S.	$2,800.00	4,500.00
Can.	$3,300.00	5,500.00
U.K.	£1,500.00	2,500.00

Note: Missing plinth.

RW4016
WELSH COB STALLION "LLANARTH FLYING COMET"
Modeller:	Lorne McKean
Height:	11", 27.9 cm
Colour:	1. Bone china: Black
	2. Bronze metal
Plinth:	Wooden
Issued:	1. Bone china: 1978 in a limited edition of 250
	2. Bronze metal: 1978 in a limited edition of 15

	Bone China	Bronze
U.S.	$1,575.00	
Can.	$1,875.00	Extremely rare
U.K.	£ 850.00	

Note: Missing plinth.

Photograph not available at press time

RW4017
DUNFERMLINE
Modeller:	Bernard Winskill
Height:	11", 27.9 cm
Colour:	Bronze metal
Issued:	1978 in a limited edition of 25

U.S.	
Can.	Extremely rare
U.K.	

RW4018
ROBIN ON CHRISTMAS ROSE
Modeller:	James Alder
Height:	7 ¾", 19.7 cm
Colour:	Red breast; grey and brown feathers; white rose; green leaves
Issued:	1978 in a limited edition of 250
Series:	British Birds, Series Two

U.S.	$325.00
Can.	$400.00
U.K.	£175.00

RW4019
WOOD WARBLER ON CHERRY
Modeller:	James Alder
Height:	7 ¾", 18.5 cm
Colour:	Green and brown bird; white flowers; brown branch; green leaves
Issued:	1978 in a limited edition of 250
Series:	British Birds, Series Two

U.S.	$325.00
Can.	$400.00
U.K.	£175.00

RW4020
KITTEN (Lying)
Style One
Modeller:	James Alder
Height:	5 ¼", 13.5 cm
Colour:	Black and white
Issued:	1979-1983
Series:	Kittens

U.S.	$120.00
Can.	$135.00
U.K.	£ 65.00

RW4023
MORNING WALK
Modeller: Donald Brindley
Height: 6", 15.0 cm
Colour: 1. White dress with blue design on bodice
2. White dress with red dots on sleeves, red sash and ribbons
Issued: 1979-1984
Varieties: Also called "Red Ribbons," Style Two
Series: Age of Romance, Series Two

U.S. $150.00
Can. $175.00
U.K. £ 85.00

RW4024
SPRING FAIR
Modeller: Donald Brindley
Height: 6", 15.0 cm
Colour: 1. White skirt with pink design; white bodice, apron and frills; basket of yellow flowers
2. Yellow skirt; white bodice and apron; basket of pink flowers
Issued: 1979-1980
Series: Age of Romance, Series Two

U.S. $150.00
Can. $175.00
U.K. £ 85.00

RW4025
WEDDING DAY (Girl)
Modeller: Donald Brindley
Height: 4", 10.1 cm
Colour: White dress and veil; pink flowers attached to veil; white posy
Issued: 1979-1980
Series: Age of Romance, Series Two

U.S. $120.00
Can. $135.00
U.K. £ 65.00

RW4026
WEDDING DAY (Boy)
Modeller: Donald Brindley
Height: 4", 10.1 cm
Colour: White jacket, shirt and top hat; blue shorts; pink tie
Issued: 1979-1980
Series: Age of Romance, Series Two

U.S. $120.00
Can. $135.00
U.K. £ 65.00

RW4027
PERSIAN KITTEN (Seated)
Modeller: James Alder
Height: 4, 10.1 cm
Colour: 1. Blue
2. Cream
Issued: 1978-1985
Series: Kittens

U.S. $120.00
Can. $135.00
U.K. £ 65.00

RW4028
OLD ENGLISH SHEEPDOG (Seated)
Modeller: Kenneth Potts
Height: 5", 12.5 cm
Colour: 1. Bone china: Grey and white
2. Bronze metal
Issued: 1. Bone china: 1978
2. Bronze metal: 1978 Ltd. edition of 75

	Bone China	Bronze
U.S.	$275.00	925.00
Can.	$325.00	1,100.00
U.K.	£150.00	500.00

RW4029
BLUE TIT ON HOGWEED
Modeller:	James Alder
Height:	8", 20.3 cm
Colour:	Green and yellow
Issued:	1978 in a limited edition of 250
Series:	British Birds, Series Two

U.S.	$325.00
Can.	$400.00
U.K.	£175.00

RW4030
LITTLE OWL ON IVY
Modeller:	James Alder
Height:	7 ¼", 18.4 cm
Colour:	1. Bone china: Brown, cream, yellow and green
	2. Bronze metal
Issued:	1. Bone china: 1978 in a limited edition of 250
	2. Bronze metal: 1978 in a limited edition of 25
Series:	British Birds, Series Two

	Bone China	Bronze
U.S.	$325.00	
Can.	$400.00	Rare
U.K.	£175.00	

RW4031
H.R.H. PRINCE CHARLES ON PANS FOLLY
Modeller:	Lorne McKean
Height:	16", 40.6 cm
Colour:	1. Bone china: Green shirt; white jodhpurs; brown boots; black hat; brown horse
	2. Bronze metal
Plinth:	Wooden
Issued:	1. Bone china: 1978 in a limited edition of 250
	2. Bronze metal: 1878 in a limited edition of 15

	Bone China	Bronze
U.S.	$1,875.00	2,800.00
Can.	$2,250.00	3,300.00
U.K.	£1,000.00	1,500.00

RW4032
CRINOLINE LADY
Modeller:	Donald Brindley
Height:	6", 15.0 cm
Colour:	1. Lilac patterned dress, white frills, deep lilac bow and ribbons; straw hat with deep lilac ribbon and bow
	2. White dress with lemon highlights; yellow bow and ribbons; straw hat with yellow ribbon and bow
Issued:	1979-1980
Series:	Age of Romance, Series Two

U.S.	$150.00
Can.	$175.00
U.K.	£ 85.00

RW4033
WINTER WALTZ
Modeller:	Donald Brindley
Height:	6", 15.0 cm
Colour:	1. Red skirt; white coat with brown fur trim and buttons; red ruff at neck; brown fur muff and hat
	2. White skirt; yellow coat with brown fur trim and buttons; yellow ruff at neck; brown fur hat and muff
Issued:	1979-1980
Series:	Age of Romance, Series Two

U.S.	$150.00
Can.	$175.00
U.K.	£ 85.00

RW4034
RICHARD COEUR DE LION
Modeller:	Bernard Winskill
Height:	15 ½", 39.4 cm
Colour:	1. Bone china: Red cape and reins; grey tunic and horse
	2. Bronze metal
Issued:	1. Bone china: 1978 in a limited edition of 250
	2. Bronze metal: 1978 in a limited edition of 15
Series:	Military Commanders

	Bone China	Bronze
U.S.	$3,700.00	7,400.00
Can.	$4,500.00	8,500.00
U.K.	£2,000.00	4,000.00

RW4035
BOXER (Seated)
Modeller:	Kenneth Potts
Height:	9 ½", 24.0 cm
Colour:	1. Bone china: Tan with black facial markings
	2. Bronze metal
Issued:	1. Bone china: 1978 in a limited edition of 250
	2. Bronze metal: 1978 in a limited edition of 25

	Bone China	Bronze
U.S.	$375.00	
Can.	$450.00	Rare
U.K.	£200.00	

RW4036
LABRADOR (Seated)
Modeller:	Kenneth Potts
Height:	10 ¼", 26.0 cm
Size:	Large
Colour:	1. Bone china: Golden
	2. Bronze metal
Issued:	1. Bone china: 1978 in a limited edition of 250
	2. Bronze metal: 1978 in a limited edition of 25

	Bone China	Bronze
U.S.	$375.00	
Can.	$450.00	Rare
U.K.	£200.00	

RW4037
CONNEMARA
Modeller:	Lorne McKean
Height:	13 ½", 34.3 cm
Colour:	1. Bone china: Grey
	2. Bronze metal
Issued:	1. Bone china: 1978 in a limited edition of 250
	2. Bronze metal: 1978 in a limited edition of 25

	Bone China	Bronze
U.S.	$1,575.00	
Can.	$1,900.00	Rare
U.K.	£ 850.00	

RW4038
INVITATION
Style Two
Modeller:	Donald Brindley
Height:	6", 15.0 cm
Colour:	1. Lemon dress; pink roses on skirt; lemon fan
	2. White dress; patterned blue underskirt and fan
Issued:	1979-1984
Series:	Age of Romance, Series Two
U.S.	$150.00
Can.	$175.00
U.K.	£ 85.00

RW4039
FRAGRANCE
Modeller:	Donald Brindley
Height:	6", 15.0 cm
Colour:	1. Pink dress; white jacket
	2. Yellow dress; white jacket
Issued:	1979-1984
Series:	Age of Romance, Series Two
U.S.	$150.00
Can.	$175.00
U.K.	£ 85.00

RW4040
YELLOW BUNTING ON
BLACKBERRY
Modeller:	James Alder
Height:	6", 15.0 cm
Colour:	Yellow, green and orange bird; purple berries; white flowers
Issued:	1978 in a limited edition of 250
Series:	British Birds, Series Two
U.S.	$325.00
Can.	$400.00
U.K.	£175.00

RW4041
SUNDAY MORNING
Modeller:	Donald Brindley
Height:	6", 15.0 cm
Colour:	1. Green skirt and hat; dark green jacket and umbrella
	2. Pale brown skirt; dark brown jacket and hat; yellow umbrella
Issued:	1979-1984
Series:	Age of Romance, Series Two
U.S.	$150.00
Can.	$175.00
U.K.	£ 85.00

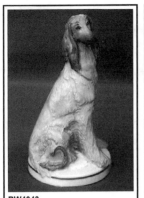

RW4043
AFGHAN HOUND
Modeller:	Kenneth Potts
Height:	5 ¾", 14.6 cm
Colour:	Golden brown
Issued:	1978
U.S.	$225.00
Can.	$275.00
U.K.	£125.00

RW4044
CHARITY
Modeller:	Donald Brindley
Height:	6", 15.0 cm
Colour:	1. Cream dress with brown flowers; golden ribbons
	2. Salmon pink dress; rust ribbons
Issued:	1980-1984
Series:	Age of Romance, Series Two
U.S.	$150.00
Can.	$175.00
U.K.	£ 85.00

RW4045
PERSIAN KITTEN (On hind legs)
Modeller:	James Alder
Height:	4", 10.1 cm
Colour:	White kitten, blue bow
Issued:	1979-1985
Series:	Kittens
U.S.	$120.00
Can.	$135.00
U.K.	£ 65.00

RW4046
SIAMESE KITTEN (Seated)
Modeller:	James Alder
Height:	4", 10.1 cm
Colour:	Sealpoint with grey markings; blue eyes
Issued:	1979-1985
Series:	Kittens
U.S.	$120.00
Can.	$135.00
U.K.	£ 65.00

RW4047
TABBY KITTEN (Lying)
Modeller:	James Alder
Height:	4", 10.1 cm
Colour:	Dark and light brown with white markings
Issued:	1979-1985
Series:	Kittens
U.S.	$120.00
Can.	$135.00
U.K.	£ 65.00

RW4048
LINNET ON WILD ROSE
Modeller:	James Alder
Height:	7", 17.8 cm
Colour:	Brown, cream and red bird; pink flower; green leaves
Issued:	1980 in a limited edition of 250
Series:	British Birds, Series Two
U.S.	$375.00
Can.	$450.00
U.K.	£200.00

RW4055
EUGÉNE DE BEAUHARNAIS / CHASSEUR AND CHAVAL
Modeller:	Bernard Winskill
Height:	Unknown
Colour:	1. Red and black jacket; cream jodhpurs; black saddle pad; brown horse
	2. Red and yellow jacket; white jodhpurs; cream and gold saddle pad; light brown horse
Plinth:	Wooden
Issued:	1980 in a limited edition of 250
Series:	**Eugéne De Beauharnais:** Military Commanders
U.S.	$2,800.00
Can.	$3,300.00
U.K.	£1,500.00

Note: Missing plinth.

RW4056
MARSH TIT ON DAPHNE
Modeller: James Alder
Height: 7 ¾", 19.7 cm
Colour: Brown, black and white
              bird; pink flowers;
              brown stalk
Issued: 1979 in a limited
              edition of 250
Series: British Birds,
              Series Two

U.S. $375.00
Can. $450.00
U.K.   £200.00

RW4057
GREENFINCH ON FORSYTHIA
Modeller: James Alder
Height: Unknown
Colour: Yellow and green
Issued: 1979 in a limited
              edition of 250
Series: British Birds,
              Series Two

U.S. $375.00
Can. $450.00
U.K.   £200.00

RW4058
SUMMERTIME
Modeller: Donald Brindley
Height: 6", 15.0 cm
Colour: 1. White dress with blue flowers and ribbon; blue hat and
                  ribbon
              2. White dress with lemon shading; yellow hat with cream
                  ribbon
Issued: 1980-1985
Series: Age of Romance, Series Two

U.S. $150.00
Can. $175.00
U.K.   £ 85.00

RW4059
SAVED
Modeller: Kenneth Potts
Height: 8", 20.3 cm
Colour: Black uniform; gold
              helmet; light grey dress
Issued: 1979
Comm. by: Phoenix World

U.S. $ 925.00
Can. $1,100.00
U.K.   £ 500.00

RW4061
GREENFINCH ON BRONZE
Modeller: James Alder
Height: 4", 10.1 cm
Colour: Green, black and brown
Issued: 1979
Series: British Birds,
              Series Three

U.S. $120.00
Can. $135.00
U.K.   £ 65.00

RW4062
SINCERITY
Modeller: Donald Brindley
Height: 6", 15.0 cm
Colour: 1. Lilac
              2. Spring green
Issued: 1980-1985
Series: Age of Romance,
              Series Two

U.S. $150.00
Can. $175.00
U.K.   £ 85.00

RW4064
COMING OF AGE
Modeller: Donald Brindley
Height: 6", 15.0 cm
Colour: 1. White, green trim
              2. White, maroon trim
              3. Red
Issued: 1980-1984
Series: Age of Romance,
              Series Two

U.S. $150.00
Can. $175.00
U.K.   £ 85.00

RW4065
FLIRTATION
Style One
Modeller: Donald Brindley
Height: 6", 15.0 cm
Colour: 1. Light blue dress
2. Pink dress
Issued: 1980-1984
Series: Age of Romance,
Series Two

U.S. $150.00
Can. $175.00
U.K. £ 85.00

RW4066
EQUESTRIENNE
Modeller: Donald Brindley
Height: 6", 15.0 cm
Colour: 1. Red riding jacket;
grey skirt; black hat
2. Blue riding jacket
and hat; peach skirt
Issued: 1980-1985
Series: Age of Romance,
Series Two

U.S. $150.00
Can. $175.00
U.K. £ 85.00

RW4067
WILLIAM THE CONQUEROR
Modeller: Bernard Winskill
Height: Unknown
Colour: 1. Bone china: Dark brown, tan and blue
2. Bronze metal
Plinth: Wooden
Issued: 1. Bone china: 1980 in a limited edition of 250
2. Bronze metal: 1980 in a limited edition of 15
Series: Military Commanders

	Bone China	Bronze
U.S.	$2,800.00	3,700.00
Can.	$3,300.00	4,450.00
U.K.	£1,500.00	2,000.00

RW4068
REDSTART
Modeller: James Alder
Height: 4 ½", 11.9 cm
Colour: Grey, red and black
Issued: 1979
Series: British Birds,
Series Three

U.S. $120.00
Can. $135.00
U.K. £ 65.00

RW4070
GREY WAGTAIL
Modeller: James Alder
Height: 3 ½", 8.9 cm
Colour: Grey and yellow
Issued: 1979
Series: British Birds,
Series Three

U.S. $120.00
Can. $135.00
U.K. £ 65.00

RW4071
ROBIN ON HOLLY
Style One
Modeller: James Alder
Height: 4", 10.1 cm
Colour: Brown and red bird;
yellow berries; green
leaves
Issued: 1979
Series: British Birds,
Series Three

U.S. $120.00
Can. $135.00
U.K. £ 65.00

RW4072
GERMAINE
Modeller: Kenneth Potts
Height: 8 ¾", 22.2 cm
Colour: Pink, blue and yellow
skirt; yellow and blue
blouse and hat; pink
and blue umbrella
Issued: 1979 in a limited
edition of 500
Series: The World of the
Impressionists

U.S. $500.00
Can. $600.00
U.K. £275.00

RW4073
JEANNE
Modeller:	Kenneth Potts
Height:	8 ¼", 21.0 cm
Colour:	White dress shaded in lilac, yellow and blue; dark blue bows and underskirt
Issued:	1979 in a limited edition of 500
Series:	The World of the Impressionists
U.S.	$500.00
Can.	$600.00
U.K.	£275.00

RW4076
SIMÓN BOLÍVAR
Modeller:	Bernard Winskill
Height:	15 ½", 39.4 cm
Colour:	Rider: Navy jacket with gold epaulettes; white jodhpurs Horse: Grey
Plinth:	Wooden
Issued:	1979 in a limited edition of 250
Series:	Military Commanders
U.S.	$2,800.00
Can.	$3,300.00
U.K.	£1,500.00

Note: Missing plinth.

RW4077
STONECHAT
Modeller:	James Alder
Height:	4", 10.1 cm
Colour:	Yellow breast; black head and wings; yellow flower; green-brown base
Issued:	1979
Series:	British Birds, Series Three
U.S.	$120.00
Can.	$135.00
U.K.	£ 65.00

RW4078
CRESTED TIT
Modeller:	James Alder
Height:	3 ¾", 9.5 cm
Colour:	Pale brown; cream; black and white
Issued:	1979
Series:	British Birds, Series Three
U.S.	$120.00
Can.	$135.00
U.K.	£ 65.00

RW4079
BELLE OF THE BALL (Style One) / EMILY (Style Two)
Modeller:	Donald Brindley	
Height:	7 ¾", 19.7 cm	
Colour:	1. **Belle of the Ball:** White dress with pink flowers, green trim	
	2. **Emily:** Lilac and white dress	
Issued:	1. **Belle of the Ball:** 1979-1991	
	2. **Emily:** 1988-1991	
Series:	Age of Romance, Series Two	

Name:	Belle	Emily
U.S.	$150.00	150.00
Can.	$175.00	175.00
U.K.	£ 85.00	85.00

RW4080
EASTER PARADE
Modeller:	Donald Brindley
Height:	Unknown
Colour:	Unknown
Issued:	1979
U.S.	
Can.	Extremely rare
U.K.	

RW4081
OLD ENGLISH SHEEPDOG PUPPY (Playing)
Modeller:	Kenneth Potts
Height:	10", 25.4 cm
Size:	Large
Colour:	Grey and white
Issued:	1979 in a limited edition of 250
U.S.	$425.00
Can.	$500.00
U.K.	£225.00

RW4083
REBECCA (Style Two) / WINTER'S MORN
Modeller:	Donald Brindley
Height:	7 ¾", 19.7 cm
Colour:	1. **Rebecca:** Blue jacket and hat; yellow and blue skirt; fur trim
	2. **Winter's Morn:** Blue jacket and hat; pale yellow and white skirt; fur trim
Issued:	1. **Rebecca:** 1988-1991
	2. **Winter's Morn:** 1979-1991
Series:	Age of Romance, Series Two

Name:	Rebecca	Winter's Morn
U.S.	$150.00	150.00
Can.	$175.00	175.00
U.K.	£ 85.00	85.00

RW4084
CAMILLE
Modeller:	Kenneth Potts
Height:	8 ½", 21.6 cm
Colour:	Pink dress with blue shading; navy shawl with white trim; straw hat with navy ribbon; pale blue umbrella
Issued:	1979 in a limited edition of 500
Series:	The World of the Impressionists
U.S.	$500.00
Can.	$600.00
U.K.	£275.00

RW4085
ALPHONSINE
Modeller:	Kenneth Potts
Height:	7", 17.8 cm
Colour:	Burgundy skirt; white top with yellow and red design; yellow straw hat with blue bow
Issued:	1979 in a limited edition of 500
Series:	The World of the Impressionists
U.S.	$500.00
Can.	$600.00
U.K.	£275.00

RW4086
MODESTY
Modeller:	Donald Brindley
Height:	5", 12.7 cm
Colour:	Pink dress with white frills; bouquet of red roses
Issued:	1981-1984
Series:	Age of Romance, Miniatures
U.S.	$120.00
Can.	$165.00
U.K.	£ 65.00

RW4087
AUTUMN SONG
Modeller:	Donald Brindley
Height:	6", 15.0 cm
Colour:	1. Pale blue skirt, darker blue jacket and hat
	2. Pale brown skirt, darker brown jacket and hat
Issued:	1980-1984
Series:	Age of Romance, Series Two
U.S.	$150.00
Can.	$175.00
U.K.	£ 85.00

RW4088
MARGUERITE AND DON PEDRO
Modeller:	Kenneth Potts
Height:	8 ½", 21.6 cm
Colour:	Marguerite: Shaded pink, blue and yellow dress; dark blue collar, bows and underskirt
	Don Pedro: Yellow trousers; blue jacket, hat and tie; white shirt
Issued:	1980 in a limited edition of 500
Series:	The World of the Impressionists

U.S.	$600.00
Can.	$725.00
U.K.	£325.00

RW4089
NORBERT
Modeller:	Kenneth Potts
Height:	8 ¼", 21.0 cm
Colour:	Dark blue suit; white shirt; dark yellow tie; light yellow hat
Issued:	1980 in a limited edition of 500
Series:	The World of the Impressionists

U.S.	$500.00
Can.	$600.00
U.K.	£275.00

RW4090
DEBUTANTE / DIANA (Style One)
Modeller:	Donald Brindley
Height:	7 ¾", 19.7 cm
Colour:	1. **Debutante:** White skirt; green and white top
	2. **Diana:** Pink dress with white trim
Issued:	1. **Debutante:** 1980-1991
	2. **Diana:** 1988-1991
Series:	Age of Romance, Series Two

Name	Debutante	Diana
U.S.	$150.00	150.00
Can.	$175.00	175.00
U.K.	£ 85.00	85.00

RW4091
COQUETTE
Style Two
Modeller:	Donald Brindley
Height:	5", 12.7 cm
Colour:	Pale blue dress, white underskirt and bow
Issued:	1981-1984
Series:	Age of Romance, Miniatures

U.S.	$120.00
Can.	$135.00
U.K.	£ 65.00

RW4093
BOXER (Standing)
Modeller:	Doris Lindner
Height:	10 ¼", 26.0 cm
Size:	Large
Colour:	Brown and white
Plinth:	Wooden
Issued:	1981 in a limited edition of 1,000
Series:	Final Collection by Doris Lindner

U.S.	$750.00
Can.	$900.00
U.K.	£400.00

Note: Missing plinth.

RW4094
SALUKI (The)

Modeller:	Doris Lindner
Height:	9 ¼", 23.5 cm
Size:	Large
Colour:	White with grey and tan
Plinth:	Wooden
Issued:	1981 in a limited edition of 1,000
Series:	Final Collection by Doris Lindner
U.S.	$ 825.00
Can.	$1,000.00
U.K.	£ 450.00

RW4095
PONY STALLION

Modeller:	Doris Lindner
Height:	Unknown
Colour:	Brown
Plinth:	Wooden
Issued:	1981 in a limited edition of 500
Series:	Final Collection by Doris Lindner
U.S.	$1,400.00
Can.	$1,675.00
U.K.	£ 750.00

Note: Missing plinth.

RW4096
HUNTER

Modeller:	Doris Lindner
Height:	11 ½", 29.2 cm
Colour:	Grey
Plinth:	Wooden
Issued:	1981 in a limited edition of 1,000
Series:	Final Collection by Doris Lindner
U.S.	$1,200.00
Can.	$1,450.00
U.K.	£ 650.00

RW4097
PARTY DRESS

Modeller:	Donald Brindley
Height:	4", 10.1 cm
Colour:	Yellow dress
Issued:	1981-1984
Series:	Age of Romance, Miniatures
U.S.	$120.00
Can.	$135.00
U.K.	£ 65.00

RW4098
MARY MARY

Modeller:	Donald Brindley
Height:	5", 12.7 cm
Colour:	Rose-pink pinafore; white dress and cap; yellow watering can
Issued:	1981-1984
Series:	Age of Romance, Miniatures
U.S.	$120.00
Can.	$135.00
U.K.	£ 65.00

RW4100
LA MIDINETTE

Modeller:	Kenneth Potts
Height:	8", 20.3 cm
Colour:	Mottled green and blue dress; yellow basket, blue contents
Issued:	1980 in a limited edition of 500
Series:	The World of the Impressionists
U.S.	$500.00
Can.	$600.00
U.K.	£275.00

RW4101
WREN ON CLEMATIS

Modeller:	James Alder
Height:	7 ¼", 18.4 cm
Colour:	Brown bird; pink and yellow flower; bronze stem and leaves
Issued:	1981
Series:	Nature Studies
U.S.	$225.00
Can.	$275.00
U.K.	£125.00

RW4102
NIGHTINGALE ON HONEYSUCKLE

Modeller:	James Alder
Height:	10", 25.4 cm
Colour:	Brown and cream bird; pink and yellow flowers; bronze stem and leaves
Issued:	1981
Series:	Nature Studies
U.S.	$225.00
Can.	$275.00
U.K.	£125.00

RW4103
ROBIN ON HOLLY
Style Two
Modeller:	James Alder
Height:	7 ¼", 18.4 cm
Colour:	Brown and red bird; red berries; bronze stem and leaves
Issued:	1981
Series:	Nature Studies
U.S.	$225.00
Can.	$275.00
U.K.	£125.00

RW4106
THOROUGHBRED FOAL
Modeller:	Doris Lindner
Height:	6", 15.0 cm
Colour:	Brown and cream
Plinth:	Wooden
Issued:	1981 in a limited edition of 1,000
Series:	Final Collection by Doris Lindner
U.S.	$ 825.00
Can.	$1,000.00
U.K.	£ 450.00

RW4107
THOROUGHBRED MARE
Modeller:	Doris Lindner
Height:	10 ¼", 26.0 cm
Colour:	Palomino
Plinth:	Wooden
Issued:	1981 in a limited edition of 1,000
Series:	Final Collection by Doris Lindner
U.S.	$1,200.00
Can.	$1,450.00
U.K.	£ 650.00

RW4108
WATERLILY AND BUTTERFLY
Modeller:	James Alder
Height:	9 ¼", 24.0
Colour:	Crimson flower; white butterfly; bronze stem and leaves
Issued:	1981
Series:	Nature Studies
U.S.	$225.00
Can.	$275.00
U.K.	£125.00

RW4109
CURTSEY (Style Two) /
LITTLE MAID
Modeller:	Donald Brindley
Height:	4", 10.1 cm
Colour:	Orange dress; white apron, cuffs and petticoat; brown hair
Issued:	1980
U.S.	Only
Can.	trial pieces
U.K.	exist

Photograph not
available
at press time

RW4111
HEDGEHOG ON BRONZE
Style One
Modeller:	James Alder
Height:	4", 10.1 cm
Colour:	Brown
Issued:	1980
Series:	Nature Studies
U.S.	$150.00
Can.	$175.00
U.K.	£ 85.00

RW4112
RENDEZVOUS
Modeller:	Donald Brindley
Height:	6", 15.0 cm
Colour:	Brown-orange dress
Issued:	1981-1984
Series:	Age of Romance, Miniatures
U.S.	$150.00
Can.	$175.00
U.K.	£ 85.00

RW4113
AFFECTION
Modeller:	Donald Brindley
Height:	5", 12.7 cm
Colour:	Pale green dress with dark green trim
Issued:	1981-1984
Series:	Age of Romance, Miniatures
U.S.	$120.00
Can.	$135.00
U.K.	£ 65.00

RW4114
EVENING ENGAGEMENT
Modeller:	Donald Brindley
Height:	6", 15.0 cm
Colour:	White dress with pink trim; brown cape and hat trimmed with yellow; blue lining
Issued:	1981-1984
Series:	Age of Romance, Miniatures
U.S.	$150.00
Can.	$175.00
U.K.	£ 85.00

RW4115
MARCH WINDS
Modeller:	Donald Brindley
Height:	4", 10.1 cm
Colour:	Pale green and yellow
Issued:	1981-1984
Series:	Age of Romance, Miniatures
U.S.	$120.00
Can.	$135.00
U.K.	£ 65.00

RW4116
GOLDCREST ON BRONZE
Style One
Modeller:	James Alder
Height:	Unknown
Colour:	Greenish-yellow and brown bird; bronze branch
Issued:	1981
Series:	Nature Studies
U.S.	$120.00
Can.	$135.00
U.K.	£ 65.00

RW4117
BLUE TIT ON BRONZE
Style One
Modeller:	James Alder
Height:	7", 17.8 cm
Colour:	Yellow, blue and black bird; bronze branch and leaves
Issued:	1981
Series:	Nature Studies
U.S.	$120.00
Can.	$135.00
U.K.	£ 65.00

RW4118
BULLFINCH ON BRONZE
Modeller:	James Alder
Height:	5 ½", 14.0 cm
Colour:	Grey, black and red bird; white flowers; bronze branch and leaves
Issued:	1981
Series:	Nature Studies
U.S.	$120.00
Can.	$135.00
U.K.	£ 65.00

RW4119
THE BRIDE
Modeller:	Donald Brindley
Height:	6", 15.0 cm
Colour:	White dress and veil; pink rose; green leaves pale blue ribbon
Issued:	1981-1984
Series:	Age of Romance, Series Two
U.S.	$150.00
Can.	$175.00
U.K.	£ 85.00

RW4124
BALLET MASTER
Modeller:	Kenneth Potts
Height:	9", 22.9 cm
Colour:	Green-grey jacket; brown-green trousers; white shirt; red neck tie
Issued:	1982 in a limited edition of 500
Series:	The World of the Impressionists
U.S.	$500.00
Can.	$600.00
U.K.	£275.00

RW4126
LA LEÇON
Modeller:	Kenneth Potts
Height:	7", 17.8 cm
Colour:	White dress with yellow highlights; black sash and bow
Issued:	1980 in a limited edition of 500
Series:	The World of the Impressionists
U.S.	$750.00
Can.	$900.00
U.K.	£400.00

RW4127
L'ÉTUDE
Modeller: Kenneth Potts
Height: 6", 15.0 cm
Colour: Mottled blue and pink
 dress; pink ballet
 slippers
Issued: 1982 in a limited
 edition of 500
Series: The World of the
 Impressionists
U.S. $500.00
Can. $600.00
U.K. £275.00

RW4129
POPE JOHN PAUL II
(Bust on plinth)
Designer: Donald Brindley
Height: 11 ½", 29.2 cm
Colour: Cream; gilding; pink
 flowers in mitre (matt)
Issued: c.1980 in a limited
 edition of 250
U.S. $750.00
Can. $900.00
U.K. £400.00

RW4139
EN REPOSE (1926)
Modeller: Kenneth Potts
Height: Unknown
Colour: White jacket with blue
 stripes; rust and blue
 trim; light blue shirt and
 trousers; burgundy
 couch
Issued: 1981 in a limited
 edition of 500
Series: À La Mode
U.S. $550.00
Can. $675.00
U.K. £300.00

RW4140
SOIREE (1926)
Modeller: Kenneth Potts
Height: Unknown
Colour: Green coat, striped
 scarf; yellow hair
Issued: 1981 in a limited
 edition of 500
Series: À la Mode
U.S. $550.00
Can. $675.00
U.K. £300.00

RW4144
FRENCH BULLDOG "WINSTON"
Modeller: James Alder
Height: 3", 7.6 cm
Colour: Black with white patch
 on chest
Issued: Unknown
U.S.
Can. Extremely rare
U.K.

Note: Approximately 15 models were
 made. The dog "Winston"
 belonged to Lynn Davies,
 Managing Director of Royal
 Worcester 1977-1979 and
 Chief Executive 1979-1984.

RW4148
SKATER
Modeller: Donald Brindley
Height: Unknown
Colour: Unknown
Issued: 1982
Series: Age of Romance
U.S. Possibly
Can. not put into
U.K. production

RW4149
MASQUERADE
Style Two
Modeller: Donald Brindley
Height: 6", 15.0 cm
Colour: Light blue overcoat;
 pale pink skirt; light
 blue hat with pink
 feather; black mask
Issued: 1982
Series: Age of Romance,
 Series Two
U.S. $150.00
Can. $175.00
U.K. £ 85.00

RW4150
CHIC (1933)
Modeller: Kenneth Potts
Height: Unknown
Colour: Peach dress, white
 collar, gold buttons and
 shoes; yellow dog;
 peach flowered hat
Issued: 1981 in a limited
 edition of 500
Series: À La Mode
U.S. $500.00
Can. $600.00
U.K. £275.00

LIMITED EDITIONS

RW4703
Secret Garden
Limited edition of 1,000

RW4633
Midnight Rendezvous
Limited edition of 1,000

RW4628
With Love, Style One
Limited edition of 500

RW4722
True Love
Limited edition of 500

DAY DREAMS

RW4654A
Reflection, Style One

RW4604
Wistful

RW4666
Thoughtful

GOLDEN MOMENTS

RW4661
Birthday Wish

RW4603
Ruby Anniversary
Style One

RW4634
Mother and Child, Style One

GLITTERING OCCASIONS

RW4659
Masked Ball

RW4707
Grand Entrance

RW4638
Night at the Opera

HIGH SOCIETY

RW4711
Tea at the Ritz

RW4700
Knightsbridge

RW4662
Ascot Lady

PREMIERE FIGURINE OF THE YEAR

RW4725
Grace, Style Four
1999

RW4795
Margaret
2000

RW4873
Isabella, Style Two
2001

RW4955
Diana, Style Three
2002

RW5017
Eleanor, Style Two
2003

RW5024
Alexandra
2004

SUMMER ROMANCE

RW4595A
Charlotte, Style One

RW4877
Amanda, Style Two

RW5035
Carmen

RW4615
Jessica, Style One

RW4653
Claire

RW4647
Alice, Style Three

FORCES OF CREATION

RW4689
Flame Dance (Fire)

RW4694
Aquamarine (Water)

RW4697
Mistral (Air)

RW4699
Earth Song

LIVING SCULPTURES

RW5004
Elation

RW4996
Desire

RW4998
Fantasy

RW4992
Harmony

RW4993
Reflection, Style Three

RW4999
Eternal Love

STREET SELLERS

RW4958
Rose Seller

RW4961
Lavender Seller

RW4966
Apple Seller

LES PETITES

RW4715
Christina

RW5027
Emma

RW5028
Megan

RW4152
DIANA, PRINCESS OF WALES
(Bust on plinth)
Modeller: Donald Brindley
Height: Unknown
Colour: Cream (Wallbody)
Issued: 1982 in a limited edition of 100

U.S. $550.00
Can. $675.00
U.K. £300.00

Note: Issued in 1982 to celebrate Diana's 21st birthday.

RW4153
PROMENADE (1922)
Modeller: Kenneth Potts
Height: Unknown
Colour: Green dress and hat with red edging; white greyhound
Issued: 1982 in a limited edition of 500
Series: À la Mode

U.S. $650.00
Can. $775.00
U.K. £350.00

RW4154
KATIE
Style One
Modeller: Freda Doughty
Height: 3", 7.6 cm
Colour: Blue dress; yellow hair
Issued: 1982-1985
Series: The Worcester Children

U.S. $175.00
Can. $200.00
U.K. £100.00

RW4155
LITTLE GRANDMOTHER'S DRESS
Modeller: Freda Doughty
Height: 3", 7.6 cm
Colour: 1. Green dress; yellow hair
2. Yellow dress; brown hair
Issued: 1982-1985
Series: The Worcester Children

U.S. $175.00
Can. $200.00
U.K. £100.00

Note: See also RW4155 Grandmother's Dress.

RW4156
CHRISTOPHER
Modeller: Freda Doughty
Height: 3", 7.6 cm
Colour: Yellow shirt and hat; brown shorts; green shoes
Issued: 1982-by 1985
Series: The Worcester Children

U.S. $275.00
Can. $325.00
U.K. £150.00

Note: See also RW3457 September / Snowy.

RW4157
WOODLAND WALK
Modeller: Freda Doughty
Height: 3", 7.6 cm
Colour: Grey-blue
Issued: 1982-by 1985
Series: The Worcester Children

U.S. $225.00
Can. $275.00
U.K. £125.00

Note: See also RW3417 October.

RW4158
THREE'S COMPANY
Modeller: Freda Doughty
Height: 3", 7.6 cm
Colour: Brown shorts and hair
Issued: 1982-by 1985
Series: The Worcester Children

U.S. $225.00
Can. $275.00
U.K. £125.00

Note: See also RW3519 Monday's Child (Boy) / All Mine.

RW4159
HOMETIME
Modeller: Freda Doughty
Height: 3", 7.6 cm
Colour: Blue coat and shoes
Issued: 1982-by 1985
Series: The Worcester Children

U.S. $225.00
Can. $275.00
U.K. £125.00

Note: See also RW3522 Thursday's Child (Girl).

RW4160
TEATIME
Style One
Modeller:	Freda Doughty
Height:	3", 7.6 cm
Colour:	Blue dungarees; yellow hair; brown bird
Issued:	1982-by 1985
Series:	The Worcester Children
U.S.	$275.00
Can.	$325.00
U.K.	£150.00

Note: See also RW3523 Friday's Child (Girl).

RW4161
LET'S RUN
Modeller:	Freda Doughty
Height:	3", 7.6 cm
Colour:	Red dress and shoes; white hat with red band; metal windmill
Issued:	1982-by 1985
Series:	The Worcester Children
U.S.	$175.00
Can.	$200.00
U.K.	£100.00

Note: See also RW3518 Sunday's Child (Girl).

Photograph not
available
at press time

RW4162
ARAB STALLION
Modeller:	Donald Brindley
Height:	Unknown
Colour:	Unknown
Plinth:	Wooden
Issued:	1982 in a limited edition of 500
Comm. by:	L'Atelier Art Editions
U.S.	$1,575.00
Can.	$1,900.00
U.K.	£ 850.00

RW4163
LITTLE PARAKEET BOY
Modeller:	Freda Doughty
Height:	3", 7.6 cm
Colour:	Green suit; yellow hair
Issued:	1982-1985
Series:	The Worcester Children
U.S.	$175.00
Can.	$200.00
U.K.	£100.00

Note: See also RW3087 Boy With Parakeet.

RW4164
SUNSHINE DAYS
Modeller:	Freda Doughty
Height:	3", 7.6 cm
Colour:	Blue outfit; blonde hair; red ball; yellow sandy base
Issued:	1982-1985
Series:	The Worcester Children
U.S.	$175.00
Can.	$200.00
U.K.	£100.00

Note: See also RW3256 Sunday's Child (Boy).

RW4165
FISHERMAN
Modeller:	Freda Doughty
Height:	3", 7.6 cm
Colour:	Yellow raincoat; green hat; black wellingtons
Issued:	1982-by 1985
Series:	The Worcester Children
U.S.	$225.00
Can.	$275.00
U.K.	£125.00

Note: See also RW3453 February.

RW4166
SNOWBALL
Modeller:	Freda Doughty
Height:	3", 7.6 cm
Colour:	Red coat with white trim
Issued:	1982-by 1985
Series:	The Worcester Children
U.S.	$325.00
Can.	$400.00
U.K.	£175.00

Note: See also RW3458 December.

RW4167
PEACE
Modeller:	Freda Doughty
Height:	3", 7.6 cm
Colour:	Pink hat and coat; brown shoes
Issued:	1982-by 1985
Series:	The Worcester Children
U.S.	$275.00
Can.	$325.00
U.K.	£150.00

Note: See also RW3418 November.

RW4168A
SPRINGTIME
Modeller: Freda Doughty
Height: 3", 7.6 cm
Colour: White bodice, green skirt; yellow hair
Issued: 1982-by 1985
Series: The Worcester Children

U.S. $225.00
Can. $275.00
U.K. £125.00

Note: See also RW3416 April.

RW4168B
SPRING
Style Four
Modeller: Kenneth Potts
Height: 9", 22.9 cm
Colour: Pink and silver dress; gilt mounts
Issued: 1982
Series: The Four Seasons, Series Three

U.S. $450.00
Can. $550.00
U.K. £250.00

RW4172
POINTER SLEEPING
Modeller: Kenneth Potts
Height: 1 ¼", 3.1 cm
Colour: White and gold
Issued: 1985-1991
Series: Country Life Cameos

U.S. $65.00
Can. $75.00
U.K. £35.00

RW4173
FOXHOUND (Standing)
Style Three
Modeller: Kenneth Potts
Height: 1 ¼", 3.1 cm
Colour: 1. White and gold
2. White and tan
Issued: 1985-1991
Series: Country Life Cameos

	White/gold	White/tan
U.S.	$65.00	90.00
Can.	$75.00	110.00
U.K.	£35.00	50.00

RW4174
SALMON
Style Three
Modeller: Kenneth Potts
Height: 1 ¼", 3.1 cm
Colour: 1. Creamy-yellow with red spots and gilt highlights
2. White and gold
Issued: 1985-1991
Series: Country Life Cameos

	Cream	White
U.S.	$ 90.00	65.00
Can.	$110.00	75.00
U.K.	£ 50.00	35.00

RW4175
FOX
Style Two
Modeller: Kenneth Potts
Height: 1 ¼", 3.1 cm
Colour: 1. Grey with gilt highlights
2. White and gold
Issued: 1985-1991
Series: Country Life Cameos

	Grey/gilt	White/gold
U.S.	$ 90.00	65.00
Can.	$110.00	75.00
U.K.	£ 50.00	35.00

RW4176
MALLARDS
Modeller: Kenneth Potts
Height: 1 ¾", 4.5 cm
Colour: White and gold
Issued: 1985-1991
Series: Country Life Cameos

U.S. $65.00
Can. $75.00
U.K. £35.00

RW4177
OTTER
Modeller: Kenneth Potts
Height: 1", 2.5 cm
Colour: 1. White and gilt otter; blue base
2. White; gold line around base
Issued: 1985-1991
Series: Country Life Cameos

	White/gilt	White/gold
U.S.	$ 90.00	65.00
Can.	$110.00	75.00
U.K.	£ 50.00	35.00

Photograph not
available
at press time

RW4178
CAROLINA WREN AND WILD ROSE
Modeller:	David Fryer
Height:	4 ½", 11.9 cm
Colour:	Unknown
Issued:	1985
Series:	American Birds on Bronze (Small size)
U.S.	$120.00
Can.	$135.00
U.K.	£ 65.00

RW4179
ROBIN AND NARCISSUS
Modeller:	David Fryer
Height:	6 ¾", 17.2 cm
Colour:	Red and brown bird; lemon-yellow flowers; bronze leaves and base
Issued:	1985
Series:	American Birds on Bronze (Small size)
U.S.	$120.00
Can.	$135.00
U.K.	£ 65.00

RW4180
RED CARDINAL ON BRONZE
Modeller:	David Fryer
Height:	4", 10.1 cm
Colour:	Red bird; pink flowers; bronze stems, leaves and base
Issued:	1985
Series:	American Birds on Bronze (Small size)
U.S.	$120.00
Can.	$135.00
U.K.	£ 65.00

RW4181
CHICKADEE AND DAISIES
Modeller:	David Fryer
Height:	5 ½", 14.0 cm
Colour:	Brown, white and black bird; white flowers; bronze stem, leaves and base
Issued:	1985
Series:	American Birds on Bronze (Small size)
U.S.	$120.00
Can.	$135.00
U.K.	£ 65.00

RW4186
BLUEBIRD AND PINE CONES
Modeller:	David Fryer
Height:	5", 12.7 cm
Colour:	Blue and orange bird; brown pine cones; bronze foliage and
Issued:	1985
Series:	American Birds on Bronze (Small size)
U.S.	$120.00
Can.	$135.00
U.K.	£ 65.00

RW4188
BALLERINA
Modeller:	Freda Doughty
Height:	3", 7.6 cm
Colour:	Pink tutu; yellow hair
Issued:	1983-1985
Series:	The Worcester Children
U.S.	$225.00
Can.	$275.00
U.K.	£125.00

Note: See also RW3258 Tuesday's Child (Girl) / Red Shoes.

RW4189
THE SLIDE
Modeller:	Freda Doughty
Height:	3", 7.0 cm
Colour:	Light brown coat; dark brown shoes; blue scarf; yellow hair
Issued:	1982-1988
Series:	The Worcester Children
U.S.	$175.00
Can.	$200.00
U.K.	£100.00

Note: See also RW3452 January.

RW4190
AT THE SEASIDE
Modeller:	Freda Doughty
Height:	3", 7.5 cm
Colour:	Yellow bathing suit; brown hair
Issued:	1982-by 1985
Series:	The Worcester Children
U.S.	$275.00
Can.	$325.00
U.K.	£150.00

Note: See also RW3440 July.

RW4191
LITTLE MERMAID
Modeller:	Freda Doughty
Height:	3", 7.6 cm
Colour:	Fleshtones; blue base
Issued:	1982-by 1985
Series:	The Worcester Children

U.S.	$225.00
Can.	$275.00
U.K.	£125.00

Note: See also RW3441 August.

RW4192
GARDENER
Modeller:	Freda Doughty
Height:	3", 7.6 cm
Colour:	Green dungarees; yellow hair
Issued:	1982-by 1985
Series:	The Worcester Children

U.S.	$225.00
Can.	$275.00
U.K.	£125.00

Note: See also RW3524 Saturday's Child (Boy).

RW4193
OLD FRIENDS
Modeller:	Freda Doughty
Height:	3", 7.6 cm
Colour:	Blue top; dark blue shorts; yellow hair
Issued:	1982-1985
Series:	The Worcester Children

U.S.	$175.00
Can.	$200.00
U.K.	£100.00

Note: See also RW3261 Friday's Child (Boy) / My Pet.

RW4194
BIRTHDAY GIRL
Style One
Modeller:	Freda Doughty
Height:	3", 7.6 cm
Colour:	White dress; blue bow and trim; yellow hair
Issued:	1982-1985
Series:	The Worcester Children

U.S.	$175.00
Can.	$200.00
U.K.	£100.00

Note: See also RW3257 Monday's Child (Girl) / Susie

RW4195
POOR TEDDY
Modeller:	Freda Doughty
Height:	3", 7.5 cm
Colour:	Yellow smock; brown hair
Issued:	1982-by 1985
Series:	The Worcester Children

U.S.	$225.00
Can.	$275.00
U.K.	£125.00

Note: See also RW3521 Wednesday's Child (Boy).

Photograph not available at press time

RW4196
STAG BEETLE
Modeller:	Kenneth Potts
Height:	1", 2.5 cm
Colour:	Unknown
Issued:	1983
Series:	Country Life Cameos

U.S.	$ 90.00
Can.	$110.00
U.K.	£ 50.00

RW4197
SNAIL
Style Two
Modeller:	Kenneth Potts
Height:	¾", 1.90 cm
Colour:	1. Pale blue and gold
	2. White and gold
Issued:	1989-1991
Series:	Country Life Cameos

	Blue	White
U.S.	$ 90.00	65.00
Can.	$110.00	75.00
U.K.	£ 50.00	35.00

RW4198
FROG
Modeller:	Kenneth Potts
Height:	1 ¼", 3.1 cm
Colour:	Creamy-yellow with gold spots
Issued:	1989-1991
Series:	Country Life Cameos

U.S.	$ 90.00
Can.	$110.00
U.K.	£ 50.00

RW4199
SKATING
Modeller: Freda Doughty
Height: 3", 7.6 cm
Colour: Red coat
Issued: 1982-by 1985
Series: The Worcester Children

U.S. $225.00
Can. $275.00
U.K. £125.00

Note: See also RW3534 Tuesday's Child (Boy).

RW4200
LOST SLIPPER
Modeller: Freda Doughty
Height: 3", 7.6 cm
Colour: Blue dress; brown hair
Issued: 1982-1985
Series: The Worcester Children

U.S. $175.00
Can. $200.00
U.K. £100.00

Note: See also RW3259 Wednesday's Child (Girl).

RW4201
COUNTRY BOY
Modeller: Freda Doughty
Height: 3", 7.6 cm
Colour: Blue coat; yellow hair
Issued: 1982-1985
Series: The Worcester Children

U.S. $175.00
Can. $200.00
U.K. £100.00

Note: See also RW3260 Thursday's Child (Boy) / Smiling Through.

RW4202
WINDY
Modeller: Freda Doughty
Height: 3", 7.0 cm
Colour: White dress trimmed in green; green belt; brown hat and hair
Issued: 1982-by 1985
Series: The Worcester Children

U.S. $450.00
Can. $550.00
U.K. £250.00

Note: See also RW3454 March.

RW4203
DAISY CHAIN
Modeller: Freda Doughty
Height: 3", 7.6 cm
Colour: Pink dress; brown hair; yellow flowers and base
Issued: 1982-by 1985
Series: The Worcester Children

U.S. $425.00
Can. $500.00
U.K. £225.00

Note: See also RW3455 May.

RW4204
MUSICAL MOMENTS
Modeller: Freda Doughty
Height: 3", 7.0 cm
Colour: Yellow shirt and hair; blue shorts
Issued: 1982-by 1985
Series: The Worcester Children

U.S. $225.00
Can. $275.00
U.K. £125.00

Note: See also RW3456 June (Style Two).

RW4205
MOTHER'S HELPER / POLLY KETTLE
Modeller: Freda Doughty
Height: 3", 7.6 cm
Colour: Pink apron; gold kettle
Issued: 1982-1985
Series: The Worcester Children

U.S. $375.00
Can. $450.00
U.K. £200.00

Note: See also RW3303 Polly Put the Kettle On.

RW4206
SOLITAIRE
Modeller: Freda Doughty
Height: 3", 7.6 cm
Colour: Yellow dress with an orange border; dark brown hair; yellow base
Issued: 1983-1985
Series: The Worcester Children

U.S. $450.00
Can. $550.00
U.K. £250.00

Note: See also RW3226 Only Me.

Photograph not available at press time

RW4207
WINTER
Style Three
Modeller:	Kenneth Potts
Height:	9", 22.9 cm
Colour:	Unknown; gilt mounts
Issued:	1983
Series:	The Four Seasons, Series Three
U.S.	
Can.	Very few made
U.K.	

RW4209
HARVEST MOUSE ON BRONZE
Modeller:	David Fryer
Height:	5 ½", 14.0 cm
Colour:	Grey mouse; white flowers; bronze foliage and base
Issued:	1984-1986
Series:	Woodland Animals on Bronze
U.S.	$140.00
Can.	$165.00
U.K.	£ 75.00

RW4210
BARN OWL (TYTO ALBA)
Modeller:	David Fryer
Height:	25", 63.5 cm
Colour:	Bone china bird and ivy; bronze and glass window
Plinth:	Wooden
Issued:	1984 in a limited edition of 100
Series:	Ornamental Studio (Large size)
U.S.	$2,775.00
Can.	$3,300.00
U.K.	£1,500.00

Note: A variation of RW4210 was commissioned with white flowers around the lower corner of the window frame. Few models were made.

RW4211
HARE ON BRONZE
Modeller:	David Fryer
Height:	4 ¾", 12.1 cm
Colour:	Brown and white hare; red flowers; bronze foliage and base
Issued:	1984-1986
Series:	Woodland Animals on Bronze
U.S.	$140.00
Can.	$165.00
U.K.	£ 75.00

RW4212
HEDGEHOG ON BRONZE
Style Two
Modeller:	David Fryer
Height:	4 ¼", 10.8 cm
Colour:	Brown hedgehog; mauve flower; bronze foliage and base
Issued:	1984-1986
Series:	Woodland Animals on Bronze
U.S.	$140.00
Can.	$165.00
U.K.	£ 75.00

Photograph not available at press time

RW4214
BELTED KINGFISHER AND WATER LILY
Modeller:	David Fryer
Height:	7", 17.8 cm
Colour:	Blue and orange bird; yellow flower; bronze foliage and base
Issued:	1985
Series:	American Birds on Bronze
U.S.	$120.00
Can.	$135.00
U.K.	£ 65.00

RW4215
NINA LA LOGE
Modeller:	Kenneth Potts
Height:	Unknown
Colour:	Black and white striped dress
Issued:	1983 in a limited edition of 500
Series:	The World of the Impressionists
U.S.	
Can.	Extremely rare
U.K.	

Note: Possibly only prototype models available.

196

RW4216
CHA-U-KAO (Female clown)
Modeller: Ken Potts
Height: 8 ¾", 22.2 cm
Colour: Yellow and blue dress;
 yellow hair
Issued: 1983
Varieties: Also known as 'Jester'
 (Style One) RW3483

U.S. Only trial
Can. models
U.K. produced

Note: Not produced commercially.

RW4219
FOX ON BRONZE
Modeller: David Fryer
Height: 3 ½", 8.9 cm
Colour: Red-brown and white
 fox; lemon-yellow
 narcissus; bronze
 foliage and base
Issued: 1984-1986
Series: Woodland Animals
 on Bronze

U.S. $140.00
Can. $165.00
U.K. £ 75.00

RW4222
NYMPH WITH DAISY
Modeller: David Fryer
Height: 8 ½", 21.6 cm
Colour: Light blue dress; yellow
 hair and flowers;
 bronze leaves, stem
 and base
Issued: 1984-1988
Series: Sylvan Nymphs

U.S. $150.00
Can. $175.00
U.K. £ 85.00

RW4223
NYMPH WITH WINTER JASMINE
Modeller: David Fryer
Height: 8 ½", 21.6 cm
Colour: Lemon dress; yellow
 flowers; bronze stem
 and base
Issued: 1984-1988
Series: Sylvan Nymphs

U.S. $150.00
Can. $175.00
U.K. £ 85.00

RW4226
NYMPH WITH CONVOULVULUS
MOdeller: David Fryer
Height: 8 ½", 21.6 cm
Colour: Pink flowers, dress and
 butterfly; ginger hair;
 bronze stem, leaves
 and base
Issued: 1984-1988
Series: Sylvan Nymphs

U.S. $150.00
Can. $175.00
U.K. £ 85.00

RW4227
NYMPH WITH SNOWDROP
Modeller: David Fryer
Height: 8 ½", 21.6 cm
Colour: White flowers;
 white / green dress;
 ginger hair; bronze
 leaves, stems and base
Issued: 1984-1988
Series: Sylvan Nymphs

U.S. $150.00
Can. $475.00
U.K. £ 85.00

RW4228
NYMPH WITH HAIRBELL
Modeller: David Fryer
Height: 8 ½", 21.6 cm
Colour: Pink dress; pale lilac
 flowers; bronze stem,
 leaves and base
Issued: 1984-1988
Series: Sylvan Nymphs

U.S. $150.00
Can. $175.00
U.K. £ 85.00

RW4229
NYMPH WITH VIOLA
Modeller: David Fryer
Height: 8 ½", 21.6 cm
Colour: Lemon dress and
 flowers; bronze stem,
 leaves and base
Issued: 1984-1988
Series: Sylvan Nymphs

U.S. $150.00
Can. $175.00
U.K. £ 85.00

RW4230
MARY CASSAT

Modeller:	Kenneth Potts
Height:	Unknown
Colour:	Brown dress, bonnet and bag
Issued:	1983
Series:	The World of the Impressionists
U.S.	Small number
Can.	of trial models
U.K.	produced

RW4231
LE CERCEAU

Modeller:	Kenneth Potts
Height:	6", 15.0 cm
Colour:	Dark blue and yellow
Issued:	1980
Series:	The World of the Impressionists
U.S.	Small number
Can.	of trial models
U.K.	produced

Note: This model comes with a hoop which is missing from this illustration.

RW4234
BLUE COAT SCHOOL (Boy)

Modeller:	Kenneth Potts
Height:	6", 15.0 cm
Colour:	Blue
Issued:	1983 in a limited edition of 200
U.S.	$225.00
Can.	$275.00
U.K.	£125.00

RW4235
BLUE COAT SCHOOL (Girl)

Modeller:	Kenneth Potts
Height:	6", 15.0 cm
Colour:	Blue
Issued:	1983 in a limited edition 200
U.S.	$225.00
Can.	$275.00
U.K.	£125.00

RW4237
DORMOUSE ON BRONZE

Modeller:	David Fryer
Height:	5 ½", 14.0 cm
Colour:	Brown mouse; pink flowers; bronze foliage and base
Issued:	1984-1986
Series:	Woodland Animals on Bronze
U.S.	$140.00
Can.	$165.00
U.K.	£ 75.00

RW4238
RED SQUIRREL ON BRONZE

Modeller:	David Fryer
Height:	5 ½", 14.0 cm
Colour:	Red-brown and white squirrel; yellow flowers; bronze foliage and base
Issued:	1984-1986
Series:	Woodland Animals on Bronze
U.S.	$140.00
Can.	$165.00
U.K.	£ 75.00

Photograph not available at press time

RW4240
KESTREL (Domed)

Modeller:	David Fryer
Height:	7", 17.8 cm
Colour:	Golden and dark brown and white bird; pink flowers; bronze foliage and base
Issued:	1984-1987
Series:	Birds of Prey on Bronze (Small size)
U.S.	$275.00
Can.	$325.00
U.K.	£150.00

Note: Issued with a wooden plinth and a glass dome (8" x 4").

RW4241
BARN OWL (Domed)

Modeller:	David Fryer
Height:	7", 17.8 cm
Colour:	Golden brown and cream bird; pink flowers; bronze foliage and base
Issued:	1984-1987
Series:	Birds of Prey on Bronze (Small size)
U.S.	$275.00
Can.	$325.00
U.K.	£150.00

Note: Issued with a wooden plinth and a glass dome (8" x 4").

RW4243
PEREGRINE FALCON (Domed)
Style Two
Modeller:	David Fryer
Height:	7", 17.8 cm
Colour:	Brown and white bird; bronze foliage and base
Issued:	1985
Series:	Birds of Prey on Bronze (Small size)
U.S.	$275.00
Can.	$325.00
U.K.	£150.00

Note: Issued with a wooden plinth and a glass dome (8" x 4").

Photograph not available at press time

RW4246
MARSH HARRIER (Domed)
Modeller:	David Fryer
Height:	7", 17.8 cm
Colour:	Grey and white bird; white flowers; bronze foliage and base
Issued:	1984-1987
Series:	Birds of Prey on Bronze (Small size)
U.S.	$275.00
Can.	$325.00
U.K.	£150.00

Note: Issued with a wooden plinth and a glass dome (8" x 4").

Photograph not available at press time

RW4260
SHORT-EARED OWL
Modeller:	David Fryer
Height:	7", 17.8 cm
Colour:	Golden and dark brown; white flowers; bronze foliage and base
Issued:	1984-1987
Series:	Birds of Prey on Bronze (Small size)
U.S.	$275.00
Can.	$325.00
U.K.	£150.00

Note: Issued with a wooden plinth and a glass dome (8" x 4").

RW4261
SUMMER
Style Three
Modeller:	Kenneth Potts
Height:	9", 22.9 cm
Colour:	Unknown; gilt mounts
Issued:	1984
Series:	The Four Seasons, Series Three
U.S.	
Can.	Very few made
U.K.	

RW4262
AUTUMN
Style Three
Modeller:	Kenneth Potts
Height:	9", 22.9 cm
Colour:	Unknown; gilt mounts
Issued:	1984
Series:	The Four Seasons, Series Three
U.S.	
Can.	Very few made
U.K.	

RW4264
BUMBLEBEE
Modeller:	Kenneth Potts
Height:	1 ¼", 3.1 cm
Colour:	Yellow, black and white with gilt highlights
Issued:	1989-1991
Series:	Country Life Cameos
U.S.	$ 90.00
Can.	$110.00
U.K.	£ 50.00

RW4265
GRASSHOPPER
Modeller:	Kenneth Potts
Height:	1 ¼", 3.1 cm
Colour:	Green, gilt highlights
Issued:	1989-1991
Series:	Country Life Cameos
U.S.	$ 90.00
Can.	$110.00
U.K.	£ 50.00

RW4267
BUTTERFLY
Modeller:	Kenneth Potts
Height:	1 ¼", 3.1 cm
Colour:	Cream with gilt highlights
Issued:	1989-1991
Series:	Country Life Cameos
U.S.	$ 90.00
Can.	$110.00
U.K.	£ 50.00

RW4270
BALD EAGLE (Domed)

Photograph not
available
at press time

Modeller:	David Fryer
Height:	7", 17.8 cm
Colour:	Brown and white bird; orange flowers; bronze foliage and base
Issued:	1984-1987
Series:	Birds of Prey on Bronze (Small size)
U.S.	$275.00
Can.	$325.00
U.K.	£150.00

Note: Issued with a wooden plinth and a glass dome (8: x 4").

RW4272
PEREGRINE FALCON
Style One

Modeller:	David Fryer
Height:	17 ½", 44.5 cm
Colour:	Brown, black and white china bird; bronze foliage and base
Issued:	1983 in a limited edition of 150
Series:	Ornamental Studio (Large size)
U.S.	$ 925.00
Can.	$1,100.00
U.K.	£ 500.00

RW4283
MARSH TIT
Style Two

Modeller:	David Fryer
Height:	Unknown
Colour:	Yellow, green and brown bird; yellow flowers; bronze foliage and base
Issued:	1986-1988
Series:	British Birds on Bronze (Large size)
U.S.	$225.00
Can.	$275.00
U.K.	£125.00

RW4284
GOLDEN EAGLE (AQUILA CHRYSAETOS)

Modeller:	David Fryer
Height:	27" x 39 ½", 68.6 x 100.3 cm
Colour:	Golden and dark brown bone china bird; cast crystal base
Plinth:	Wooden (mahogany)
Issued:	1986 in a limited edition of 15
Series:	Ornamental Studio (Large size)
U.S.	
Can.	Extremely rare
U.K.	

Note: This model, the largest ever produced by Royal Worcester, has a cast crystal base and a 48" wooden plinth. Due to firing problems only five models were produced.

RW4287
REED WARBLER

Modeller:	David Fryer
Height:	Unknown
Colour:	Brown, white and black bird; green acorns; bronze foliage and base
Issued:	1986-1988
Series:	British Birds on Bronze (Large size)
U.S.	$225.00
Can.	$275.00
U.K.	£125.00

RW4288
RICHMOND GIRL

Modeller:	Timothy Potts
Height:	8 ¼", 21.3 cm
Colour:	Pale blue dress and hat
Issued:	1989
Series:	English Girls
U.S.	$175.00
Can.	$200.00
U.K.	£100.00

RW4289
TRUSH
Style Two
Modeller:	David Fryer
Height:	Unknown
Colour:	Brown bird; purple flowers; bronze foliage and base
Issued:	1986-1988
Series:	British Birds on Bronze (Large size)
U.S.	$225.00
Can.	$275.00
U.K.	£125.00

RW4290
CHAFFINCH
Style Two
Modeller:	David Fryer
Height:	Unknown
Colour:	Orange, blue, black and white bird; pink flowers; bronze foliage and base
Issued:	1986-1988
Series:	British Birds on Bronze (Large size)
U.S.	$225.00
Can.	$275.00
U.K.	£125.00

RW4318
CAT (Seated)
Modeller:	Carol Gladman	
Height:	Unknown	
Colour:	1.	Black
	2.	Black with white nose, bib and paws
	3.	Ginger and white
	4.	Tabby
	5.	Tortoiseshell
Issued:	1985	
Series:	Severn Street Kittens	
U.S.	$120.00	
Can.	$135.00	
U.K.	£ 65.00	

Note: Sold at the Severn Street factory site only.

RW4319
TABBY KITTEN (Seated)
Modeller:	Carol Gladman	
Height:	Unknown	
Colour:	1.	Black with white nose, bib and tail
	2.	Ginger and white
	3.	Tabby
	4.	Tortoiseshell
	5.	White
Issued:	1985	
Series:	Severn Street Kittens	
U.S.	$ 90.00	
Can.	$110.00	
U.K.	£ 50.00	

Note: Sold at the Severn Street factory site only.

RW4320
KITTEN (Lying)
Style Two
Modeller:	Carol Gladman	
Height:	Unknown	
Colour:	1.	Black and white
	2.	Ginger and white
	3.	Tabby
	4.	Tortoiseshell
	5.	White
Issued:	1985	
Series:	Severn Street Kittens	
U.S.	$ 90.00	
Can.	$110.00	
U.K.	£ 50.00	

Note: Sold at the Severn Street factory site only.

RW4322
ROSIE PICKING APPLES
Modeller:	Sheila Mitchell
Height:	8 ½", 21.6 cm
Colour:	Peach skirt; blue blouse with yellow flowers, white collar and cuffs; white apron; blue cap; yellow basket of apples
Issued:	1986 in a limited edition of 9,500
Series:	Old Country Ways
Comm. by:	Compton & Woodhouse Ltd.

U.S.	$150.00
Can.	$175.00
U.K.	£ 85.00

RW4323
LOVE
Modeller:	Sheila Mitchell
Height:	7", 17.8 cm
Colour:	Girl: Pale blue dress; brown hair
	Baby: Peach dress; white pinafore; blonde hair
Issued:	1989 in a limited edition of 9,500
Series:	NSPCC
Comm. by:	Compton & Woodhouse Ltd.

U.S.	$150.00
Can.	$175.00
U.K.	£ 85.00

RW4332
AMERICAN ROBIN ON BRONZE
Modeller:	James Alder
Height:	Unknown
Colour:	Brown and red bird; red berries; bronze foliage
Issued:	1981

U.S.	$225.00
Can.	$275.00
U.K.	£125.00

RW4337
SYMBOLI RUDOLF
Modeller:	Kenneth Potts
Height:	Unknown
Colour:	Chestnut
Plinth:	Wooden
Issued:	1987 in a limited edition of 250
Series:	Japanese Throughbred
Comm. by:	Barbizon

U.S.	$1,475.00
Can.	$1,775.00
U.K.	£ 800.00

Note: Missing plinth.

RW4347
EMMA WOODHOUSE
Style One
Modeller:	Kenneth Potts
Height:	9", 22.9 cm
Colour:	Blue dress; yellow hat with blue ribbon
Issued:	1988-1991
Series:	Jane Austen Collection

U.S.	$175.00
Can.	$200.00
U.K.	£100.00

RW4348
ELIZABETH BENNET
Modeller:	Kenneth Potts
Height:	9", 22.9 cm
Colour:	Yellow and white dress; yellow hat
Issued:	1988-1991
Series:	Jane Austen Collection

U.S.	$175.00
Can.	$200.00
U.K.	£100.00

RW4349
ANNE ELLIOT
Modeller:	Kenneth Potts
Height:	9", 22.0 cm
Colour:	Light blue dress; pink shawl and bow
Issued:	1988-1991
Series:	Jane Austen Collection
U.S.	$175.00
Can.	$200.00
U.K.	£100.00

Photograph not
available
at press time

RW4353
APHRODITE (La Tendresse)
Modeller:	Unknown
Height:	32 ½", 82.55 cm
Colour:	Gold
Issued:	1987 in a limited edition of 1,000
Comm. by:	Goldshieder
U.S.	
Can.	Extremely rare
U.K.	

RW4355
SAFE AT LAST
Modeller:	Sheila Mitchell
Height:	5", 12.7 cm
Colour:	White dress with blue design; pale blue pinafore; ginger cat
Issued:	1988 in a limited edition of 12,500
Series:	RSPCA
Comm. by:	Compton & Woodhouse Ltd.
U.S.	$175.00
Can.	$200.00
U.K.	£100.00

RW4356
QUEEN ELIZABETH I
Style Three
Modeller:	Kenneth Potts
Height:	15 ½", 39.4 cm
Colour:	Creamy-white gown and cape; gold decoration; burgundy cap; grey horse; blue and gold saddle cloth
Plinth:	Wooden
Issued:	1998 in a limited edition of 100
U.S.	—
Can.	—
U.K.	£7,800.00

RW4357
LAUNDRY MAID
Designer:	Maureen Halson
Modeller:	Kenneth Potts
Height:	9 ¼", 23.5 cm
Colour:	Grey dress; white underskirt, apron and mob cap
Issued:	1987-c.1990
Series:	Upstairs, Downstairs
U.S.	$425.00
Can.	$500.00
U.K.	£225.00

RW4361
FANNY PRICE
Modeller:	Kenneth Potts
Height:	9", 22.9 cm
Colour:	Pale green dress with yellow trim
Issued:	1988-1991
Series:	Jane Austen Collection
U.S.	$175.00
Can.	$200.00
U.K.	£100.00

RW4362
CATHERINE MORLAND
Modeller:	Kenneth Potts
Height:	9", 22.9 cm
Colour:	Cream dress with peach shading
Issued:	1988-1991
Series:	Jane Austen Collection
U.S.	$175.00
Can.	$200.00
U.K.	£100.00

RW4363
LADY SUSAN
Modeller:	Kenneth Potts
Height:	9", 22.5 cm
Colour:	Yellow dress; lilac coat, hat and parasol
Issued:	1988-1991
Series:	Jane Austen Collection
U.S.	$175.00
Can.	$200.00
U.K.	£100.00

RW4368
CHAMBER MAID
Designer: Maureen Halson
Modeller: Timothy Potts
Height: 8", 20.3 cm
Colour: Pink dress; white apron,
            petticoats, collar,
            towel and cap; white
            jug with pink flowers
Issued: 1989-1991
Series: Upstairs, Downstairs

U.S. $425.00
Can. $500.00
U.K.   £225.00

RW4369
PARLOUR MAID
Designer: Maureen Halson
Modeller: Timothy Potts
Height: 9 ¼", 23.5 cm
Colour: Blue dress; white apron,
            petticoats and cap;
            ginger cat
Issued: 1989-1991
Series: Upstairs, Downstairs

U.S. $425.00
Can. $500.00
U.K.   £225.00

RW4371
SCULLERY MAID
Designer: Maureen Halson
Modeller: Timothy Potts
Height: 8 ¾", 22.2 cm
Colour: Grey dress and coal
            scuttle; white pinafore
            and cap; ginger cats
Issued: 1988-c.1990
Series: Upstairs, Downstairs

U.S. $425.00
Can. $500.00
U.K.   £225.00

RW4372
THE REGENCY
Modeller: Sandro Maggioni
Height: 9", 22.9 cm
Colour: Lilac coat and hat
            with pink trim
Issued: 1989 in a limited edition
            of 9,500
Series: Walking-Out Dresses of
            the 19th Century
            (Victoria and Albert
            Museum)
Comm. by: Compton & Woodhouse
            Ltd.

U.S. $225.00
Can. $275.00
U.K.   £125.00

RW4373
A FARMER'S WIFE
Modeller: Maureen Halson
Height: 8 ½", 21.6 cm
Colour: Lilac, peach and white
Issued: 1988 in a limited edition
            of 9,500
Series: Old Country Ways
Comm. by: Compton & Woodhouse
            Ltd.

U.S. $150.00
Can. $175.00
U.K.   £ 85.00

RW4381
KNIGHTSBRIDGE GIRL
Modeller: Timothy Potts
Height: 8 ¼", 21.0 cm
Colour: Blue skirt; yellow shirt
Issued: 1989
Series: English Girls

U.S. $150.00
Can. $175.00
U.K.   £ 85.00

RW4385
COOK
Designer: Maureen Halson
Modeller: Timothy Potts
Height: 8", 20.3 cm
Colour: Blue-grey dress; white
            apron and mob cap;
            pale yellow dog
Issued: 1989-1991
Series: Upstairs, Downstairs

U.S. $425.00
Can. $500.00
U.K.   £225.00

RW4408
SWEET DREAMS
Style One
Modeller: Maureen Halson
Height: 8 ¼", 21.0 cm
Colour: Cream (Wallbody)
Issued: 1989-2000
Series: Mother's Love
Comm. by: Compton & Woodhouse
            Ltd.

U.S. $150.00
Can. $175.00
U.K.   £ 85.00

RW4409
ROMANTIC (The)
Style One
Modeller:	Sandro Maggioni
Height:	9", 22.9 cm
Colour:	White dress with blue flower pattern; white shoulder cape and gloves; beige bonnet with pink roses
Issued:	1990 in a limited edition of 9,500
Series:	Walking-Out Dresses of the 19th Century (Victoria and Albert Museum)
Comm. by:	Compton & Woodhouse Ltd.
U.S.	$225.00
Can.	$275.00
U.K.	£125.00

RW4411
MAYFAIR GIRL
Modeller:	Timothy Potts
Height:	8 ¼", 21.0 cm
Colour:	Orange dress; dark brown coat
Issued:	1989
Series:	English Girls
U.S.	$175.00
Can.	$200.00
U.K.	£100.00

RW4412
COUNTRY GIRL
Modeller:	Timothy Potts
Height:	8 ¼", 21.0 cm
Colour:	Blue shirt, darker blue collar; blue denim skirt; white shoes with pink laces
Issued:	1989
Series:	English Girls
U.S.	$175.00
Can.	$200.00
U.K.	£100.00

RW4413
WEST END GIRL
Modeller:	Timothy Potts
Height:	8 ½", 21.6 cm
Colour:	Red-brown skirt and jacket; beige shirt; brown shoes and bag; yellow-beige hat
Issued:	1989
Series:	English Girls
U.S.	$175.00
Can.	$200.00
U.K.	£100.00

RW4414
WEEKEND GIRL
Modeller:	Timothy Potts
Height:	8 ¼", 21.0 cm
Colour:	Cream shirt with green, red and blue design; blue trousers
Issued:	1989
Series:	English Girls
U.S.	$175.00
Can.	$200.00
U.K.	£100.00

RW4415
LADY OF THE HOUSE
Modeller:	Glenis Devereux
Height:	9 ¾", 24.7 cm
Colour:	Pale blue dress; white fan; pink rose and gloves
Issued:	1989-1991
Series:	Upstairs, Downstairs
U.S.	$425.00
Can.	$500.00
U.K.	£225.00

RW4422
THE CRINOLINE
Modeller:	Sandro Maggioni
Height:	9", 22.9 cm
Colour:	Pink dress and hat with white shading; lilac parasol and ribbons
Issued:	1990 in a limited edition of 9,500
Series:	Walking-Out Dresses of the 19th Century (Victoria and Albert Musuem)
Comm. by:	Compton & Woodhouse Ltd.
U.S.	$225.00
Can.	$275.00
U.K.	£125.00

RW4423
CITY GIRL
Modeller:	Timothy Potts
Height:	8 ¼", 21.0 cm
Colour:	Navy suit; stocks and shares newspaper
Issued:	1989
Series:	English Girls
U.S.	$175.00
Can.	$200.00
U.K.	£100.00

RW4428
GENTLEMAN OF THE HOUSE
Modeller:	Glenis Devereux
Height:	9 ¾", 24.7 cm
Colour:	Black evening suit, bowtie, cape, and shoes; white shirt and gloves; blue waistcoat
Issued:	1989-1991
Series:	Upstairs, Downstairs
U.S.	$425.00
Can.	$500.00
U.K.	£225.00

RW4440
DAUGHTER OF THE HOUSE
Modeller:	Glenis Devereux
Height:	8", 20.3 cm
Colour:	Yellow dress; rose-pink belt and hair ribbon
Issued:	1990-1991
Series:	Upstairs, Downstairs
U.S.	$425.00
Can.	$500.00
U.K.	£225.00

RW4441
SHEPHERDESS (The)
Style Two
Modeller:	Maureen Halson
Height:	8 ½", 21.6 cm
Colour:	Pale blue skirt and cap; peach bodice; white apron and lambs
Issued:	1990 in a limited edition of 9,500
Series:	Old Country Ways
Comm. by:	Compton & Woodhouse Ltd.
U.S.	$150.00
Can.	$175.00
U.K.	£ 85.00

RW4442
LULLABY
Modeller:	Sheila Mitchell
Height:	7", 17.8 cm
Colour:	Lilac nightdress with white frills
Issued:	1988 in a limited edition of 9,500
Series:	NSPCC
Comm. by:	Compton & Woodhouse Ltd.
U.S.	$175.00
Can.	$200.00
U.K.	£100.00

RW4446
GOVERNESS AND CHILD
Modeller:	Glenis Devereux
Height:	8", 20.3 cm
Colour:	Governess: Blue dress; white apron and cap; brown book Child: Lemon dress with pink sash
Issued:	1990-1991
Series:	Upstairs, Downstairs
U.S.	$425.00
Can.	$500.00
U.K.	£225.00

RW4454
THE BUSTLE
Modeller:	John Bromley
Height:	9", 22.9 cm
Colour:	Blue dress with white shading; rose-pink gloves, shoe and hat ribbon; yellow hat
Issued:	1990 in a limited edition of 9,500
Series:	Walking-Out Dresses of the 19th Century (Victoria and Albert Museum)
Comm. by:	Compton & Woodhouse Ltd.
U.S.	$225.00
Can.	$275.00
U.K.	£125.00

RW4458
THE MILKMAID
Modeller:	Maureen Halson
Height:	8 ½", 21.6 cm
Colour:	Blue skirt, bonnet and ribbons; yellow blouse with red design and white frills; white apron; brown bucket and kitten
Issued:	1989 in a limited edition of 9,500
Series:	Old Country Ways
Comm. by:	Compton & Woodhouse Ltd.
U.S.	$150.00
Can.	$175.00
U.K.	£ 85.00

RW4459
FIRST STEPS
Modeller:	Glenis Devereux
Height:	8 ¼", 21.0 cm
Colour:	Cream (Wallbody)
Issued:	1989-2000
Series:	Mother's Love
Comm. by:	Compton & Woodhouse Ltd.
U.S.	$160.00
Can.	$185.00
U.K.	£ 90.00

RW4464
QUEEN MOTHER
Style One
Modeller:	Kenneth Potts
Height:	9", 22.9 cm
Colour:	Pink dress; blue sash
Issued:	1989 in a limited edition of 9,000
Comm. by:	Mulberry Hall, York
U.S.	$150.00
Can.	$175.00
U.K.	£ 85.00

RW4466
BATH TIME
Modeller:	Glenis Devereux
Height:	6 ¾", 17.2 cm
Colour:	Pink towel; white cap; rag doll has yellow hair and blue trousers
Issued:	1994-1999
Series:	Katie's Day
U.S.	$175.00
Can.	$200.00
U.K.	£100.00

RW4468
ONCE UPON A TIME
Modeller:	Glenis Devereux
Height:	8 ¼", 21.0 cm
Colour:	Cream (Wallbody)
Issued:	1990-2000
Series:	Mother's Love
Comm. by:	Compton & Woodhouse Ltd.
U.S.	$160.00
Can.	$185.00
U.K.	£ 90.00

RW4472
SCHOOL TIME
Modeller:	Glenis Devereux
Height:	6 ¼", 15.9 cm
Colour:	Light grey pinafore and hat; white blouse; yellow sash and ribbons; black shoes; beige satchel
Issued:	1989-1999
Series:	Katie's Day
U.S.	$175.00
Can.	$200.00
U.K.	£100.00

RW4473
BED TIME
Style One
Modeller:	Glenis Devereux
Height:	4 ½", 11.9 cm
Colour:	Pale blue nightdress; rag doll has blue dress and yellow hair
Issued:	1989-1999
Series:	Katie's Day
U.S.	$175.00
Can.	$200.00
U.K.	£100.00

RW4474
TEA TIME
Style Two
Modeller:	Glenis Devereux
Height:	5 ¾", 14.6 cm
Colour:	Yellow dress and bow; white socks; blue shoes
Issued:	1989-1999
Series:	Katie's Day
U.S.	$175.00
Can.	$200.00
U.K.	£100.00

RW4482
GRANDMOTHER'S BONNET
Modeller:	Sheila Mitchell
Height:	7 ¾", 19.7 cm
Colour:	Pale blue dress
Issued:	1990 in a limited edition of 9,500
Comm. by:	Compton & Woodhouse Ltd.
U.S.	$175.00
Can.	$200.00
U.K.	£100.00

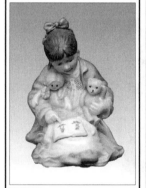

RW4483
STORY TIME
Modeller:	Glenis Devereux
Height:	4 ¼", 10.8 cm
Colour:	Blue dressing gown, bow and slippers; pale blue nightdress; doll wears blue dress; brown teddy bear
Issued:	1989-1999
Series:	Katie's Day
U.S.	$175.00
Can.	$200.00
U.K.	£100.00

RW4484
PLAY TIME
Modeller:	Glenis Devereux
Height:	5 ¾", 14.6 cm
Colour:	Blue-grey dungarees; white blouse; rag doll with yellow hair
Issued:	1990-1999
Series:	Katie's Day
U.S.	$175.00
Can.	$200.00
U.K.	£100.00

RW4487
WEDNESDAY'S CHILD
Modeller:	Carol Gladman
Height:	5", 12.7 cm
Colour:	Pink dress with white collar; brown hair and dog; grey rock; green and yellow base
Issued:	1990
U.S.	
Can.	Extremely rare
U.K.	

RW4488
NEW ARRIVAL
Style One
Modeller:	Maureen Halson
Height:	8 ¼", 21.0 cm
Colour:	Cream (Wallbody)
Issued:	1990
Series:	Mother's Love
Comm. by:	Compton & Woodhouse Ltd.
U.S.	$160.00
Can.	$185.00
U.K.	£ 90.00

RW4498
KING HENRY VIII
Modeller:	Kenneth Potts
Height:	15 ½", 39.4
Colour:	Burgundy cape; grey tunic; white stockings; bay horse; green reins and riding cloth
Issued:	1991 in a limited edition of 75
U.S.	—
Can.	—
U.K.	£9,130.00

Note: Issued to commemorate the 500th anniversary of the birth of Henry VIII (1491).

RW4499
A POSY FOR MOTHER
Modeller:	Maureen Halson
Height:	7", 17.8 cm
Colour:	Pale blue dress, shawl and hat; shawl and hat trimmed with purple; white apron with pink trim; posy of pink flowers
Issued:	1990 in a limited edition of 7,500
Series:	NSPCC
Comm. by:	Compton & Woodhouse Ltd.
U.S.	$150.00
Can.	$175.00
U.K.	£ 85.00

RW4500
OGURI CAP
Modeller:	Kenneth Potts
Height:	Unknown
Colour:	Dark grey and black
Plinth:	Wooden
Issued:	1991 in a limited edition of 100
Series:	Japanese Thoroughbreds
Comm. by:	Barbizon
U.S.	$1,575.00
Can.	$1,900.00
U.K.	£ 850.00

Note: Issued for the Japanese market, missing plinth.

RW4503
SCARF OF THE DANCE
Modeller:	Maureen Halson
Height:	10", 25.4 cm
Colour:	Cream (Wallbody) with pearl lustre
Issued:	1991 in a limited edition of 5,000
Series:	Spirit of the Dance
Comm. by:	Compton & Woodhouse Ltd.
U.S.	$225.00
Can.	$275.00
U.K.	£125.00

RW4504
SPRING
Style Five
Modeller:	Maureen Halson
Height:	9", 22.9 cm
Colour:	Pink skirt; deeper pink bodice; white apron, underskirt and gloves; cream sleeves and neckline; yellow straw hat; yellow flowers
Issued:	1992 in a limited edition of 7,500
Series:	The Four Seasons, Series Four
Comm. by:	Compton & Woodhouse Ltd.
U.S.	$275.00
Can.	$325.00
U.K.	£150.00

RW4507
THE MASQUERADE BEGINS
Modeller:	Nigel Stevens
Height:	8 ¼", 21.6 cm
Colour:	Pink gown decorated with deeper pink roses and ribbons; gold necklace and bracelets
Issued:	1991 in a limited edition of 12,500
Series:	Enchanted Evenings
Comm. by:	Compton & Woodhouse Ltd.
U.S.	$165.00
Can.	$210.00
U.K.	£ 95.00

RW4508
BALLET
Modeller:	Glenis Devereux
Height:	4 ½", 11.4 cm
Colour:	Pink ballet dress and slippers
Issued:	1992-1999
Series:	Boys and Girls Come Out to Play
U.S.	$210.00
Can.	$275.00
U.K.	£120.00

RW4509
DRESSING UP
Modeller:	Glenis Devereux
Height:	6 ¾", 17.2 cm
Colour:	Blue dress and hat; black sandal
Issued:	1992-1999
Series:	Boys and Girls Come Out to Play
U.S.	$210.00
Can.	$275.00
U.K.	£120.00

RW4510
SUMMER
Style Four
Modeller:	Maureen Halson
Height:	9", 22.9 cm
Colour:	Pale lilac dress; tan boots; yellow straw hat
Issued:	1992 in a limited edition of 7,500
Series:	The Four Seasons, Series Four
Comm. by:	Compton & Woodhouse Ltd.
U.S.	$250.00
Can.	$300.00
U.K.	£135.00

Photograph not
available
at press time

RW4511
LEGAL EAGLE
Modeller:	David Fryer and Peter Ewence
Height:	Unknown
Colour:	Unknown
Issued:	1992
Comm. by:	The Law Society
U.S.	$275.00
Can.	$325.00
U.K.	£150.00

RW4512
DIANA (1921)
Style Two
Modeller:	Nigel Stevens
Height:	8 ½", 21.6 cm
Colour:	1. Cream (Wallbody)
	2. Coloured
Issued:	1. Cream: 1992
	2. Coloured: 1992
Series:	1. The Roaring Twenties
	2. The 1920s Vogue Collection
Comm. by:	Compton & Woodhouse Ltd.
U.S.	$150.00
Can.	$175.00
U.K.	£ 85.00

RW4514
CLARA (1925)

Modeller:	Nigel Stevens
Height:	8", 20.3 cm
Colour:	1. Cream (Wallbody)
	2. Pale green dress with white and blue trim; white hat with blue trim; brown and white dog
Issued:	1. Cream: 1992
	2. Pale green: 1992
Series:	1. The Roaring Twenties
	2. The 1920s Vogue Collection
Comm. by:	Compton & Woodhouse Ltd.
U.S.	$150.00
Can.	$175.00
U.K.	£ 85.00

RW4515
SEE-SAW

Modeller:	Glenis Devereux
Height:	6 ¼", 15.9 cm
Colour:	Blue shorts; white shirt; yellow dress; brown see-saw
Issued:	1992-1999
Series:	Boys and Girls Come Out to Play
U.S.	$375.00
Can.	$495.00
U.K.	£220.00

RW4517
FIRST FLIGHT

Modeller:	Glenis Devereux
Height:	6 ½", 16.5 cm
Colour:	Blue trousers; green sweater and cap; yellow scarf and pom pon
Issued:	1992-1999
Series:	Boys and Girls Come Out to Play
U.S.	$175.00
Can.	$200.00
U.K.	£100.00

RW4518
AUTUMN
Style Four

Modeller:	Maureen Halson
Height:	9", 22.9 cm
Colour:	Mauve dress; white apron, collar and underskirt; tan shawl and straw hat; brown basket with purple flowers
Issued:	1992 in a limited edition of 7,500
Series:	The Four Seasons, Series Four
Comm. by:	Compton & Woodhouse Ltd.
U.S.	$250.00
Can.	$300.00
U.K.	£135.00

RW4519
DAISY (1922)
Style Two

Modeller:	Nigel Stevens
Height:	8 ¼", 21.0 cm
Colour:	1. Cream (Wallbody)
	2. Pink dress; cream sash; pink and cream hat
Issued:	1. Cream: 1992
	2. Pink and Lilac: 1992
Series:	1. The Roaring Twenties
	2. The 1920s Vogue Collection
Comm. by:	Compton & Woodhouse Ltd.
U.S.	$150.00
Can.	$175.00
U.K.	£ 85.00

RW4520
MILLIE (1926)
Style One
Modeller: Nigel Stevens
Height: 8 ¼", 21.0 cm
Colour: 1. Cream (Wallbody)
            2. Pale blue with pale turquoise trim
Issued: 1. Cream: 1991
            2. Pale blue: 1992
Series: 1. The Roaring Twenties
            2. The 1920s Vogue Collection
Comm. by: Compton & Woodhouse Ltd.

U.S. $150.00
Can. $175.00
U.K.   £ 85.00

RW4521
POPPY (1924)
Modeller: Nigel Stevens
Height: 8", 20.3 cm
Colour: 1. Cream (Wallbody)
            2. Pale yellow dress; blue headband and shoes
Issued: 1. Cream: 1992
            2. Pale yellow: 1992
Series: 1. The Roaring Twenties
            2. The 1920s Vogue Collection
Comm. by: Compton & Woodhouse Ltd.

U.S. $150.00
Can. $175.00
U.K.   £ 85.00

RW4522
FIRST PRIZE
Modeller: Glenis Devereux
Height: 7 ¼", 18.4 cm
Colour: 1. White shirt; yellow jodhpurs; black hat and boots;
                brown saddle
            2. Pink shirt; yellow jodhpurs; black hat and boots;
                brown saddle
Issued: 1. 1992-1999: Royal Worcester
            2. 2004 to the present: Compton & Woodhouse Ltd.
                (Commissioned piece)
Series: Boys and Girls Come Out to Play

U.S. $275.00
Can. $325.00
U.K.   £150.00

RW4523
WINTER
Style Four
Modeller: Maureen Halson
Height: 9", 22.9 cm
Colour: Pale brown jacket, skirt and boots; pink scarf and hat;
            brown muff; brown basket of holly
Issued: 1992 in a limited edition of 7,500
Series: The Four Seasons, Series Four
Comm. by: Compton & Woodhouse Ltd.

U.S. $275.00
Can. $325.00
U.K.   £150.00

RW4524
THE LAST WALTZ
Modeller:	Nigel Stevens
Height:	8 ¼", 21.0 cmcm
Colour:	Lilac gown with deeper lilac and gold design
Issued:	1992 in a limited edition of 12,500
Series:	Enchanted Evenings
Comm. by:	Compton & Woodhouse Ltd.
U.S.	$150.00
Can.	$175.00
U.K.	£ 85.00

Photograph not
available
at press time

RW4527
MOLLY
Modeller:	Nigel Stevens
Height:	8 ½", 21.6 cm
Colour:	1. Cream (Wallbody)
	2. Coloured
Issued:	1992
Series:	1. Roaring Twenties
	2. The 1920s Vogue Collection
Comm. by:	Compton & Woodhouse Ltd.
U.S.	$150.00
Can.	$175.00
U.K.	£ 85.00

RW4529
THE QUEEN OF THE MAY
Modeller:	Maureen Halson
Height:	8", 20.3 cm
Colour:	Pink dress with pale green overdress; basket of red roses; red rose crown in her hair
Issued:	1992 in a limited edition of 9,500
Series:	Festive Country Days
Comm. by:	Compton & Woodhouse Ltd.
U.S.	$150.00
Can.	$175.00
U.K.	£ 85.00

RW4532
QUEEN OF HEARTS
Designer:	Nigel Stevens
Modeller:	John Bromley
Height:	8 ¼", 21.0 cm
Colour:	Turquoise gown with deep pink roses and gold highlights
Issued:	1992 in a limited edition of 12,500
Series:	Enchanted Evenings
Comm. by:	Compton & Woodhouse Ltd.
U.S.	$160.00
Can.	$185.00
U.K.	£ 90.00

RW4533
JOY
Style Two
Modeller:	Maureen Halson
Height:	9", 22.9 cm
Colour:	1. Cream (Wallbody)
	2. Pale blue
Issued:	1. Cream: 1992 in a limited edition of 5,000
	2. Pale blue: 1992 in a limited edition of 5,000
Comm. by:	Compton & Woodhouse Ltd.
U.S.	$175.00
Can.	$200.00
U.K.	£100.00

RW4536
THE ROYAL TOURNAMENT
Modeller: David Lovegrove
Height: 5", 12.7 cm
Colour: Blue; white circular base with blue trim
Issued: 1992
U.S. $120.00
Can. $135.00
U.K. £ 65.00

RW4537
KITTY (1928)
Designer: Nigel Stevens
Modeller: John Bromley
Height: 8 ¼", 21.0 cm
Colour:
1. Cream (Wallbody)
2. Pale yellow dress and hat trimmed with red; red shoes
Issued:
1. Cream: 1992
2. Pale yellow: 1992
Series:
1. The Roaring Twenties
2. The 1920s Vogue Collection
Comm. by: Compton & Woodhouse Ltd.
U.S. $150.00
Can. $175.00
U.K. £ 85.00

RW4538
THE FIRST QUARDRILLE
[Henrietta]
Modeller: Nigel Stevens
Height: 8 ¼", 21.0 cm
Colour: Pale blue; deep blue shading; pink roses; gold highlights
Issued: 1992 in a limited edition of 12,500
Series: Enchanted Evenings
Comm. by: Compton & Woodhouse Ltd.
U.S. $225.00
Can. $275.00
U.K. £125.00

RW4539
NOELLE
Modeller: Maureen Halson
Height: 8 ½", 21.6 cm
Colour: Pink dress with red flowered trim; red shoulder cape with pink lining
Issued: 1992 in a limited edition of 9,500
Series: Festive Country Days
U.S. $225.00
Can. $275.00
U.K. £125.00

Photograph not
available
at press time

RW4540
ELLEN
Modeller: Nigel Stevens
Height: 8 ½", 21.6 cm
Colour:
1. Cream
2. Coloured
Issued: 1992
Series:
1. Roaring Twenties
2. The 1920s Vogue Collection
Comm. by: Compton & Woodhouse Ltd.
U.S. $150.00
Can. $175.00
U.K. £ 85.00

RW4543
ANNIE (1927)
Modeller: Nigel Stevens
Height: 8 ¾", 22.2 cm
Colour:
1. Cream (Wallbody)
2. Lilac with maroon
Issued: 1992
Series:
1. Roaring Twenties
2. The 1920s Vogue Collection
Comm. by: Compton & Woodhouse Ltd.
U.S. $150.00
Can. $175.00
U.K. £ 85.00

RW4544
MINNIE (1929)
Modeller:	Nigel Stevens
Height:	8 ¼", 21.0 cm
Colour:	1. Cream (Wallbody)
	2. Pale pink dress and hat; iron red sash and shoes
Issued:	1. Cream: 1992
	2. Pale pink: 1992
Series:	1. The Roaring Twenties
	2. The 1920s Vogue Collection
Comm. by:	Compton & Woodhouse Ltd.
U.S.	$150.00
Can.	$175.00
U.K.	£ 85.00

RW4545
THE CHRISTENING
Modeller:	Maureen Halson
Height:	9", 22.9 cm
Colour:	Cream (Wallbody)
Issued:	1993 in a limited edition of 9,500
Series:	Our Cherished Moments
Comm. by:	Compton & Woodhouse Ltd.
U.S.	$220.00
Can.	$265.00
U.K.	£118.50

RW4546
ARAB STALLION (and Rider)
Modeller:	Kenneth Potts
Height:	16", 40.6 cm
Colour:	Rider: Multicoloured
	Horse: Grey
Issued:	1993 in a limited edition of 50
Series:	Classic Horse and Rider
U.S.	—
Can.	—
U.K.	£6,745.00

RW4547
THE FAIREST ROSE
Modeller:	Nigel Stevens
Height:	8 ¼", 21.0 cm
Colour:	Pink gown; white frills; gold decoration
Issued:	1993 in a limited edition of 12,500
Series:	Enchanted Evenings
Comm. by:	Compton & Woodhouse Ltd.
U.S.	$225.00
Can.	$275.00
U.K.	£125.00

RW4548
THE VILLAGE BRIDE
Modeller:	Maureen Halson
Height:	8 ½", 21.6 cm
Colour:	Pale pink dress with deeper pink design, white frills and lilac ribbons; posy of yellow, red and purple flowers
Issued:	1993 in a limited edition of 9,500
Series:	Festive Country Days
Comm. by:	Compton & Woodhouse Ltd.
U.S.	$150.00
Can.	$175.00
U.K.	£ 85.00

RW4549
MARKET DAY
Modeller:	Maureen Halson
Height:	8 ½", 21.6 cm
Colour:	Peach dress; white apron; light blue shawl with white flower design; straw hat; tan basket of vegetables
Issued:	1993 in a limited edition of 5,000
Series:	Pastoral Collection
Comm. by:	Compton & Woodhouse Ltd.
U.S.	$150.00
Can.	$175.00
U.K.	£ 85.00

RW4550
BEA (1922)
Modeller:	Nigel Stevens
Height:	8 ½", 21.6 cm
Colour:	1. Cream (Wallbody)
	2. Light Pink dress and headband; lilac sash and shoes
Issued:	1. Cream: 1993
	2. Light pink: 1994
Series:	1. The Roaring Twenties
	2. The 1920s Vogue Collection
Comm. by:	Compton & Woodhouse Ltd.
U.S.	$150.00
Can.	$175.00
U.K.	£ 85.00

RW4551
THE WEDDING DAY
Style One
Modeller:	Maureen Halson
Height:	9", 22.9 cm
Colour:	Cream (Wallbody)
Issued:	1993 in a limited edition of 9,500
Series:	Our Cherished Moments
Comm. by:	Compton & Woodhouse Ltd.
U.S.	$220.00
Can.	$265.00
U.K.	£118.50

RW4552
SWEETEST VALENTINE
Modeller:	Nigel Stevens
Height:	8 ¼", 21.0 cm
Colour:	Pink gown decorated with gold highlighted roses
Issued:	1993 in a limited edition of 12,500
Series:	Enchanted Evenings
Comm. by:	Compton & Woodhouse Ltd.
U.S.	$225.00
Can.	$275.00
U.K.	£125.00

RW4554
EVIE (1923)
Modeller:	Nigel Stevens
Height:	8 ½", 21.6 cm
Colour:	1. Cream
	2. Grey coat, grey and dark grey skirt; pink tie and cap
Issued:	1. Cream: 1994
	2. Grey: 1992
Series:	1. The Roaring Twenties
	2. The 1920s Vogue Collection
Comm. by:	Compton & Woodhouse Ltd.
U.S.	$150.00
Can.	$175.00
U.K.	£ 85.00

RW4555
ELEANOR (1928)
Style One
Modeller: Nigel Stevens
Height: 8 ¾", 22.2 cm
Colour: 1. Cream (Wallbody)
        2. Turquoise dress and hat; pink sash, bow and shoes
Issued: 1. Cream: 1994
        2. Turquoise: 1994
Series: 1. The Roaring Twenties
        2. The 1920s Vogue Collection
Comm. by: Compton & Woodhouse Ltd.

U.S. $150.00
Can. $175.00
U.K.   £ 85.00

RW4556
SUMMER'S SWEET KISS
Modeller: Nigel Stevens
Height: 8 ½", 21.6 cm
Colour: White dress decorated
        with rose-pink roses;
        pink shawl; straw hat
Issued: 1995 in a limited
        edition of 4,900

U.S. $175.00
Can. $200.00
U.K.   £100.00

RW4557
SUNDAY BEST
Modeller: Maureen Halson
Height: 8 ½", 21.6 cm
Colour: Peach jacket; pale peach skirt and shawl with deeper peach
        design; straw hat; tan boots
Issued: 1993 in a limited edition of 9,500
Series: Pastoral Collection
Comm. by: Compton & Woodhouse Ltd.

U.S. $150.00
Can. $175.00
U.K.   £ 85.00

RW4560
MOTHERING SUNDAY
Modeller: Maureen Halson
Height: 9", 22.9 cm
Colour: 1. Cream (Wallbody)
        2. Mother: Blue and white dress
            Daughter: Pink dress, white petticoats
Issued: 1. 1994 in a limited edition of 9,500
        2. 1994 in a limited edition of 750
Series: Our Cherished Moments
Comm. by: Compton & Woodhouse Ltd.

	Cream	Blue/Pink
U.S.	$140.00	275.00
Can.	$165.00	325.00
U.K.	£ 75.00	150.00

RW4561
CONSTANCE (1924)
Modeller:	Nigel Stevens
Height:	8 ¼", 21.0 cm
Colour:	1. Cream (Wallbody)
	2. Lilac dress; white feather boa, fan and shoes
Issued:	1. Cream: 1994
	2. Lilac: 1992
Series:	1. The Roaring Twenties
	2. The 1920s Vogue Collection
Comm. by:	Compton & Woodhouse Ltd.
U.S.	$150.00
Can.	$175.00
U.K.	£ 85.00

RW4562
BELLE OF THE BALL
Style Two
Modeller:	Nigel Stevens
Height:	8 ¼", 21.0 cm
Colour:	Lilac and ecru gown; gold decoration
Issued:	1994 in a limited edition of 12,500
Series:	Enchanted Evenings
Comm. by:	Compton & Woodhouse Ltd.
U.S.	$150.00
Can.	$175.00
U.K.	£ 85.00

RW4565
A PRESENT FOR SANTA
Modeller:	Maureen Halson
Height:	9", 22.9 cm
Colour:	Cream (Wallbody)
Issued:	1995 in a limited edition of 9,500
Series:	Our Cherished Moments
Comm. by:	Compton & Woodhouse Ltd.
U.S.	$130.00
Can.	$150.00
U.K.	£ 70.00

RW4566
GOOSE GIRL
Modeller:	Maureen Halson
Height:	8 ½", 21.6 cm
Colour:	Light blue skirt; white apron; peach and white top; straw basket of lilac flowers; white goose
Issued:	1994 in a limited edition of 5,000
Series:	Pastoral Collection
Comm. by:	Compton & Woodhouse Ltd.
U.S.	$150.00
Can.	$175.00
U.K.	£ 85.00

RW4567
IRENE (Miss 1920)
Modeller:	Maureen Halson
Height:	8 ¼", 21.0 cm
Colour:	1. Cream (Wallbody)
	2. Pale pink dress; rose-pink sash
Issued:	1. Cream: 1994
	2. Pale pink: 1994
Series:	1. Roaring Twenties
	2. The 1920s Vogue Collection
U.S.	$150.00
Can.	$175.00
U.K.	£ 85.00

RW4569
ROYAL DEBUT
Designer:	Raymond Hughes
Modeller:	John Bromley
Height:	8 ¼", 21.0 cm
Colour:	White gown with pink frills and gold stars
Issued:	1994 in a limited edition of 12,500
Series:	Enchanted Evenings
Comm. by:	Compton & Woodhouse Ltd.
U.S.	$160.00
Can.	$185.00
U.K.	£ 90.00

RW4571
OLIVIA
Style One
Modeller:	David Lyttleton
Height:	9 ½", 24.0 cm
Colour:	Tiger-striped black and orange dress; white wrap; feathered hat
Issued:	1995 in a limited edition of 12,500
Series:	Hollywood Glamour
Comm. by:	Compton & Woodhouse Ltd
U.S.	$150.00
Can.	$175.00
U.K.	£ 85.00

RW4572
FIRST TOUCH
Modeller:	Maureen Halson
Height:	8 ¼", 21.0 cm
Colour:	Cream (Wallbody)
Issued:	1994 in a limited edition of 7,500
Series:	Tender Moments
Comm. by:	Compton & Woodhouse Ltd
U.S.	$140.00
Can.	$165.00
U.K.	£ 70.00

RW4573
LIZ
Modeller:	David Lyttleton
Height:	9 ½", 24.0 cm
Colour:	Black and leopard print; white and gold
Issued:	1994 Ltd. Ed. of 12,500
Series:	Hollywood Glamour
Comm. by:	Compton & Woodhouse Ltd.
U.S.	$175.00
Can.	$200.00
U.K.	£100.00

RW4574
SWEET ROSE
Modeller:	David Lyttleton
Height:	6 ¾", 17.2 cm
Colour:	Pink bodice, shawl and hat; white skirt with pink roses and shading
Issued:	1995 in a limited edition of 9,500
Series:	Sweet Posy Collection
Comm. by:	Compton & Woodhouse Ltd.
U.S.	$150.00
Can.	$175.00
U.K.	£ 80.00

RW4575
BETTE
Modeller:	David Lyttleton
Height:	9 ½", 24.0 cm
Colour:	Black spotted dress; fur and feather wrap; black feathered hat
Issued:	1995 in a limited edition of 12,500
Series:	Hollywood Glamour
Comm. by:	Compton & Woodhouse Ltd.
U.S.	$175.00
Can.	$200.00
U.K.	£100.00

RW4576
DOLLY
Modeller:	Nigel Stevens
Height:	8 ¼", 21.0 cm
Colour:	1. Cream (Wallbody)
	2. Mauve and white dress; ruby sash; mauve hat and gloves
Issued:	1. Cream: 1994
	2. Mauve and white: 1992
Series:	1. The Roaring Twenties
	2. The 1920s Vogue Collection
Comm. by:	Compton & Woodhouse Ltd.
U.S.	$150.00
Can.	$175.00
U.K.	£ 85.00

RW4577
LADY VIOLET
Modeller:	Jack Glynn
Height:	9½", 24.0 cm
Colour:	Lilac dress and hat with mauve trim; mauve and white parasol; gold highlights
Issued:	1996 in a limited edition of 9,500
Series:	Fashion Figurine of the Year (1909)
Comm. by:	Compton & Woodhouse Ltd.
U.S.	$160.00
Can.	$185.00
U.K.	£ 90.00

RW4578
TAKAI TEIO
Modeller:	Kenneth Potts
Height:	Unknown
Colour:	Brown with black markings
Plinth:	Wooden
Issued:	1990 in a limited edition of 75
Series:	Japanese Thoroughbreds
Comm. by:	Barbizon
U.S.	$1,575.00
Can.	$1,900.00
U.K.	£ 850.00

Note: Issued for the Japanese market, missing plinth.

RW4579
PAINTING
Modeller:	Maureen Halson
Height:	8 ¼", 22.2 cm
Colour:	White underskirt with pink flowers; pale pink dress with white frills; white shawl with pink design; gilt highlights
Issued:	1995 in a limited edition of 2,500
Series:	The Graceful Arts
Comm. by:	Compton & Woodhouse Ltd.
U.S.	$375.00
Can.	$450.00
U.K.	£200.00

RW4580
LADY EMMA
Style One
Modeller:	Richard Moore
Height:	5", 12.7 cm
Colour:	Rose-pink dress and hat; pink collar, frills and parasol
Issued:	1995 in a limited edition of 9,500
Series:	The Fashionable Victorians (Victoria and Albert Museum)
Comm. by:	Compton & Woodhouse Ltd.
U.S.	$130.00
Can.	$155.00
U.K.	£ 70.00

RW4581
LADY ELIZABETH

Photograph not available at press time

Modeller:	David Lyttleton
Height:	5", 12.7 cm
Colour:	Crimson dress
Issued:	1995 in a limited edition of 9,500
Series:	The Fashionable Victorians (Victoria and Albert Museum)
Comm. by:	Compton & Woodhouse Ltd.
U.S.	$130.00
Can.	$155.00
U.K.	£ 70.00

RW4582
LADY JANE

Modeller:	Richard Moore
Height:	5", 12.7 cm
Colour:	Purple and white dress
Issued:	1995 in a limited edition of 9,500
Series:	The Fashionable Victorians (Victoria and Albert Museum)
Comm. by:	Compton & Woodhouse Ltd.
U.S.	$130.00
Can.	$155.00
U.K.	£ 70.00

RW4583
BAKER'S WIFE

Modeller:	Maureen Halson
Height:	8 ½", 21.6 cm
Colour:	Peach skirt; blue bodice with white frills; white apron and petticoat; straw hat with blue ribbon; brown basket of bread
Issued:	1995 in a limited edition of 5,000
Series:	Pastoral Collection
Comm. by:	Compton & Woodhouse Ltd.
U.S.	$160.00
Can.	$185.00
U.K.	£ 90.00

RW4584
SWEET HOLLY

Modeller:	David Lyttleton
Height:	6 ¾", 17.2 cm
Colour:	Green coat and hat trimmed with rose-pink; white skirt decorated with holly and flowers
Issued:	1995 in a limited edition of 9,500
Series:	Sweet Posy Collection
Comm. by:	Compton & Woodhouse Ltd.
U.S.	$150.00
Can.	$175.00
U.K.	£ 80.00

RW4585
SWEET VIOLET

Modeller:	David Lyttleton
Height:	6 ¾", 17.2 cm
Colour:	Lilac bodice and hat; white skirt decorated with lilacs; straw basket of lilacs
Issued:	1995 in a limited edition of 9,500
Series:	Sweet Posy Collection
Comm. by:	Compton & Woodhouse Ltd.
U.S.	$150.00
Can.	$175.00
U.K.	£ 80.00

RW4586
A ROYAL PRESENTATION
Designer:	Raymond Hughes
Modeller:	John Bromley
Height:	8 ½", 21.6 cm
Colour:	Lilac; gold highlights
Issued:	1995 in a limited edition of 12,500
Series:	Splendour at Court
Comm. by:	Compton & Woodhouse Ltd.

U.S.	$225.00
Can.	$275.00
U.K.	£125.00

RW4587
JULIETTE / RACHEL (Style Two) / THANK YOU
Designer: Elizabeth Greenshields
Modeller: Jack Glynn
Height: 6 ½", 16.5 cm
Colour:
1. **Juliette:** Peach dress; darker peach highlights and shawl
2. **Rachel:** Pink dress; white petticoats lilac trim and shawl
3. **Thank You:** White with gold highlights
Issued:
1. **Juliette:** 1996-2002
2. **Rachel:** 1996 to the present
3. **Thank You:** 1998-2003
Series:
1. **Juliette:** Les Petites
2. **Rachel:** High Society
3. **Thank You:** Golden Moments

Name:	Juliette	Rachel	Thank You
U.S.	$140.00	140.00	130.00
Can.	$165.00	165.00	155.00
U.K.	£ 75.00	75.00	70.00

RW4588A
LADY HANNAH
Style One
Modeller:	David Lyttleton
Height:	5", 12.7 cm
Colour:	White dress with blue flowers, frills and neckline; gold highlights
Issued:	1995 in a limited edition of 9,500
Series:	The Fashionable Victorians (Victoria and Albert Museum)
Comm. by:	Compton & Woodhouse Ltd.

U.S.	$130.00
Can.	$155.00
U.K.	£ 70.00

RW4588B
LADY SARAH
Style One
Modeller:	Richard Moore
Height:	5", 12.7 cm
Colour:	White skirt with pink roses; green overdress; white hat with green ribbons
Issued:	1995 in a limited edition of 9,500
Series:	The Fashionable Victorians (Victoria and Albert Museum)
Comm. By:	Compton & Woodhouse Ltd.

U.S.	$130.00
Can.	$155.00
U.K.	£ 70.00

RW4589
FIRST KISS

Modeller:	Maureen Halson
Height:	8 ½", 21.6 cm
Colour:	Cream (Wallbody)
Issued:	1995 in a limited edition of 7,500
Varieties:	RW4777 Mother and Child
Series:	Tender Moments
Comm. by:	Compton & Woodhouse Ltd.
U.S.	$150.00
Can.	$175.00
U.K.	£ 80.00

RW4591
FIRST DANCE
Style Two

Modeller:	Brian Diment
Height:	8 ½", 21.6 cm
Colour:	Pink dress with red trim; white gloves with black ribbons; gold fan
Issued:	1995 in a limited edition of 7,500
Series:	Tissot Collection
U.S.	$225.00
Can.	$275.00
U.K.	£125.00

RW4594
THE WEDDING DAY
Style Two

Designer:	Elizabeth Greenshields
Modeller:	Richard Moore
Height:	9 ½", 24.0 cm
Colour:	1. White dress; brown hair
	2. Ivory dress; blonde hair
Issued:	1996-1998
Series:	Golden Moments
U.S.	$160.00
Can.	$185.00
U.K.	£ 90.00

RW4595A
CHARLOTTE
Style One

Designer:	Elizabeth Greenshields
Modeller:	Jack Glynn
Height:	9 ½", 24.0 cm
Colour:	Pale yellow dress; pale blue overskirt decorated with white flowers; darker blue shawl; pale blue parasol
Issued:	1996 to the present
Series:	Summer Romance
U.S.	—
Can.	—
U.K.	£165.00

Note: The same mould used to make Charlotte was also used to make Glyndebourne. Charlotte holds an open parasol in her right hand, Glyndebourne a rose.

RW4595B
GLYNDEBOURNE

Designer:	Elizabeth Greenshields
Modeller:	Jack Glynn
Height:	9", 22.9 cm
Colour:	Pale pink dress decorated with salmon-pink roses and edging; salmon-pink shawl; red rose
Issued:	1996-2003
Series:	High Society
U.S.	$225.00
Can.	$275.00
U.K.	£125.00

RW4597
A CELEBRATION AT WINDSOR

Modeller:	Nigel Stevens
Height:	8 ½", 21.6 cm
Colour:	Pink gown decorated with red roses, deeper pink underskirt and bow; gold highlights
Issued:	1995 in a limited edition of 12,500
Series:	Splendour at Court
Comm. By:	Compton & Woodhouse Ltd.
U.S.	$270.00
Can.	$320.00
U.K.	£145.00

RW4599
SWEET FORGET-ME-NOT / AUTUMN (Style Six)

Modeller:	David Lyttleton
Height:	6 ¾", 17.2 cm
Colour:	1. **Sweet Fotget-me-not:** Blue bodice with white frill and bow; white skirt decorated with forget-me-not flowers
	2. **Autumn:** Purple dress and hat; white and gold sash
Issued:	1. **Sweet Fotget-me-not:** 1995 in a limited edition of 9,500
	2. **Autumn:** 2001 in a limited edition of 9,500
Series:	1. **Sweet Forget-me-not:** Sweet Posy Collection
	2. **Autumn:** The Four Seasons Elite Edition
Comm. by:	Compton & Woodhouse Ltd.

Name:	Sweet Forget-Me-Not	Autumn
U.S.	$150.00	150.00
Can.	$175.00	175.00
U.K.	£ 80.00	80.00

RW4600
EMBROIDERY

Modeller:	Maureen Halson
Height:	8 ¼", 21.0 cm
Colour:	Lilac and pink dress and hat decorated with pink roses
Issued:	1997 in a limited edition of 2,500
Series:	The Graceful Arts
Comm. by:	Compton & Woodhouse Ltd.
U.S.	$375.00
Can.	$450.00
U.K.	£200.00

RW4601
FRIENDSHIP / LAURA (Style One)

Designer:	Elizabeth Greenshields
Modeller:	Jack Glynn
Height:	8 ¼", 21.0 cm
Colour:	1. **Friendship:** White dress and hat; gold highlights
	2. **Laura:** Pale blue dress; gold highlights; straw hat
Issued:	1. **Friendship:** 1996 to the present
	2. **Laura:** 1996-1999
Series:	1. **Friendship:** Golden Moments
	2. **Laura:** Summer Romance

Name:	Friendship	Laura
U.S.	$160.00	160.00
Can.	$185.00	185.00
U.K.	£ 90.00	90.00

RW4602A
SWEET PRIMROSE
Modeller: David Lyttleton
Height: 6 ¾", 17.2 cm
Colour: Pale green dress; white underskirt with green shading and primrose flowers
Issued: 1995 in a limited edition of 9,500
Series: Sweet Posy Collection
Comm. by: Compton & Woodhouse Ltd.

U.S.	$150.00
Can.	$175.00
U.K.	£ 80.00

RW4602B
SWEET DAISY / SUMMER (Style Six)
Modeller: David Lyttleton
Height: 6 ¾", 17.2 cm
Colour: 1. **Sweet Daisy:** Blue bodice and overskirt; white underskirt with blue shading and daisies; yellow hat and shawl
2. **Summer:** Blue dress and hat with gold accents
Issued: 1. **Sweet Daisy:** 1995 in a limited edition of 9,500
2. **Summer:** 2001 in a limited edition of 9,500
Series: 1. **Sweet Daisy:** Sweet Posy Collection
2. **Summer:** The Four Seasons' Elite Edition
Comm. by: Compton & Woodhouse Ltd.

Name:	Sweet Daisy	Summer
U.S.	$150.00	150.00
Can.	$175.00	175.00
U.K.	£ 80.00	80.00

RW4603
ANNIVERSARY / GOLDEN ANNIVERSARY / ROYAL PREMIERE / RUBY ANNIVERSARY (Style One) / SILVER ANNIVERSARY
Designer: Elizabeth Greenshields
Modeller: Jack Glynn
Height: 6 ¾", 18.4cm
Colour: 1. **Anniversary:** White with gold highlights
2. **Golden Anniversary:** Gold dress; pale yellow shawl
3. **Royal Premiere:** Peach dress; white shawl
4. **Ruby Anniversary:** Ruby dress; white shawl
5. **Silver Anniversary:** Silver-grey dress with silver highlights
6. **Pearl Anniversary:** Metallic silver dress; white shawl
Issued: 1. **Anniversary:** 1996 to the present
2. **Golden Anniversary:** 1999 to the present
3. **Royal Premiere:** 1996-2001
4. **Ruby Anniversary:** 1999 to the present
5. **Silver Anniversary:** 1999 to the present
6. **Pearl Anniversary:** 2002 to the present
Series: 1. Anniversary Collection
2. Golden Moments
3. Glittering Occasions

Name:	Anniversary	Golden	Royal	Ruby	Silver	Pearl
U.S.	$210.00	210.00	210.00	210.00	210.00	210.00
Can.	$255.00	255.00	255.00	255.00	255.00	255.00
U.K.	£115.00	115.00	115.00	115.00	115.00	115.00

RW4604
JANE / SARAH (Style Three) / WISTFUL

Designer:	Elizabeth Greenshields
Modeller:	Jack Glynn
Height:	8 ¾", 22.2 cm
Colour:	1. **Jane:** Pale green skirt and scarf, darker green bodice
	2. **Sarah:** Lavender skirt and scarf, deeper lavender bodice; gold highlights
	3. **Wistful:** Yellow skirt and scarf; deeper yellow bodice
Issued:	1. **Jane:** 1998 to the present
	2. **Sarah:** 2000 in a limited edition of 950
	3. **Wistful:** 1996-1999
Series:	1. **Jane:** Summer Romance
	3. **Wistful:** Day Dreams
Comm. by:	2. **Sarah:** Compton & Woodhouse Ltd.

Name:	Jane	Sarah	Wistful
U.S.	—	350.00	225.00
Can.	—	425.00	275.00
U.K.	£115.00	190.00	125.00

RW4605
HOLLY

Designer:	Elizabeth Greenshields
Modeller:	Maureen Halson
Height:	8", 20.3 cm
Colour:	Blue dress; pink bow; white apron; brown dog
Issued:	1995 in a limited edition of 7,500
Comm. by:	The Juvenile Diabetes Foundation

U.S.	$160.00
Can.	$185.00
U.K.	£ 90.00

RW4606
SWEET ANEMONE

Modeller:	David Lyttleton
Height:	6 ¾", 17.2 cm
Colour:	Mauve dress; white underskirt decorated with anemone flowers; yellow hat with pink and mauve flowers
Issued:	1995 in a limited edition of 9,500
Series:	Sweet Posy Collection
Comm. by:	Compton & Woodhouse Ltd.

U.S.	$150.00
Can.	$175.00
U.K.	£ 80.00

RW4607
LUCY
Style One

Designer:	Elizabeth Greenshields
Modeller:	Jack Glynn
Height:	4", 10.1 cm
Colour:	White dress and hat; tan dog
Issued:	1999
Series:	Collectors Club Figure

U.S.	$120.00
Can.	$135.00
U.K.	£ 65.00

RW4608
CAROLINE (Style Two) / FIONA

Designer:	Elizabeth Greenshields
Modeller:	Jack Glynn
Height:	6 ¾", 17.3 cm
Colour:	1. **Caroline:** Pale brown skirt and hat; brown bows, ribbons and bag; dark brown jacket
	2. **Fiona:** Blue dress, hat and bag; pink bows and ribbons
Issued:	1. **Caroline:** 1996 to the present
	2. **Fiona:** 1996-2002
Series:	1. **Caroline:** Les Petites
	2. **Fiona:** High Society

Name:	Caroline	Fiona
U.S.	—	165.00
Can.	—	200.00
U.K.	£87.50	90.00

RW4609
GRACE
Style Three

Modeller:	John Bromley
Height:	8 ½", 21.6 cm
Colour:	Pink dress and shawl; red roses
Issued:	1996-1996
Series:	Figurine of the Year
U.S.	$175.00
Can.	$200.00
U.K.	£100.00

RW4611
CATHERINE (Style One) / CONGRATULATIONS

Designer:	Elizabeth Greenshields
Modeller:	Jack Glynn
Height:	6 ¾", 17.3 cm
Colour:	1. **Catherine:** Pale blue dress and hat
	2. **Congratulations:** White with gold highlights
Issued:	1. **Catherine:** 1996 to the present
	2. **Congratulations:** 1998 to the present
Series:	1. **Catherine:** High Society
	2. **Congratulations:** Golden Moments

Name:	Catherine	Congratulations
U.S.	—	—
Can.	—	—
U.K.	£87.50	87.50

RW4612
SPECIAL OCCASION

Designer:	Elizabeth Greenshields
Modeller:	Richard Moore
Height:	8 ¾", 22.2 cm
Colour:	White with gold highlights
Issued:	1996 to the present
Varieties:	RW4676 May Ball
Series:	Golden Moments
U.S.	—
Can.	—
U.K.	£105.00

RW4613
SWEET PEONY

Modeller:	David Lyttleton
Height:	6 ¾", 17.2 cm
Colour:	Rose-pink dress and hat; white overskirt decorated with peony flowers
Issued:	1995 Ltd. Ed. of 9,500
Series:	Sweet Posy Collection
Comm. by:	Compton & Woodhouse Ltd.
U.S.	$150.00
Can.	$175.00
U.K.	£ 80.00

RW4614
THE FLIRTATION
Style Two
Modeller:	Maureen Halson
Height:	9 ½", 24.0 cm
Colour:	Female: Pink skirt; rose-pink bodice decorated with flowers
	Male: Blue suit; white waistcoat with blue and red design; white frills and cravat; brown shoes
Issued:	1996 in a limited edition of 2,450
Comm. by:	Compton & Woodhouse Ltd.

U.S.	$500.00
Can.	$600.00
U.K.	£275.00

RW4615
JESSICA
Style One
Designer:	Elizabeth Greenshields
Modeller:	Jack Glynn
Height:	9", 22.9 cm
Colour:	Mauve and lilac dress; pink roses; gold highlights
Issued:	1996 to the present
Series:	Summer Romance

U.S.	—
Can.	—
U.K.	£115.00

RW4616
LADY CHARLOTTE
Modeller:	Martin Evans
Height:	5", 12.7 cm
Colour:	Turquoise dress with white bows
Issued:	1995 in a limited edition of 9,500
Series:	The Fashionable Victorians (Victoria and Albert Museum)
Comm. by:	Compton & Woodhouse Ltd.

U.S.	$130.00
Can.	$155.00
U.K.	£ 70.00

RW4617
THE GOLDEN JUBILEE BALL
Designer:	Raymond Hughes
Modeller:	John Bromley
Height:	8 ½", 21.6 cm
Colour:	Blue dress trimmed with gold and red roses; white underskirt; pink gloves
Issued:	1996 in a limited edition of 12,500
Series:	Splendour at Court
Comm. by:	Compton & Woodhouse Ltd.

U.S.	$250.00
Can.	$300.00
U.K.	£135.00

RW4619
THE LAST DANCE
Modeller:	David Lyttleton
Height:	9", 22.9 cm
Colour:	1. Cream dress with gold design on bodice
	2. Purple dress with gold design on bodice
Issued:	1. 1997
	2. 2003 to the present
Series:	Classical Sentiments
Comm. by:	Compton & Woodhouse Ltd.

	Cream	Purple
U.S.	$185.00	—
Can.	$225.00	—
U.K.	£100.00	140.00

RW4620
EMILY (Style Three) / KATE
Designer:	Elizabeth Greenshields
Modeller:	Jack Glynn
Height:	5 ¾", 14.6 cm
Colour:	1. **Emily:** Pale blue dress, hat and parasol, gold parasol stem
	2. **Kate:** Pale green dress, hat and parasol; gold parasol stem
Issued:	1. **Emily:** 1996-1999
	2. **Kate:** 1996-2002
Series:	Les Petites

Name:	Emily	Kate
U.S.	$130.00	130.00
Can.	$155.00	155.00
U.K.	£ 70.00	70.00

RW4621
REBECCA (Style Three) / SARAH (Style Two)
Designer:	Elizabeth Greenshields
Modeller:	Richard Moore
Height:	6 ¼", 15.9 cm
Colour:	1. **Rebecca:** Red dress and hat; white petticoat
	2. **Sarah:** Pink dress with rose-pink bows; white petticoat
Issued:	1. **Rebecca:** 1996 to the present
	2. **Sarah:** 1996-2002
Series:	Les Petites

Name:	Rebecca	Sarah
U.S.	—	165.00
Can.	—	200.00
U.K.	£87.50	90.00

RW4622
FIRST SMILE
Modeller:	Maureen Halson
Height:	8 ¼", 21.0 cm
Colour:	Cream (Wallbody)
Issued:	1996 in a limited edition of 7,500
Series:	Tender Moments
Comm. by:	Compton & Woodhouse Ltd.

U.S.	$165.00
Can.	$195.00
U.K.	£ 89.00

RW4623
SWEET ASTOR / WINTER (Style Six)
Modeller:	David Lyttleton
Height:	6 ¾", 17.2 cm
Colour:	1. **Sweet Astor:** Dark peach, peach, orange and white
	2. **Winter:** Pink, gold, white and cream
Issued:	1. **Sweet Astor:** 1995 in a limited edition of 9,500
	2. **Winter:** 2001 in a limited edition of 9,500
Series:	1. **Sweet Astor:** Sweet Posy Collection
	2. **Winter:** The Four Seasons' Elite Edition
Comm. by:	Compton & Woodhouse Ltd.

Name:	Sweet Astor	Winter
U.S.	$150.00	150.00
Can.	$175.00	175.00
U.K.	£ 80.00	80.00

RW4624
LADY ALICE
Modeller:	Martin Evans
Height:	5", 12.7 cm
Colour:	Yellow dress; black hat and gloves
Issued:	1995 in a limited edition of 9,500
Series:	The Fashionable Victorians
Comm. by:	Compton & Woodhouse Ltd.

U.S.	$130.00
Can.	$155.00
U.K.	£ 70.00

RW4625
LADY VICTORIA
Modeller: Martin Evans
Height: 5", 12.7 cm
Colour: White, purple, pink, blue and gold
Issued: 1995 in a limited edition of 9,500
Series: The Fashionable Victorians
Comm. by: Compton & Woodhouse Ltd.

U.S. $130.00
Can. $155.00
U.K. £ 70.00

RW4627
SOPHIE / VIENNESE WALTZ / FRANCESCA (Style Two)
Designer: Elizabeth Greenshields
Modeller: Richard Moore
Height: 8 ¼", 21.0 CM
Colour:
1. **Sophie:** Pink dress with deeper pink shading; gold purse
2. **Viennese Waltz:** Pale yellow dress; darker yellow shawl; gold purse
3. **Francesca:** Dark blue dress with red rose
Issued:
1. **Sophie:** 1996 to the present
2. **Viennese Waltz:** 1996-2001
3. **Francesca:** 2002 to the present
Series:
1. **Sophie:** Summer Romance
2. **Viennese Waltz:** Glittering Occasions
Comm. by: **Francesca:** Compton & Woodhouse Ltd.

Name:	Sophie	Viennese	Francesca
U.S.	$225.00	225.00	—
Can.	$275.00	275.00	—
U.K.	£125.00	125.00	189.00

RW4628
WITH LOVE
Style One
Designer: Elizabeth Greenshields
Modeller: Jack Glynn
Height: 9", 22.9 cm
Colour: Female: Pink dress; white underskirt; rose-pink hat
Male: Dark grey suit; white shirt; grey stockings; black shoes
Issued: 1996 in a limited edition of 500
Series: Age of Romance (Series Three)

U.S. $500.00
Can. $600.00
U.K. £275.00

RW4629
BRIDESMAID (Style Two) / NICOLA
Designer: Elizabeth Greenshields
Modeller: Maureen Halson
Height: 6", 15.0 cm
Colour:
1. **Bridesmaid:** Pink and white dress; gold highlights
2. **Nicola:** Grey-blue and white dress; gold highlights
Issued:
1. **Bridesmaid:** 1996-1998
2. **Nicola:** 1996-1998
Series:
1. **Bridesmaid:** Golden Moments
2. **Nicola:** Les Petites

Name:	Bridesmaid	Nicola
U.S.	$130.00	130.00
Can.	$155.00	155.00
U.K.	£ 70.00	70.00

RW4630
LADY SOPHIE
Style One
Designer: Elizabeth Greenshields
Modeller: Maureen Halson
Height: 5", 12.7 cm
Colour: White overdress with pink edging; pink underskirt with white shading; beige hat with pink ribbon; gold highlights
Issued: 1996 in a limited edition of 9,500
Series: The Fashionable Victorians
Comm. by: Compton & Woodhouse Ltd.

U.S.	$130.00
Can.	$155.00
U.K.	£ 70.00

RW4631
LADY BEATRICE
Modeller: Martin Evans
Height: 5", 12.7 cm
Colour: Dark blue jacket and skirt with pale blue shading; gold highlights
Issued: 1996 in a limited edition of 9,500
Series: The Fashionable Victorians
Comm. by: Compton & Woodhouse Ltd.

U.S.	$130.00
Can.	$155.00
U.K.	£ 70.00

RW4632
BRIDE AND GROOM
(Cake Decoration)
Designer: Elizabeth Greenshields
Modeller: Maureen Halson
Height: 4 ¾", 12.1 cm
Colour: White with gold highlights
Issued: 1996 to the present
Series: Golden Moments

U.S.	$110.00
Can.	$130.00
U.K.	£ 60.00

RW4633
MIDNIGHT RENDEZVOUS
Designer: Elizabeth Greenshields
Modeller: Maureen Halson
Height: 9", 22.9 cm
Colour: Red dress; white underskirt; white and grey marbled staircase; pink roses
Issued: 1996 in a limited edition of 1000
Series: Precious Moments

U.S.	$375.00
Can.	$450.00
U.K.	£200.00

RW4634
MOTHER AND CHILD
Style One
Designer: Elizabeth Greenshields
Modeller: Jack Glynn
Height: 9", 22.9 cm
Colour: Peach and white
Issued: 1996-2001
Series: Golden Moments

U.S.	$225.00
Can.	$275.00
U.K.	£125.00

RW4635
SWEET SNOWDROP
Modeller: David Lyttleton
Height: 6 ¾", 17.2 cm
Colour: Green dress and hat; white skirt with green shading / snowdrops
Issued: 1996 in a limited edition of 9,500
Series: Sweet Posy Collection
Comm. by: Compton & Woodhouse Ltd.

U.S.	$150.00
Can.	$175.00
U.K.	£ 80.00

RW4637
AMY
Style One
Designer: Elizabeth Greenshields
Modeller: Jack Glynn
Height: 8 ¾", 22.2 cm
Colour: Yellow dress, gold trim; black hair
Issued: 1996-1998
Series: Summer Romance

U.S. $160.00
Can. $185.00
U.K. £ 90.00

RW4638
FROM ALL OF US / NIGHT AT THE OPERA
Designer: Elizabeth Greenshields
Modeller: Maureen Halson
Height: 9", 22.9 cm
Colour: 1. **From All of Us:** White with gold highlights
2. **Night at the Opera:** Blue dress, cream fan, gold highlights
Issued: 1. **From All of Us:** 1999-2002
2. **Night at the Opera:** 1996-2001
Series: 1. **From All of Us:** Golden Moments
2. **Night at the Opera:** Glittering Occasions

Name:	From all of Us	Night at the Opera
U.S.	$160.00	160.00
Can.	$185.00	185.00
U.K.	£ 90.00	90.00

RW4639
OLIVIA
Style Two
Designer: Elizabeth Greenshields
Modeller: Jack Glynn
Height: 8 ¼", 21.0 cm
Colour: Pale aquamarine dress, gold trim
Issued: 1996-1999
Varieties: Also known as Jessica, RW5038
Series: Summer Romance

U.S. $225.00
Can. $275.00
U.K. £125.00

RW4641
ROYAL ENCLOSURE
Designer: Elizabeth Greenshields
Modeller: Richard Moore
Height: 9", 22.9 cm
Colour: Pale yellow skirt; white underskirt; dark green riding jacket and hat; yellow band and bow on hat; gold riding crop
Issued: 1996-2003
Series: High Society

U.S. $220.00
Can. $265.00
U.K. £120.00

RW4642
SWEET PANSY
Modeller: David Lyttleton
Height: 6 ¾", 17.2 cm
Colour: Lilac jacket and hat, white skirt decorated with pansies; tan basket of flowers
Issued: 1996 in a limited edition of 9,500
Series: Sweet Posy Collection
Comm. by: Compton & Woodhouse Ltd.

U.S. $150.00
Can. $175.00
U.K. £ 80.00

RW4643
SWEET DAFFODIL / SPRING (Style Six)
Modeller: David Lyttleton
Height: 6 ¾", 17.2 cm
Colour: 1. **Sweet Daffodil:** Blue bodice and hat; white skirt decorated with daffodils; yellow overskirt
2. **Spring:** Green dress; gold highlights; white shawl and hat
Issued: 1. **Sweet Daffodil:** 1996 in a limited edition of 9,500
2. **Spring:** 2001 in a limited edition of 9,500
Series: 1. **Sweet Daffodil:** Sweet Posy Collection
2. **Spring:** The Four Seasons' Elite Edition
Comm. by: Compton & Woodhouse Ltd.

Name:	Sweet Daffodil	Spring
U.S.	$150.00	150.00
Can.	$175.00	175.00
U.K.	£ 80.00	80.00

RW4644
STROLLING IN SATIN
Modeller: John Bromley
Height: 8 ½", 21.6 cm
Colour: White
Issued: 1996 in a limited edition of 12,500
Series: House of Elliot
Comm. by: Compton & Woodhouse Ltd.

U.S.	$155.00
Can.	$185.00
U.K.	£ 85.00

RW4645
SISTER, GUYS HOSPITAL, 1960
Designer: Elizabeth Greenshields
Modeller: Kenneth Potts
Height: 9", 22.9 cm
Colour: White uniform and cap; black and red cape
Issued: 1996
Series: Nursing Sisters

U.S.	$450.00
Can.	$550.00
U.K.	£250.00

RW4646
ANNABEL / JUST FOR YOU
Designer: Elizabeth Greenshields
Modeller: Maureen Halson
Height: 6 ¼", 15.9 cm
Colour: 1. **Annabel:** Pale yellow skirt; blue jacket; blue hat with yellow ribbon
2. **Just for You:** Red jacket; pale yellow skirt; black hat
Issued: 1. **Annabel:** 1997 to the present
2. **Just for You:** 2000 to the present
Series: 1. **Annabel:** Les Petites

Name:	Annabel	Just for You
U.S.	—	—
Can.	—	—
U.K.	£87.50	87.50

Note: Just For You is available only at the Royal Worcester Factory Shop. The name of your choice can be inscribed on the base of the figurine.

RW4647
ALICE (Style Three) / CELEBRATION / GARDEN PARTY
Designer: Elizabeth Greenshields
Modeller: Richard Moore
Height: 9", 22.9 cm
Colour: 1. **Alice:** Brown and peach dress; brown hat with peach ribbon
2. **Celebration:** White dress and hat, gold highlights
3. **Garden Party:** Pale yellow skirt; darker yellow bodice and overskirt
Issued: 1. **Alice:** 1996 to the present
2. **Celebration:** 1996-2003
3. **Garden Party:** 1996-1999
Series: 1. **Alice:** Summer Romance
2. **Celebration:** Golden Moments
3. **Garden Party:** High Society

Name:	Alice	Celebration	Garden Party
U.S.	$175.00	175.00	175.00
Can.	$200.00	200.00	200.00
U.K.	£100.00	100.00	100.00

RW4648
GRADUATION NIGHT
Designer: Elizabeth Greenshields
Modeller: Jack Glynn
Height: 8 ¾", 22.2 cm
Colour: Peach dress, gold highlights
Issued: 1996-1998
Series: Glittering Occasions
U.S. $160.00
Can. $185.00
U.K. £ 90.00

RW4649
LADY ALEXANDRA
Modeller: Martin Evans
Height: 5", 12.7 cm
Colour: Lilac overdress; white skirt with lilac and pink flowers; gold trim
Issued: 1995 in a limited edition of 9,500
Series: The Fashionable Victorians
Comm. by: Compton & Woodhouse Ltd.

U.S. $130.00
Can. $155.00
U.K. £ 70.00

RW4650
LADY LOUISE
Modeller: Martin Evans
Height: 5", 12.7 cm
Colour: Pale green crinoline; white sleeves and hat; gold highlights
Issued: 1995 in a limited edition of 9,500
Series: The Fashionable Victorians
Comm. by: Compton & Woodhouse Ltd.

U.S. $130.00
Can. $155.00
U.K. £ 70.00

RW4651
QUEEN ELIZABETH I
Style Four

Modeller:	Michael Talbot
Height:	9", 22.9 cm
Colour:	Ivory sleeves and skirt with gold design; dark green overdress and cape with gold bows; white ruff with gold design; white ostrich feather fan
Issued:	1997 in a limited edition of 4,500
Comm. by:	Compton & Woodhouse Ltd.
U.S.	$450.00
Can.	$540.00
U.K.	£245.00

RW4652
DANCE OF TIME

Modeller:	Maureen Halson
Height:	11", 27.9 cm
Colour:	Cream (Wallbody) with pearl lustre
Issued:	1997 in a limited edition of 5,000
Series:	Spirit of the Dance
Comm. by:	Compton & Woodhouse Ltd.
U.S.	$325.00
Can.	$400.00
U.K.	£175.00

Note: This figure also appears on a lamp base.

RW4653
CLAIRE

Designer:	Elizabeth Greenshields
Modeller:	Richard Moore
Height:	8", 20.3 cm
Colour:	Peach dress, gold highlights; brown hair and shoes
Issued:	1996-1998
Series:	Summer Romance
U.S.	$225.00
Can.	$275.00
U.K.	£125.00

RW4654A
REFLECTION (Style One) / SPECIAL MUM (First Version)

Designer:	Elizabeth Greenshields
Modeller:	Jack Glynn
Height:	8 ½", 21.6 cm
Colour:	1. **Reflection:** Pale blue, yellow and gold
	2. **Special Mum:** White with gold highlights; hand holds gold mirror
Issued:	1. **Reflection:** 1996-1999
	2. **Special Mum:** 1999-2002
Series:	1. **Reflection:** Day Dreams
	2. **Special Mum:** Golden Moments

Name:	Reflection	Special Mum
U.S.	$160.00	160.00
Can.	$185.00	185.00
U.K.	£ 90.00	90.00

RW4654B
SPECIAL MUM (Second Version)

Designer:	Elizabeth Greenshields
Modeller:	Jack Glynn
Height:	8 ¾", 22.2 cm
Colour:	White with gold highlights; hand holds a rose
Issued:	1999 to the present
Series:	Golden Moments
U.S.	—
Can.	—
U.K.	£105.00

RW4656
MEMORIES

Designer:	Elizabeth Greenshields
Modeller:	Jack Glynn
Height:	4 ¾" x 7 ½", 12.1 x 19.1 cm
Colour:	Peach and yellow dress; brown and green chaise-lounge
Issued:	1996-1998
Series:	Day Dreams
U.S.	$175.00
Can.	$200.00
U.K.	£ 90.00

235

RW4657
LADY MARGARET
Modeller:	Jack Glynn
Height:	6", 15.0 cm
Colour:	Rose-pink and pale pink
Issued:	1994 in a limited edition of 15,000
Series:	My Fair Ladies
Comm. by:	Compton & Woodhouse Ltd.
U.S.	$130.00
Can.	$155.00
U.K.	£ 70.00

RW4658
ANNE
Style One
Modeller:	Maureen Halson
Height:	9 ¼", 23.5 cm
Colour:	Peach
Issued:	1997-1997
Series:	Special Events
U.S.	$225.00
Can.	$275.00
U.K.	£125.00

RW4659
MASKED BALL
Designer:	Elizabeth Greenshields
Modeller:	Maureen Halson
Height:	8 ¾", 22.2 cm
Colour:	Purple and lilac gown; gold mask
Issued:	1996-2000
Series:	Glittering Occasions
U.S.	$225.00
Can.	$275.00
U.K.	£125.00

RW4660
NEW ARRIVAL
Style Two
Designer:	Elizabeth Greenshileds
Modeller:	Jack Glynn
Size:	3 ½" x 4 ½", 8.9 x 11.9 cm
Colour:	1. Blue 2. Pink
Issued:	1996-2002
Series:	Golden Moments
U.S.	$ 80.00
Can.	$100.00
U.K.	£ 45.00

RW4661
BIRTHDAY WISH / SUMMER REGATTA
Designer:	Elizabeth Greenshields
Modeller:	Richard Moore
Height:	8 ¾", 22.2 cm
Colour:	1. **Birthday Wish:** White with gold highlights 2. **Summer Regatta:** Green dress, black gloves and hat
Issued:	1. **Birthday Wish:** 1997 to the present 2. **Summer Regatta:** 1996-1999
Series:	1. **Birthday Wish:** Golden Moments 2. **Summer Regatta:** High Society

Name:	Birthday Wish	Summer Regatta
U.S.	$ —	175.00
Can.	$ —	200.00
U.K.	£ 70.00	100.00

RW4662
ASCOT LADY / ANNA (Style Two)
Designer:	Elizabeth Greenshields
Modeller:	Richard Moore
Height:	9", 22.9 cm
Colour:	1. **Ascot Lady:** Light and dark blue, and yellow 2. **Anna:** Red and black
Issued:	1. **Ascot Lady:** 1996-2000 2. **Anna:** 2002 in a limited edition of 950
Series:	1. **Ascot Lady:** High Society
Comm. by:	2. **Anna:** Compton & Woodhouse Ltd.

Name:	Ascot Lady	Anna
U.S.	$225.00	325.00
Can.	$275.00	400.00
U.K.	£125.00	175.00

RW4664
LADY LOUISA

Modeller:	Martin Evans
Height:	4 ½", 11.9 cm
Colour:	Pink, rose-pink and gold
Issued:	1996 in a limited edition of 15,000
Series:	Debutantes
Comm. by:	Compton & Woodhouse Ltd.
U.S.	$130.00
Can.	$155.00
U.K.	£ 70.00

RW4665
LADY EMMA
Style Two

Modeller:	Martin Evans
Height:	4 ½", 11.9
Colour:	Pale blue, dark blue and gold
Issued:	1996 in a limited edition of 15,000
Series:	Debutantes
Comm. by:	Compton & Woodhouse Ltd.
U.S.	$130.00
Can.	$155.00
U.K.	£ 70.00

RW4666
LOVING YOU / THOUGHTFUL

Designer:	Elizabeth Greenshields
Modeller:	Richard Moore
Height:	8 ¼", 21.0 cm
Colour:	1. **Loving You:** White with gold highlights
	2. **Thoughtful:** Pale blue dress and jacket trimmed with lilac
Issued:	1. **Loving You:** 1997-2001
	2. **Thoughtful:** 1996-1998
Series:	1. **Loving You:** Golden Moments
	2. **Thoughtful:** Day Dreams

Name:	Loving You	Thoughtful
U.S.	$160.00	160.00
Can.	$185.00	185.00
U.K.	£ 90.00	90.00

RW4667
ESPECIALLY FOR YOU / LADIES DAY / CHRISTMAS

Designer:	Elizabeth Greenshields
Modeller:	Maureen Halson
Height:	8 ¾", 22.2 cm
Colour:	1. **Especially For You:** Blue dress
	2. **Ladies Day:** Pale tan dress and hat; white petticoats; blue coat trimmed with fur; brown boot
	3. **Christmas:** Red bodice; green skirt and jacket with fur trim; black hat
Issued:	1. **Especially For You:** 2000 to the present
	2. **Ladies Day:** 1996-1998
	3. **Christmas:** 2001 in a limited edition of 750
Series:	2. **Ladies Day:** High Society
Comm. by:	3. **Christmas:** Compton & Woodhouse Ltd.

Name:	Especially For You	Ladies Day	Christmas
U.S.	—	175.00	375.00
Can.	—	200.00	450.00
U.K.	£100.00	100.00	200.00

RW4668
LADY EMILY

Designer:	Unknown
Modeller:	Jack Glynn
Height:	6", 15.0 cm
Colour:	Green and white dress with black edging
Issued:	1996 in a limited edition of 15,000
Series:	My Fair Ladies
Comm. by:	Compton & Woodhouse Ltd.
U.S.	$130.00
Can.	$155.00
U.K.	£ 70.00

Note: Especially For You is available only at the Royal Worcester factory shop. The name of your choice can be inscribed on the base of the figurine.

RW4669
LADY HANNAH
Style Two
Modeller: Martin Evans
Height: 4 ½", 11.9 cm
Colour: Pale green, yellow and gold
Issued: 1996 in a limited edition of 15,000
Series: Debutantes
Comm. by: Compton & Woodhouse Ltd.

U.S. $130.00
Can. $155.00
U.K. £ 70.00

RW4670
LADY CICELY
Designer: Unknown
Modeller: Richard Moore
Height: 4 ½", 11.9 cm
Colour: Mauve, white, deep mauve, rose-pink and gold
Issued: 1996 in a limited edition of 15,000
Series: Debutantes
Comm. by: Compton & Woodhouse Ltd.

U.S. $130.00
Can. $155.00
U.K. £ 70.00

RW4671
LADY SOPHIE
Style Two
Designer: Unknown
Modeller: Richard Moore
Height: 4 ½", 11.9 cm
Colour: Pink, rose-pink, white and gold
Issued: 1996 in a limited edition of 15,000
Series: Debutantes
Comm. by: Compton & Woodhouse Ltd.

U.S. $130.00
Can. $155.00
U.K. £ 70.00

RW4672
LADY CAMILLE
Designer: Unknown
Modeller: Jack Glynn
Height: 6", 15.9 cm
Colour: Pink and burgundy
Issued: 1996 in a limited edition of 15,000
Series: My Fair Ladies
Comm. by: Compton & Woodhouse Ltd.

U.S. $130.00
Can. $155.00
U.K. £ 70.00

RW4674
ROYAL ANNIVERSARY
Style Two
Modeller: John Bromley
Height: 8 ½", 21.6 cm
Colour: Pale aqua, white, red and gold
Issued: 1996 in a limited edition of 12,500
Series: Splendour at Court
Comm. by: Compton & Woodhouse Ltd.

U.S. $225.00
Can. $275.00
U.K. £125.00

RW4676
MAY BALL
Designer: Elizabeth Greenshields
Modeller: Richard Moore
Height: 8 ¾", 22.2 cm
Colour: Pink dress; white fan; gold highlights
Issued: 1996-2001
Varieties: RW4612 Special Occasion
Series: Glittering Occasions

U.S. $175.00
Can. $200.00
U.K. £100.00

RW4677
KATIE
Style Two
Designer: Elizabeth Greenshields
Modeller: Maureen Halson
Height: 5 ¾", 14.0 cm
Colour: White dress and hat; yellow hair
Issued: 2000-2000
Series: Collectors Club Figure

U.S. $140.00
Can. $165.00
U.K. £ 75.00

RW4678
LADY DOROTHY
Modeller: Jack Glynn
Height: 6", 15.0 cm
Colour: Turquoise, cream, black and grey
Issued: 1994 in a limited edition of 15,000
Series: My Fair Ladies
Comm. by: Compton & Woodhouse Ltd.

U.S. $130.00
Can. $155.00
U.K. £ 70.00

238

RW4679
LADY HELENA
Modeller:	Jack Glynn
Height:	6", 15.0 cm
Colour:	White, blue, black and grey
Issued:	1997 in a limited edition of 15,000
Series:	My Fair Ladies
Comm. by:	Compton & Woodhouse Ltd.
U.S.	$130.00
Can.	$155.00
U.K.	£ 70.00

RW4680
MUSIC
Modeller:	Maureen Halson
Height:	8 ¼", 21.0 cm
Colour:	Turquoise, white, pink and gold
Issued:	1997 in a limited edition of 2,500
Series:	The Graceful Arts
Comm. by:	Compton & Woodhouse Ltd.
U.S.	$550.00
Can.	$675.00
U.K.	£300.00

RW4681
SERENA
Modeller:	John Bromley
Height:	9", 22.9 cm
Colour:	Pale green
Issued:	1997-1997
Varieties:	Also known as Olivia (Style Three) RW4965
Series:	Figurine of the Year
U.S.	$175.00
Can.	$200.00
U.K.	£100.00

RW4682
FIRST TEDDY
Modeller:	Maureen Halson
Height:	8 ¼", 21.0 cm
Colour:	Cream (Wallbody)
Issued:	1997 in a limited edition of 7,500
Series:	Tender Moments
Comm. by:	Compton & Woodhouse Ltd.
U.S.	$160.00
Can.	$185.00
U.K.	£ 90.00

RW4683
JEWEL IN THE CROWN
Modeller:	John Bromley
Height:	8 ½", 21.6 cm
Colour:	Pink gown with gold design
Issued:	1997 in a limited edition of 12,500
Series:	Splendour at Court
Comm. by:	Compton & Woodhouse Ltd.
U.S.	$225.00
Can.	$275.00
U.K.	£125.00

RW4685
NATASHIA
Style Two
Designer:	Elizabeth Greenshields
Modeller:	Richard Moore
Height:	9 ½", 24.0 cm
Colour:	Tan skirt; coffee coloured coat; dark brown fur collar, hat and muff
Issued:	1998-1998
Series:	Premiere Figurine of the Year
U.S.	$225.00
Can.	$275.00
U.K.	£125.00

RW4686
SUMMER'S LEASE
Modeller:	Maureen Halson
Height:	9 ½", 24.0 cm
Colour:	Pink, white and red
Issued:	1998 in a limited edition of 2,950
Comm. by:	Compton & Woodhouse Ltd.
U.S.	$450.00
Can.	$550.00
U.K.	£250.00

RW4687
THE TRYST
Modeller:	Maureen Halson
Height:	9 ½", 24.0 cm
Colour:	Female: Pale blue dress, white frills, gold edging; pink underskirt decorated with pink roses; pink shoes
	Male: Blue jacket with gold edging; flowered beige waistcoat; tan breeches; brown shoe
Issued:	1998 in a limited edition of 2,450
Series:	Dancing Lovers
Comm. by:	Compton & Woodhouse Ltd.
U.S.	$550.00
Can.	$675.00
U.K.	£300.00

RW4688
ISABELLE
Modeller:	John Bromley
Height:	8 ¼", 21.0 cm
Colour:	Pale blue dress with darker blue and gold top; pale blue and gold bow in hair
Issued:	1998-1998
Series:	Figurine of the Year
Comm. by:	Compton & Woodhouse Ltd.
U.S.	$250.00
Can.	$300.00
U.K.	£135.00

RW4689
FLAME DANCE (Fire)
Modeller:	Richard Moore
Height:	11 ½", 29.2 cm
Colour:	Red and yellow
Issued:	1997-1999
Series:	Forces of Creation
U.S.	$265.00
Can.	$320.00
U.K.	£145.00

RW4690
A GIFT OF LOVE
Modeller:	Richard Moore
Height:	9", 22.9 cm
Colour:	Female: Peach dress and shoes; white petticoats
	Male: Hunter green jacket with tan lapels and cuffs; yellow waistcoat; white cravat and gloves
Issued:	1998 in a limited edition of 500
Series:	Age of Romance, Series Three
U.S.	$550.00
Can.	$675.00
U.K.	£300.00

RW4691
THE EMBASSY BALL
Modeller:	John Bromley
Height:	10", 25.4 cm
Colour:	White, pale yellow, gold and orange
Issued:	1997 in a limited edition of 12,500
Series:	Splendour at Court
Comm. by:	Compton & Woodhouse Ltd.
U.S.	$225.00
Can.	$275.00
U.K.	£125.00

RW4692
FIRST LOVE
Modeller:	Maureen Halson
Height:	8 ¼", 21.0 cm
Colour:	Cream (Wallbody)
Issued:	1998 in a limited edition of 7,500
Series:	Tender Moments
Comm. by:	Compton & Woodhouse Ltd.
U.S.	$160.00
Can.	$185.00
U.K.	£ 90.00

240

RW4694
AQUAMARINE (Water)
Designer: Elizabeth Greenshields
Modeller: Richard Moore
Height: 9 ¼", 23.5 cm
Colour: Aquamarine and white
Issued: 1997-1999
Series: Forces of Creation

U.S. $265.00
Can. $320.00
U.K. £145.00

RW4695
MARY
Designer: Elizabeth Greenshields
Modeller: Carol Gladman
Height: 6 ¼", 15.9 cm
Colour: Peach skirt; brown
jacket with fur trim;
brown hat with peach
ribbon and bow
Issued: 1998-1999
Series: Les Petites

U.S. $160.00
Can. $185.00
U.K. £ 90.00

RW4696
JENNIFER
Designer: Elizabeth Greenshields
Modeller: Maureen Halson
Height: 6 ¾", 15.9 cm
Colour: Rose-pink dress and
hat with deep pink bow
and ribbon
Issued: 1997-2002
Series: Les Petites

U.S. $160.00
Can. $185.00
U.K. £ 90.00

RW4697
MISTRAL (Air)
Designer: Elizabeth Greenshields
Modeller: Richard Moore
Height: 11", 27.9 cm
Colour: Purple and pink
Issued: 1997-1999
Series: Forces of Creation

U.S. $265.00
Can. $320.00
U.K. £145.00

RW4698
I WISH
Modeller: Sheila Mitchell
Height: 8 ¼", 21.0 cm
Colour: Blue dress with pink
trim; brown teddy
bear
Issued: 1998 in a limited
edition of 5,000
Series: Children of the Future
(NSPCC)
Comm. by: Compton &
Woodhouse Ltd.

U.S. $225.00
Can. $275.00
U.K. £125.00

RW4699
EARTH SONG
Designer: Elizabeth Greenshields
Modeller: Richard Moore
Height: 11", 27.9 cm
Colour: Peach and yellow
Issued: 1997-1999
Series: Forces of Creation

U.S. $265.00
Can. $320.00
U.K. £145.00

RW4700
KNIGHTSBRIDGE / SABRINA / PHILLIPA
Designer: Elizabeth Greenshields
Modeller: Maureen Halson
Height: 9 ½", 24.0 cm
Colour: 1. **Knightsbridge:** Pale peach, white, gold and black
2. **Sabrina:** Green, gold, peach and light green
3. **Phillipa:** Purple and peach
Issued: 1. **Knightsbridge:** 1997 to the present
2. **Sabrina:** 2001 in a limited edition of 750
3. **Phillipa:** 2001 in a limited edition of 750
Series: 1. **Knightsbridge:** High Society
Comm. by: Sabrina / Phillipa: Compton & Woodhouse Ltd.

Name:	Knightsbridge	Sabrina	Phillipa
U.S.	$275.00	375.00	375.00
Can.	$325.00	450.00	450.00
U.K.	£150.00	200.00	200.00

RW4701
MARY, QUEEN OF SCOTS
Style Two
Modeller:	Michael Talbot
Height:	9", 22.9 cm
Colour:	Burgundy and gold
Issued:	1998 in a limited edition of 4,500
Series:	Queens of Britain
Comm. by:	Compton & Woodhouse Ltd.
U.S.	—
Can.	—
U.K.	£245.00

RW4702
THE PAINTED FAN (Lucinda)
Modeller:	John Bromley
Height:	9 ½", 24.0 cm
Colour:	Rose-pink, pale pink and gold
Issued:	1998 in a limited edition of 12,500
Series:	Age of Elegance, Series Two
Comm. by:	Compton & Woodhouse Ltd.
U.S.	$275.00
Can.	$325.00
U.K.	£150.00

RW4703
SECRET GARDEN
Designer:	Elizabeth Greenshields
Modeller:	Maureen Halson
Height:	9 ¼", 23.5 cm
Colour:	Lilac gown decorated with red roses and bows
Issued:	1998 in a limited edition of 1,000
Series:	Precious Moments
U.S.	—
Can.	—
U.K.	£230.00

RW4705
EMMA (Woodhouse)
Style Two
Modeller:	Richard Moore
Height:	8 ½", 21.6 cm
Colour:	Pink and white
Issued:	1998 in a limited edition of 4,500
Series:	Jane Austin Heroines (Museum of Costume, Bath)
Comm. by:	Compton & Woodhouse Ltd.
U.S.	$375.00
Can.	$450.00
U.K.	£200.00

RW4706
MOONLIGHT CASCADE
Modeller:	Martin Evans
Height:	8 ¾", 22.2 cm
Colour:	Blue lustre, platinum
Issued:	1998 in a limited edition of 9,500
Series:	The House of Eliott
Comm. by:	Compton & Woodhouse Ltd.
U.S.	$275.00
Can.	$325.00
U.K.	£150.00

RW4707
GRAND ENTRANCE
Designer:	Elizabeth Greenshields
Modeller:	Richard Moore
Height:	9 ¼", 23.5 cm
Colour:	Rose-pink, white and gold
Issued:	1997-2000
Series:	Glittering Occasions
U.S.	$225.00
Can.	$275.00
U.K.	£125.00

RW4708
POETRY
Modeller:	Maureen Halson
Height:	8 ¼", 21.0 cm
Colour:	Pale green dress; white underdress decorated with red roses
Issued:	1998 in a limited edition of 2,500
Series:	The Graceful Arts
Comm. by:	Compton & Woodhouse Ltd.
U.S.	$450.00
Can.	$550.00
U.K.	£250.00

RW4709
A DAY TO REMEMBER
Modeller:	Maureen Halson
Height:	9 ¼", 23.5 cm
Colour:	Pearl lustre gown
Issued:	1998-1998
Series:	Anniversary Figurine of the Year
Comm. by:	Compton & Woodhouse Ltd.
U.S.	$225.00
Can.	$275.00
U.K.	£125.00

RW4710
DINNER AT EIGHT

Modeller:	John Bromley
Height:	8 ¾", 22.2 cm
Colour:	Pearl lustre gown with platinum highlights
Issued:	1998 in a limited edition of 9,500
Series:	Brief Encounters
Comm. by:	Compton & Woodhouse Ltd.
U.S.	$225.00
Can.	$275.00
U.K.	£125.00

RW4711
TANYA / TEA AT THE RITZ

Designer:	Elizabeth Greenshields
Modeller:	Richard Moore
Height:	8 ¾", 22.2 cm
Colour:	1. **Tanya:** Cream dress and hat; gold sash and bow on hat
	2. **Tea at the Ritz:** Blue dress and hat; gold sash and bow on hat
Issued:	1. **Tanya:** 1997-1998
	2. **Tea at the Ritz:** 1997-2003
Series:	1. **Tanya:** Special Events
	2. **Tea at the Ritz:** High Society

Name:	Tanya	Tea at the Ritz
U.S.	$225.00	225.00
Can.	$275.00	275.00
U.K.	£125.00	125.00

RW4712
EVENING ROMANCE

Designer:	Elizabeth Greenshields
Modeller:	Maureen Halson
Height:	9", 22.9 cm
Colour:	Salmon-pink dress with gold decorated border
Issued:	1997-2001
Series:	Glittering Occasions
U.S.	$225.00
Can.	$275.00
U.K.	£125.00

RW4713
MOTHER'S LOVE

Modeller:	Maureen Halson
Height:	7 ¾", 19.7 cm
Colour:	Cream (Wallbody)
Issued:	1998-1998
Series:	Mother of the Year Figurine
Comm. by:	Compton & Woodhouse Ltd.
U.S.	$160.00
Can.	$185.00
U.K.	£ 90.00

RW4715
CHRISTINA

Designer:	Elizabeth Greenshields
Modeller:	Richard Moore
Height:	6 ¾, 17.2 cm
Colour:	Red dress; black hat with pink flowers; gold highlights
Issued:	1997 to the present
Series:	Les Petites
U.S.	—
Can.	—
U.K.	£87.50

RW4716
ELIZABETH
Style Two

Designer:	Elizabeth Greenshields
Modeller:	Richard Moore
Height:	9", 22.0 cm
Colour:	Dark blue jacket trimmed with paler blue fur; lemon overskirt; pale blue underskirt; blue hat with yellow band and feather; yellow gloves; blue umbrella
Issued:	1998-1998
Series:	Special Events
Comm. by:	Compton & Woodhouse Ltd.
U.S.	$175.00
Can.	$200.00
U.K.	£100.00

RW4717
JOANNE
Designer:	Elizabeth Greenshields
Modeller:	Ruth Hook
Height:	6 ½", 16.5 cm
Colour:	Cream skirt with pink shading, black bodice and hat, gold highlights
Issued:	1997-2001
Series:	Les Petites
U.S.	$140.00
Can.	$165.00
U.K.	£ 75.00

RW4718
A DAZZLING CELEBRATION
(Lady Cecilia)
Modeller:	John Bromley
Height:	9 ½", 24.0 cm
Colour:	Ivory-white, pale pink, pearl and gold
Issued:	1998 in a limited edition of 12,500
Series:	Age of Elegance, Series Two
Comm. by:	Compton & Woodhouse Ltd.
U.S.	$225.00
Can.	$275.00
U.K.	£125.00

RW4720
SONG OF SPRING
Modeller:	Maureen Halson
Height:	9 ½", 24.0 cm
Colour:	Pink, deeper pink, blue, green and white
Issued:	1998 in a limited edition of 2,950
Comm. by:	Compton & Woodhouse Ltd.
U.S.	$450.00
Can.	$550.00
U.K.	£250.00

RW4721
MILLENNIA
Modeller:	Richard Moore
Height:	9 ½", 24.0 cm
Colour:	White dress, shawl and dove; gold necklace and dials
Issued:	1999 in a limited edition of 1,000
Series:	Millennium Collection
U.S.	$375.00
Can.	$450.00
U.K.	£200.00

RW4722
TRUE LOVE
Designer:	Elizabeth Greenshields
Modeller:	Richard Moore
Height:	9 ½", 24.0 cm
Colour:	Female: Red and cream Male: Dark green, pale green and black
Plinth:	Wooden
Issued:	1998 in a limited edition of 500
Series:	Age of Romance, Series Three
U.S.	—
Can.	—
U.K.	£330.00

RW4723
THE PROPOSAL
Modeller:	Maureen Halson
Height:	9 ½", 24.0 cm
Colour:	Female: Pale lilac dress decorated with flowers Male: Purple coat with gold decoration; brown hair and breeches; black boots
Issued:	1999 in a limited edition of 2,450
Comm. by:	Compton & Woodhouse Ltd.
U.S.	$550.00
Can.	$675.00
U.K.	£300.00

RW4724
LADY SARAH
Style Two
Modeller:	Richard Moore
Height:	4 ½", 11.9 cm
Colour:	Blue crinoline with gold highlights
Issued:	1999 in a limited edition of 15,000
Series:	Debutantes
Comm. by:	Compton & Woodhouse Ltd.
U.S.	$130.00
Can.	$155.00
U.K.	£ 70.00

244

RW4725
GRACE
Style Four
Designer:	Elizabeth Greenshields
Modeller:	Richard Moore
Height:	9 ½", 24.0 cm
Colour:	Cream skirt; tan and dark brown patterned top; gold highlights
Issued:	1999-1999
Series:	Premiere Figurine of the Year
U.S.	$275.00
Can.	$325.00
U.K.	£150.00

RW4726
ETERNITY
Designer:	Elizabeth Greenshields
Modeller:	Richard Moore
Height:	6 ½", 16.5 cm
Colour:	White dress and shawl; gold trim, leaves and clock face
Issued:	1999-2000
Series:	Millennium Collection
U.S.	$175.00
Can.	$200.00
U.K.	£100.00

RW4727
I DREAM
Modeller:	Sheila Mitchell
Height:	8 ¼", 21.0 cm
Colour:	Pink dress
Issued:	1999 in a limited edition of 5,000
Series:	Children of the Future (NSPCC)
Comm. by:	Compton & Woodhouse Ltd.
U.S.	$225.00
Can.	$275.00
U.K.	£125.00

RW4728
LADY HENRIETTA
Modeller:	Martin Evans
Height:	4 ½", 11.9 cm
Colour:	Pale blue crinoline
Issued:	1999 in a limited edition of 15,000
Series:	Debutantes
Comm. by:	Compton & Woodhouse Ltd.
U.S.	$130.00
Can.	$155.00
U.K.	£ 70.00

RW4730A
THE FAN BEARER
Modeller:	John Bromley
Height:	8", 20.3 cm
Colour:	White, turquoise, lapis lazuli and terra cotta
Issued:	1999 in a limited edition of 500
Series:	The Court of Tutankhamun
Comm. by:	Compton & Woodhouse Ltd.
U.S.	$275.00
Can.	$325.00
U.K.	£150.00

Note: Models RW4703A, B and C were issued as a set.

RW4730B
TUTANKHAMUN
Modeller:	John Bromley
Height:	6 ¼", 15.9 cm
Colour:	White robes; gold headdress, amulets and sandals; turquoise, lapis lazuli, terra cotta decoration; brown and blue chair
Issued:	1999 in a limited edition of 500
Series:	The Court of Tutankhamen
Comm. by:	Compton & Woodhouse Ltd.
U.S.	$275.00
Can.	$325.00
U.K.	£150.00

Note: Models RW4703A, B and C were issued as a set

RW4730C
THE WINE POURER
Modeller:	John Bromley
Height:	8", 20.3 cm
Colour:	White, turquoise lapis lazuli and terra cotta
Issued:	1999 in a limited edition of 500
Series:	The Court of Tutankhamun
Comm. by:	Compton & Woodhouse Ltd.
U.S.	$275.00
Can.	$325.00
U.K.	£150.00

Note: Models RW4703A, B and C were issued as a set.

RW4731
VICTORIA
Designer:	Elizabeth Greenshields
Modeller:	Richard Moore
Height:	9", 22.9 cm
Colour:	Cream, red, gold, white, black and green
Issued:	1999-1999
Series:	Special Events
U.S.	$275.00
Can.	$325.00
U.K.	£150.00

RW4732
MOTHER AND CHILD
Style Two
Modeller:	John Bromley
Height:	8 ¼", 21.0 cm
Colour:	White
Issued:	1999
Comm. by:	Compton & Woodhouse Ltd.
U.S.	$175.00
Can.	$200.00
U.K.	£100.00

RW4733
QUEEN VICTORIA
Style Two
Modeller:	Richard Moore
Height:	8", 20.3 cm
Colour:	Red, gold and cream
Issued:	1999 in a limited edition of 4,500
Series:	Queens of Britain
Comm. by:	Compton & Woodhouse Ltd.
U.S.	—
Can.	—
U.K.	£245.00

RW4734
HANNAH
Style One
Designer:	Elizabeth Greenshields
Modeller:	Richard Moore
Height:	6 ¼", 15.9 cm
Colour:	Pale green dress; peach rose and bows; pale yellow shawl; dark green hat
Issued:	1999 to the present
Series:	Les Petites
U.S.	—
Can.	—
U.K.	£84.50

RW4735
SPIRIT OF PEACE
Modeller:	Maureen Halson
Height:	12", 30.5 cm
Colour:	1. Pearl lustre
	2. White with pale blue highlights
Issued:	1999 in a limited edition of 2,000 each
Comm. by:	Compton & Woodhouse Ltd.
U.S.	$500.00
Can.	$600.00
U.K.	£275.00

RW4736
AMY
Style Two
Modeller:	David Lyttleton
Height:	9", 22.9 cm
Colour:	Pink dress, hat and shoe
Issued:	1999-1999
Series:	Figurine of the Year
U.S.	$325.00
Can.	$400.00
U.K.	£175.00

RW4737
FRANCESCA
Style One
Designer:	Elizabeth Greenshields
Modeller:	Richard Moore
Height:	9", 22.9 cm
Colour:	Yellow, brown and tan
Issued:	1999-1999
Series:	Collectors Society Exclusive
U.S.	$275.00
Can.	$325.00
U.K.	£150.00

RW4739
BEDTIME STORY
Modeller:	Maureen Halson
Height:	7", 17.8 cm
Colour:	White (Wallbody)
Issued:	1999-1999
Comm. by:	Compton & Woodhouse Ltd.
U.S.	$160.00
Can.	$185.00
U.K.	£ 90.00

RW4741
MAISIE
Modeller:	John Bromley
Height:	8 ½", 21.6 cm
Colour:	Cream (Wallbody)
Issued:	1999 in a limited edition of 2,000
Series:	Fashion Figurine of the Year (1920s)
Comm. by:	Compton & Woodhouse Ltd.
U.S.	$160.00
Can.	$185.00
U.K.	£ 90.00

RW4742
MARGERY
Designer:	Elizabeth Greenshields
Modeller:	Richard Moore
Height:	Unknown
Colour:	Blue
Issued:	1999
Comm. by:	The Townswomen's Guild
U.S.	$160.00
Can.	$185.00
U.K.	£ 90.00

Photograph not
available
at press time

RW4745
**WORCESTERSHIRE COUNTY
CRICKET CLUB**
Designer:	Elizabeth Greenshields
Modeller:	Tim Perks
Height:	10", 25.4 cm
Colour:	White
Issued:	1999
Comm. by:	Worcestershire Country Cricket Club
U.S.	$275.00
Can.	$325.00
U.K.	£150.00

Note: Issued to celebrate 100 years of first class cricket in Worcestershire.

RW4749
I PRAY
Modeller:	Sheila Mitchell
Height:	8 ¼", 21.0 cm
Colour:	Blue pyjamas; brown teddy bear
Issued:	2000 in a limited edition of 2,000
Series:	Children of the Future (NSPCC)
Comm. by:	Compton & Woodhouse Ltd.
U.S.	$225.00
Can.	$275.00
U.K.	£125.00

Photograph not
available
at press time

RW4754
APPLEBY FAIR
Modeller:	Tim Perks
Height:	8 ½", 21.6 cm
Colour:	Unknown
Issued:	1999
Series:	Gypsy Fairs
Comm. by:	The Guild of Specialist China & Glass Retailers
U.S.	$375.00
Can.	$450.00
U.K.	£200.00

Photograph not
available
at press time

RW4756
THE BETROTHAL
Modeller:	Maureen Halson
Height:	9 ½", 24.0 cm
Colour:	Female: Pink dress Male: Turquoise and gold
Issued:	1999 in a limited edition of 2,450
Series:	Dancing Lovers
Comm. by:	Compton & Woodhouse Ltd.
U.S.	$550.00
Can.	$675.00
U.K.	£300.00

RW4758
CELESTIA / DESTINY
Designer:	Elizabeth Greenshields
Modeller:	Richard Moore
Height:	9 ½", 24.0 cm
Colour:	1. **Celestia:** White dress; white ribbon with gold stars; gold star, crescent moon and numerals
	2. **Destiny:** Blue dress; white ribbon with gold stars; gold star, crescent moon and numerals
Issued:	1999 in a limited edition of 1,000
Series:	Millennium Collection

Name:	**Celestia**	**Destiny**
U.S.	$275.00	275.00
Can.	$325.00	325.00
U.K.	£150.00	150.00

RW4761
REFLECTION
Style Two
Modeller: John Bromley
Height: 5", 12.7 cm
Colour: White dress; pink
              ballet slippers
Issued: 1999 in a limited
              edition of 4,500
Series: Waiting in the Wings
Comm. by: Compton &
              Woodhouse Ltd.

U.S. $225.00
Can. $275.00
U.K.   £125.00

RW4765
BEST BUDDIES
Modeller: Valerie Slusar
Height: 7 ¼", 18.4 cm
Colour: Maroon, lilac, brown
              and white
Issued: 1999 in a limited edition
              of 1,000
Series: Children of the World
              (UNICEF)

U.S. $160.00
Can. $185.00
U.K.   £ 90.00

RW4767
LOVE STORY
Modeller: Martin Evans
Height: 12", 30.5 cm
Colour: Female: Brown dress
              Male: Brown trousers
Issued: 1999 in a limited
              edition of 450
Series: Signature Collection
Comm. by: Compton &
              Woodhouse Ltd.

U.S. $450.00
Can. $550.00
U.K.   £250.00

RW4768
LITTLE PRINCESS
Modeller: Valerie Slusar
Height: 6", 15.0 cm
Colour: Pale blue dress and hat;
              darker blue hat ribbon
              and shoes; doll wears
              pale pink dress
Issued: 1999 in a limited edition
              of 1,000
Series: Children of the World
              (UNICEF)

U.S. $160.00
Can. $185.00
U.K.   £ 90.00

RW4769
QUEEN ELIZABETH THE QUEEN
MOTHER
Modeller: John Bromley
Height: 9", 22.9 cm
Colour: Red
Issued: 2000 in a limited edition
              of 9,500
Comm. by: Compton &
              Woodhouse Ltd.

U.S. $375.00
Can. $450.00
U.K.   £200.00

RW4770
PURR-FECT FRIENDS
Modeller: Valerie Slusor
Height: 6", 15.0 cm
Colour: Yellow dress edged in
              white; yellow hair
              ribbon; grey kitten
Issued: 1999 in a limited edition
              of 1,000
Series: Children of the World
              (UNICEF)

U.S. $160.00
Can. $185.00
U.K.   £ 90.00

RW4771
TWO'S COMPANY
Modeller: Valerie Slusar
Height: 6', 15.0 cm
Colour: Purple, tan, white
              and black
Issued: 1999 in a limited
              edition of 1,000
Series: Children of the World
              (UNICEF)

U.S. $160.00
Can. $185.00
U.K.   £ 90.00

RW4772
I HOPE
Modeller: Sheila Mitchell
Height: 8 ¼" 21.0 cm
Colour: White dress and dove;
              auburn hair
Issued: 2000 in a limited
              edition of 5,000
Series: Children of the Future
              (RSPCC)
Comm. by: Compton &
              Woodhouse Ltd.

U.S. $225.00
Can. $275.00
U.K.   £125.00

RW4773
PRETTY IN PINK

Modeller:	Valerie Slusar
Height:	7 ¼", 18.4 cm
Colour:	Pink dress with white frills; pink hair ribbon; brown basket and shoes
Issued:	1999 in a limited edition of 1,000
Series:	Children of the World (UNICEF)
U.S.	$160.00
Can.	$185.00
U.K.	£ 90.00

RW4774
QUEEN ELIZABETH II
Style Two

Modeller:	Richard Moore
Height:	10", 25.4 cm
Colour:	Cream gown; purple cloak trimmed with ermine and decorated with gold
Issued:	1999 in a limited edition of 4,500
Comm. by:	Compton & Woodhouse
U.S.	—
Can.	—
U.K.	£245.00

RW4776
PIGGYBACK RIDE

Modeller:	Valerie Slusor
Height:	7", 17.8 cm
Colour:	White T-shirt; blue dungarees; purple shoe; golden brown teddy bear
Issued:	1999 in a limited edition of 1,000
Series:	Children of the World (UNICEF)
U.S.	$160.00
Can.	$185.00
U.K.	£ 90.00

RW4777
MOTHER AND CHILD 2000

Modeller:	Maureen Halson
Height:	8 ¾", 22.2 cm
Colour:	Pale blue
Issued:	1999 in a limited edition of 5,000
Varieties:	RW4589 First Kiss
Series:	Tender Moments
Comm. by:	Compton & Woodhouse Ltd.
U.S.	$175.00
Can.	$200.00
U.K.	£100.00

RW4778
ANNIVERSARY 2000

Modeller:	John Bromley
Height:	8 ½", 21.6 cm
Colour:	White dress; bouquet of red roses
Issued:	2000-2000
Series:	Anniversary of the Year Figurine
Comm. by:	Compton & Woodhouse Ltd.
U.S.	$325.00
Can.	$400.00
U.K.	£175.00

RW4779
HANNAH
Style Two

Modeller:	John Bromley
Height:	8 ½", 21.6 cm
Colour:	Tinted lustre dress; blonde hair; silver-plated purse
Issued:	2000-2000
Series:	Figurine of the Year
Comm. by:	Compton & Woodhouse Ltd.
U.S.	$325.00
Can.	$400.00
U.K.	£175.00

RW4780
'CHARIS' (Night-Bust)

Modeller:	Arnold Machin
Height:	10", 25.4 cm
Colour:	White
Issued:	2002
Comm. by:	Compton & Woodhouse Ltd.
U.S.	$500.00
Can.	$600.00
U.K.	£275.00

RW4791A
CHEETAH, Style Two

Modeller:	John Bromley
Height:	4", 10.1 cm
Colour:	Naturalistically coloured; bronze collar with gold cross
Issued:	2000 in a limited edition of 500
Series:	The Jewels of Cleopatra
Comm. by:	Compton & Woodhouse Ltd.
U.S.	$325.00
Can.	$400.00
U.K.	£175.00
Note:	Sold as a complete set with RW4791B, C and D.

RW4791B
CLEOPATRA
Modeller:	John Bromley
Height:	9", 22.9 cm
Colour:	White, red, blue, gold and terracotta
Issued:	2000 in a limited edition of 500
Series:	The Jewels of Cleopatra
Comm. by:	Compton & Woodhouse Ltd.
U.S.	$325.00
Can.	$400.00
U.K.	£175.00

Note: Sold as a complete set with RW4791A , C and D.

RW4791C
SLAVE
Modeller:	John Bromley
Height:	5 ½", 14.0 cm
Colour:	Blue and gold headdress
Issued:	2000 in a limited edition of 500
Series:	The Jewels of Cleopatra
Comm. by:	Compton & Woodhouse Ltd.
U.S.	$325.00
Can.	$400.00
U.K.	£175.00

Note: Sold as a complete set with RW4791A , B and D

RW4791D
JEWEL BOX
Modeller:	John Bromley
Height:	2", 5.0 cm
Colour:	Terracotta; gold treasures
Issued:	2000 in a limited edition of 500
Series:	The Jewels of Cleopatra
Comm. by:	Compton & Woodhouse Ltd.
U.S.	$45.00
Can.	$55.00
U.K.	£25.00

Note: Sold as a complete set with RW4791A, B and C.

RW4795
MARGARET
Designer:	Elizabeth Greenshields
Modeller:	Richard Moore
Height:	9 ¼", 23.5 cm
Colour:	Dark green jacket; yellow skirt and hat; gold walking cane
Issued:	2000-2000
Series:	Premier Figurine of the Year
U.S.	$225.00
Can.	$275.00
U.K.	£125.00

RW4796
CHARIS (Day-Bust)
Modeller:	Arnold Machin
Height:	10", 25.4 cm
Colour:	Porcelain, glazed
Issued:	1999 in a limited edition of 500
Varieties:	P18 Day (bust)
Comm. by:	Compton & Woodhouse Ltd.
U.S.	$500.00
Can.	$600.00
U.K.	£275.00

RW4797
MILLIE
Style Two
Designer:	Elizabeth Greenshields
Modeller:	Richard Moore
Height:	9 ¼", 23.5 cm
Colour:	Red jacket with fur trim; tan skirt; tan hat with red ribbon and bow; black and white dog
Issued:	2000-2000
Series:	Collectors Club Exclusive
U.S.	$275.00
Can.	$325.00
U.K.	£150.00

RW4803
THE ANNIVERSARY WALTZ
Modeller:	Martin Evans
Height:	9 ¼", 23.5 cm
Colour:	Female: red and white Male: Light brown, blue and red
Issued:	2001 in a limited edition of 450
Comm. by:	Compton & Woodhouse Ltd.
U.S.	$375.00
Can.	$450.00
U.K.	£200.00

RW4805
ANNE
Style Two
Designer:	Elizabeth Greenshields
Modeller:	Richard Moore
Height:	6 ¼", 15.9 cm
Colour:	Lavender and mauve
Issued:	1999 to the present
Series:	Les Petites
U.S.	—
Can.	—
U.K.	£87.50

RW4806
NEW DAWN

Modeller:	Carolyn Froud
Height:	9", 22.9 cm
Colour:	White dress; dark brown hair; circlet of flowers in her hair
Issued:	2000 in a limited edition of 4,950
Comm. by:	Compton & Woodhouse Ltd.
U.S.	$275.00
Can.	$325.00
U.K.	£150.00

RW4808
GRACE KELLY

Modeller:	John Bromley
Height:	9", 22.9 cm
Colour:	White chiffon evening gown with platinum highlights
Issued:	2000 in a limited edition of 12,500
Comm. by:	Compton & Woodhouse Ltd.
U.S.	$375.00
Can.	$450.00
U.K.	£200.00

RW4809
THE SPIRIT OF THE MILLENNIUM

Modeller:	Maureen Halson
Height:	11 ½", 29.2 cm
Colour:	1. White (Wallbody) 2. White dress and shawl
Issued:	2000 in a limited edition of 950
Comm. by:	Compton & Woodhouse Ltd.
U.S.	—
Can.	—
U.K.	£295.00

RW4819
GRACEFUL MOMENT

Modeller:	John Bromley
Height:	10 ¼", 26.0 cm
Colour:	White tutu, pink ballet slippers
Issued:	2000 in a limited edition of 4,500
Series:	Waiting in the Wings
Comm. by:	Compton & Woodhouse Ltd.
U.S.	$225.00
Can.	$275.00
U.K.	£125.00

Photograph not
available
at press time

RW4821
EL CONDOR PASA
First Version

Modeller:	Kenneth Potts
Height:	9 ½", 24.0 cm
Colour:	Unknown
Issued:	2000
Series:	Japanese Thoroughbreds
Comm. by:	Barbizon
U.S.	
Can.	Extremely rare
U.K.	

RW4822
ONLY FOR YOU

Modeller:	Martin Evans
Height:	10 ¼", 26.0 cm
Colour:	Navy blue dress; red rose
Issued:	2000-2000
Series:	Event Exclusive
U.S.	$275.00
Can.	$325.00
U.K.	£150.00

RW4823
MARIA

Modeller:	Maureen Halson
Height:	13", 33.0 cm
Colour:	White, blue, gold and red
Issued:	2000 in a limited edition of 450
Comm. by:	Compton & Woodhouse Ltd.
U.S.	$375.00
Can.	$450.00
U.K.	£200.00

Note: RW4824 was not issued.

RW4825
WITH ALL MY HEART

Modeller:	John Bromley
Height:	9", 22.9 cm
Colour:	Pale blue, light pink and gold
Issued:	2000 in a limited edition of 12,500
Comm. by:	Compton & Woodhouse Ltd.
U.S.	—
Can.	—
U.K.	£84.00

RW4827
QUEEN MARY I
Style Two
Modeller: Martin Evans
Height: 8 ¾", 22.2 cm
Colour: Dark and light grey,
dark and light gold,
white and red
Plinth: Wooden
Issued: 2001
Series: Queens
Comm. by: Compton &
Woodhouse Ltd.

U.S. $375.00
Can. $450.00
U.K. £200.00

Photograph not
available
at press time

RW4828
JULIET
Modeller: Maureen Halson
Height: 8 ¾", 22.2 cm
Colour: Unknown
Issued: Unknown
Series: Unknown
Comm. by: Pastimes / Retail
Variations

U.S. $225.00
Can. $275.00
U.K. £125.00

RW4830
QUEEN MOTHER
Style Two
Modeller: Martin Evans
Height: 8", 20.3 cm
Colour: Lilac, green, white,
red and grey
Issued: 2000 in a limited
edition of 500
Comm. by: Wheelers

U.S. $450.00
Can. $550.00
U.K. £250.00

RW4831
I LOVE EMILY
Modeller: Peter Holland
Height: 8", 20.3 cm
Colour: Girl: red, white, pale
yellow
Boy: Blue, white and
black
Issued: 2000 in a limited
edition of 500
Comm. by: Compton &
Woodhouse Ltd.

U.S. —
Can. —
U.K. £225.00

RW4836
THE DANCERS
Second Version
Modeller: Doris Lindner
Height: 9 ¼", 23.5 cm
Colour: Red dress; charcoal suit
Issued: 2001 in a limited edition of 500
Varieties: RW2949

U.S. $450.00
Can. $550.00
U.K. £250.00

RW4837
WITH LOVE
Style Two
Modeller: Richard Moore
Height: 7 ¾", 19.7 cm
Colour: White
Issued: 2000 to the present
Series: Moments Figures

U.S. —
Can. —
U.K. £43.00

RW4838
BEST DRESS
Modeller: Richard Moore
Height: 8", 20.3 cm
Colour: White
Issued: 2000-2003
Series: Moments Figures

U.S. $ 80.00
Can. $100.00
U.K. £ 45.00

Note: Produced to commemorate Royal Worcester's 250th anniversary in 2001.
A reproduction of Doris Lindner's 'Dancers' figurine.

RW4839
THE PRINCESS OF TARA
Modeller:	Peter Holland
Height:	8 ½", 21.6 cm
Colour:	Hunter green gown and robe; gold highlights; red sash
Issued:	2000 in a limited edition of 7,500
Series:	Celtic Kingdom
Comm. by:	Compton & Woodhouse Ltd.

U.S.	—
Can.	—
U.K.	£198.00

RW4840
PRETTY AS A PICTURE
Modeller:	Richard Moore
Height:	8", 20.3 cm
Colour:	White
Issued:	2000-2003
Series:	Moments Figures

U.S.	$ 80.00
Can.	$100.00
U.K.	£ 45.00

RW4841
MY PRAYER
Modeller:	Richard Moore
Height:	6", 15.0 cm
Colour:	White
Issued:	2000 to the present
Series:	Moments Figures

U.S.	—
Can.	—
U.K.	£43.00

RW4842
GOODNIGHT / AND SO TO BED (Style One)
Modeller:	Richard Moore	
Height:	7 ½", 19.1 cm	
Colour:	1. **Goodnight:** White	
	2. **And So To Bed:** Pink dressing gown, white nightgown and brown bear	
Issued:	1. **Goodnight:** 2000-2004	
	2. **And So To Bed:** 2001	
Series:	1. **Goodnight:** Moments Figures	
	2. **And So To Bed:** Charity Figurine of the Year 2001	
Comm. by:	2. **And So To Bed:** Compton & Woodhouse Ltd.	

Name:	Goodnight	And So To Bed
U.S.	$ —	160.00
Can.	$ —	185.00
U.K.	£46.00	90.00

RW4843
BIRTHDAY GIRL
Style Two
Modeller:	Richard Moore
Height:	7 ½", 19.1 cm
Colour:	White
Issued:	2000 to the present
Series:	Moments Figures

U.S.	—
Can.	—
U.K.	£46.00

RW4844
AUDREY HEPBURN
Modeller:	John Bromley
Height:	9", 22.9 cm
Colour:	Fuchsia gown with black design
Issued:	2000 in a limited edition of 12,500
Comm. by:	Compton & Woodhouse Ltd.

U.S.	$375.00
Can.	$450.00
U.K.	£200.00

RW4847A
RAMESES

Designer:	Shirley Curzon
Modeller:	John Wincentzen
Height:	9 ½", 24.0 cm
Colour:	Blue, red, gold, white, terracotta and black
Plinth:	Wooden
Issued:	2001 in a limited edition of 500
Series:	The Lion of Rameses
Comm. by:	Compton & Woodhouse Ltd.
U.S.	$275.00
Can.	$325.00
U.K.	£150.00

Note: Issued as a set with RW4847B and C.

RW4847B
NEFERTARI

Designer:	Shirley Curzon
Modeller:	John Wincentzen
Height:	9", 22.9 cm
Colour:	White, blue, red and gold
Issued:	2001 in a limited edition of 500
Series:	The Lion of Rameses
Comm. by:	Compton & Woodhouse Ltd.
U.S.	$275.00
Can.	$325.00
U.K.	£150.00

Note: Issued as a set with RW4847A and C.

RW4847C
MUSICIAN

Designer:	Shirley Curzon
Modeller:	John Wincentzen
Height:	5 ½", 14.0 cm
Colour:	Blue, gold and white
Issued:	2001 in a limited edition of 500
Series:	The Lion of Rameses
Comm. by:	Compton & Woodhouse Ltd.
U.S.	$275.00
Can.	$325.00
U.K.	£150.00

Note: Issued as a set with RW4847A and B.

Photograph not
available
at press time

RW4850
EMPRESS OF AUSTRIA

Modeller:	Maureen Halson
Height:	9 ¼", 23.5 cm
Colour:	Cream with gold highlights
Issued:	2001
Comm. by:	Compton & Woodhouse Ltd.
U.S.	$375.00
Can.	$450.00
U.K.	£200.00

RW4851
LAUREN
Style One

Modeller:	Carolyn Froud
Height:	9", 22.9 cm
Colour:	Blue dress with gold decoration, pale blue feather boa
Issued:	2001-2001
Series:	Figurine of the Year
Comm. by:	Compton & Woodhouse Ltd.
U.S.	$325.00
Can.	$400.00
U.K.	£175.00

RW4852
A GOLDEN MOMENT

Modeller:	Martin Evans
Height:	9 ¼", 23.5 cm
Colour:	Golden yellow dress with gold highlights; purple roses
Issued:	2001-2001
Series:	Anniversary Figurine of the Year
Comm. by:	Compton & Woodhouse Ltd.
U.S.	$325.00
Can.	$400.00
U.K.	£175.00

RW4860
HAND MAIDEN WITH LYRE

Modeller:	John Wincentzen
Height:	5 ¾", 14.6 cm
Colour:	Unknown
Issued:	Unknown
Comm. by:	Compton & Woodhouse Ltd.
U.S.	$175.00
Can.	$200.00
U.K.	£100.00

Photograph not
available
at press time

RW4861
MUCHA ROSE
Style One
Modeller:	Peter Holland
Height:	10 ½", 26.7 cm
Colour:	Unknown
Issued:	Unknown
Series:	Unknown
Comm. by:	Pastimes / Retail Variations

U.S.	$125.00
Can.	$150.00
U.K.	£ 70.00

RW4862
ROYAL WORCESTER 250TH ANNIVERSARY FIGURINE (The)
Designer:	Carolyn Froud
Modeller:	Maureen Halson
Height:	10 ½" x 13" x 11 ½", 26.7 x 33.0 x 29.2 cm
Colour:	Lady: Red, white, and pink Maid: Blue and white
Issued:	2001 in a limited edition of 250
Series:	The Official Royal Worcester 250th Anniversary
Comm. by:	Compton & Woodhouse Ltd.

U.S.	—
Can.	—
U.K.	£995.00

Photograph not
available
at press time

RW4864
ROSALIND
Style Two
Modeller:	Peter Holland
Height:	8 ½", 21.6 cm
Colour:	Unknown
Issued:	Unknown
Series:	Unknown
Comm. by:	Pastimes / Retail Variations

U.S.	$55.00
Can.	$65.00
U.K.	£30.00

RW4865
SEASONS OF ROMANCE
Modeller:	Martin Evans
Height:	10", 25.4 cm
Colour:	1. Green, white, blue, yellow and pink
	2. White and gold
Issued:	1. 2001 in a limited edition of 7,000
	2. 2002 in a limited edition of 500
Comm. by:	Compton & Woodhouse Ltd.

	Coloured	White
U.S.	$375.00	225.00
Can.	$450.00	275.00
U.K.	£200.00	125.00

Photograph not
available
at press time

RW4869
EL CONDOR PASA
Second Version
Modeller:	Kenneth Potts
Height:	9 ½", 24.0 cm
Colour:	Unknown
Issued:	2000
Series:	Japanese Thoroughbreds
Comm. by:	Barbizon

U.S.	
Can.	Extremely rare
U.K.	

RW4870
A KISS SO TENDER
Modeller:	Maureen Halson
Height:	9 ¼", 23.5 cm
Colour:	White (Wallbody)
Issued:	2001 in a limited edition of 7,500
Comm. by:	Compton & Woodhouse Ltd.

U.S.	$175.00
Can.	$200.00
U.K.	£100.00

RW4871
THE WILLOW PRINCESS
Modeller:	Peter Holland
Height:	11", 27.9 cm
Colour:	Green, white, pink, light blue, blue and gold
Issued:	2001 in a limited edition of 2,450
Comm. by:	Compton & Woodhouse Ltd.

U.S.	—
Can.	—
U.K.	£550.00

RW4872
SWEET DREAMS
Style Two
Modeller: Richard Moore
Height: 7 ¼", 18.4 cm
Colour: White
Issued: 2001-2001
Series: Collectors' Club
Complimentary Gift

U.S. $ 80.00
Can. $100.00
U.K. £ 45.00

RW4873
ISABELLA
Style Two
Designer: Elizabeth Greenshields
Modeller: Richard Moore
Height: 9 ½", 24.0 cm
Colour: Damask-rose dress;
platinum highlights
Issued: 2001-2001
Series: Premiere Figurine of the
Year

U.S. $ 825.00
Can. $1,000.00
U.K. £ 450.00

RW4874
PENELOPE
Style Two
Modeller: Richard Moore
Height: 9 ¾", 24.7 cm
Colour: Dusty blue dress; dark
green jacket; white and
green luggage with
gold highlights
Issued: 2001-2001
Series: Collectors Club
Exclusive

U.S. $275.00
Can. $325.00
U.K. £150.00

RW4875
ROSE MARIE
Modeller: Peter Holland
Height: 8 ¾", 22.2 cm
Colour: Purple dress and
shawl; pink rose;
platinum highlights
Issued: 2001-2001
Series: Event Exclusive

U.S. $225.00
Can. $275.00
U.K. £125.00

RW4876
JILL
Modeller: Carolyn Froud
Height: 8", 20.3 cm
Colour: Black dress with
platinum highlights
Issued: 2001 to the present
Series: Summer Romance

U.S. —
Can. —
U.K. £115.00

RW4877
AMANDA
Style Two
Modeller: Peter Holland
Height: 8 ¾", 22.2 cm
Colour: Dusty blue dress with
gold highlights
Issued: 2001 to the present
Series: Summer Romance

U.S. —
Can. —
U.K. £115.00

RW4879
JENNY
Modeller: Tim Perks
Height: 6 ¾", 17.2 cm
Colour: Blue dress with gold
highlights
Issued: 2001 to the present
Series: Les Petites

U.S. —
Can. —
U.K. £87.50

RW4880
PAULINE / LUCY (Style Two)
Modeller: Tim Perks
Height: 6 ¾", 17.2 cm
Colour: **Pauline:** Pale yellow
dress; peach shawl
Lucy: Black dress; pale
yellow shawl
Issued: **Pauline:** 2001 to the
present
Lucy: 2002 to the
present
Series: Les Petites

U.S. —
Can. —
U.K. £87.50

RW4881
SISTERLY LOVE
Modeller:	Richard Moore
Height:	7 ¼", 18.4 cm
Colour:	White
Issued:	2001 to the present
Series:	Moments Figures
U.S.	—
Can.	—
U.K.	£60.00

RW4882
SPECIAL GIFT
Modeller:	Richard Moore
Height:	7 ½", 19.1 cm
Colour:	White
Issued:	2001 to the present
Series:	Moments Figures
U.S.	—
Can.	—
U.K.	£46.00

Note: RW4887 was not issued.

RW4888
MY LITTLE BROTHER
Modeller:	Richard Moore
Height:	7 ¼", 18.4 cm
Colour:	White
Issued:	2001-2003
Series:	Moments Figures
U.S.	—
Can.	—
U.K.	£60.00

RW4889
TITANIA, THE QUEEN OF THE FAIRIES
Style One
Modeller:	Peter Holland
Height:	10 ½", 26.7 cm
Colour:	Lilac, gold, white, pink, purple and blue
Issued:	2000 in a limited edition of 2,450
Comm. by:	Compton & Woodhouse Ltd.
U.S.	—
Can.	—
U.K.	£395.00

RW4890
BEDTIME (Style Two) / AND SO TO BED (Style Two)
Modeller:	Richard Moore
Height:	7 ½", 19.1 cm
Colour:	1. **Bedtime:** White
	2. **And So To Bed:** Light blue, white and brown
Issued:	1. **Bedtime:** 2001-2004
	2. **And So To Bed:** 2001
Series:	1. **Bedtime:** Moments Figures
	2. **And So To Bed:** NSPC Charity Figure of the Year 2001
Comm. by:	**And So To Bed:** Compton & Woodhouse Ltd.

Name:	Bedtime	And So To Bed
U.S.	—	160.00
Can.	—	185.00
U.K.	£46.00	90.00

Note: RW4894 to RW4901 not issued.

RW4903
THE CHALICE OF LOVE
Modeller:	Peter Holland
Height:	9 ¼", 23.5 cm
Colour:	Blue gown, gold and red highlights; gold chalice
Issued:	2001 in a limited edition of 7,500
Series:	Celtic Kingdom
Comm. by:	Compton & Woodhouse Ltd.
U.S.	—
Can.	—
U.K.	£198.00

RW4904
ANNIVERSARY BALL
Modeller:	Maureen Halson
Height:	9 ½", 24.0 cm
Colour:	Pale blue dress, gold highlights
Issued:	2002-2002
Series:	Anniversary Figurine of the Year
Comm. by:	Compton & Woodhouse Ltd.
U.S.	$325.00
Can.	$400.00
U.K.	£175.00

257

RW4911
BLUEBELL TIME
Modeller: Carolyn Froud
Size: 9" x 9" x 7 ½",
22.9 x 22.9 x 19.1 cm
Colour: Pale blue, brown,
black, white, yellow
and green
Issued: 2001 in a limited
edition of 450
Comm. by: Compton &
Woodhouse Ltd.
U.S. $750.00
Can. $900.00
U.K. £400.00

Photograph not
available
at press time

RW4916
TITANIA 'QUEEN OF THE FAIRIES'
Style Two
Modeller: Tim Perks
Height: 9", 22.9 cm
Colour: Unknown
Issued: 2001
U.S. $550.00
Can. $675.00
U.K. £300.00

RW4917
KEEPSAKE
Modeller: John Bromley
Height: 9", 22.9 cm
Colour: Green dress; red
roses; gold highlights
Issued: 2001 in a limited
edition of 12,500
Comm. by: Compton &
Woodhouse Ltd.
U.S. $225.00
Can. $275.00
U.K. £125.00

RW4918
FELICITY
Style Two
Modeller: Richard Moore
Height: 6 ¼", 15.9 cm
Colour: Red dress; black hat,
gloves and shirt
Issued: 2001 to the present
Series: Les Petites
U.S. —
Can. —
U.K. £87.50

RW4919
SCARLETT
Modeller: Peter Holand
Height: 9 ¼", 23.5 cm
Colour: Red and white dress;
gold highlights
Issued: 2001 in a limited
edition of 1,000
Series: Southern Belles
U.S. $325.00
Can. $400.00
U.K. £175.00

RW4922
CHARLOTTE
Style Two
Modeller: Peter Holland
Height: 9", 22.9 cm
Colour: Dark purple dress;
pink underskirt;
gold highlights
Issued: 2002-2002
Series: Figurine of the Year
Comm. by: Compton &
Woodhouse Ltd.
U.S. $225.00
Can. $275.00
U.K. £125.00

RW4924
QUEEN ELIZABETH II
Style Three
Modeller: Richard Moore
Height: 10", 25.4 cm
Colour: White, blue, red
and gold
Issued: 2002 in a limited
edition of 1,000
U.S. $450.00
Can. $550.00
U.K. £250.00

Photograph not
available
at press time

RW4927
PRINCE REGENT PAVILLION
Modeller: Andrew Henshaw
Height: 4 ¼", 10.8 cm
Colour: Unknown
Issued: Unknown
Series: Unknown
Comm. by: Unknown
U.S. Information
Can. Not
U.K. Available

RW4928
THE ELIZABETH EMANUEL BLACK GOWN
Designer: Elizabeth Emanuel
Modeller: John Bromley
Height: 9 ½", 24.0 cm
Colour: Black, silver and platinum
Issued: 2001 in a limited edition of 7,500
Comm. by: Compton & Woodhouse Ltd.

U.S. —
Can. —
U.K. £189.00

RW4929
MELANIE
Style Two
Modeller: Peter Holland
Height: 9 ¼", 23.5 cm
Colour: Green dress; pink flowers; white gloves
Issued: 2001 in a limited edition of 1,000
Series: Southern Belles

U.S. —
Can. —
U.K. £170.00

RW4930
LARA
Modeller: Richard Moore
Height: 6 ¼", 15.9 cm
Colour: Green dress; brown hat
Issued: 2001 to the present
Series: Les Petites

U.S. —
Can. —
U.K. £87.50

RW4931
THE FAIR MAIDEN OF ASTOLAT
Modeller: Peter Holland
Height: 9", 22.9 cm
Colour: Red gown with gold highlights
Issued: 2001 in a limited edition of 7,500
Series: Celtic Kingdom
Comm. by: Compton & Woodhouse Ltd.

U.S. —
Can. —
U.K. £198.00

RW4932
ART DECO FIGURINE
Modeller: Martin Evans
Height: 10 ¾", 27.8 cm
Colour: Blue, green, orange with gold highlights
Issued: 2002 in a limited edition of 1,000

U.S. $450.00
Can. $550.00
U.K. £250.00

RW4933
THE ORDER OF THE GARTER
Modeller: Martin Evans
Height: 10", 25.4 cm
Colour: White, blue, red and gold
Issued: 2002 in a limited edition of 4,500
Comm. by: Compton & Woodhouse Ltd.

U.S. —
Can. —
U.K. £245.00

RW4936
FATHER CHRISTMAS
Modeller: Scott Thomas
Height: 9", 22.9 cm
Colour: Red, white and black
Issued: 2001 to the present
Comm. by: Compton & Woodhouse Ltd.

U.S. —
Can. —
U.K. £195.00

RW4937
QUEEN ELIZABETH THE QUEEN MOTHER IN HER CORONATION ROBES
Modeller: Tim Potts
Height: 9", 22.9 cm
Colour: Cream, purple, white and gold highlights
Issued: 2002 in a limited edition of 4,500
Comm. by: Compton & Woodhouse Ltd.

U.S. —
Can. —
U.K. £285.00

RW4939
FRUIT SELLER AT CAMBRIDGE FAIR
Modeller:	Tim Perks
Height:	8 ¼", 21.0 cm
Colour:	Brown, purple, red, blue and gold
Issued:	2001 in a limited edition of 500
Series:	Gypsy Fairs
Comm. by:	The Guild of Specialist China and Glass Retailers
U.S.	$375.00
Can.	$450.00
U.K.	£200.00

RW4944
MIDNIGHT ENCOUNTER
Modeller:	Carolyn Froud
Height:	9", 22.9 cm
Colour:	Blue gown, light blue underskirt; gold accessories
Issued:	2002-2002
Series:	'New Years Eve 2001'
Comm. by:	Compton & Woodhouse Ltd.
U.S.	$325.00
Can.	$400.00
U.K.	£175.00

RW4947
COUNTRY DIARY OF AN EDWARDIAN LADY
Modeller:	Maureen Halson
Height:	8 ½", 21.6 cm
Colour:	Pink dress with red roses and white trim; cream hat with red rose
Issued:	2002 in a limited edition of 2,450
Comm. by:	Compton & Woodhouse Ltd.
U.S.	$450.00
Can.	$550.00
U.K.	£250.00

RW4952
CHLOE
Style Two
Designer:	Elizabeth Greenshields
Modeller:	Richard Moore
Height:	9", 22.9 cm
Colour:	Sky blue dress; blue jacket and hat
Issued:	2002-2002
Series:	Collectors Club Exclusive
U.S.	$275.00
Can.	$325.00
U.K.	£150.00

RW4953
CLEOPATRA 'QUEEN OF KINGS'
Modeller:	Tim Potts
Height:	13", 33.0 cm
Colour:	White, blue, gold and ivory
Issued:	2002 in a limited edition of 500
Comm. by:	Compton & Woodhouse Ltd.
U.S.	—
Can.	—
U.K.	£696.00

RW4955
DIANA
Style Three
Designer:	Elizabeth Greenshields
Modeller:	Richard Moore
Height:	8 ½", 21.6 cm
Colour:	Ruby red dress and hat; black gloves, purse and shawl; platinum highlights
Issued:	2002-2002
Series:	Premier Figurine of the Year
U.S.	$275.00
Can.	$325.00
U.K.	£150.00

RW4956
YOU'RE A STAR
Modeller:	Richard Moore
Height:	7 ¼", 18.4 cm
Colour:	White
Issued:	2002-2002
Series:	Collectors Club Gift
U.S.	$ 80.00
Can.	$100.00
U.K.	£ 45.00

RW4957
SPIRIT OF BEAUTY
Modeller:	Carolyn Froud
Height:	9 ½", 24.0 cm
Colour:	1. Cream (Wallbody) 2. Cobalt blue and gold
Issued:	1. 2002 Ltd. Ed. 1,550 2. 2003 Ltd. Ed. 450
Comm. by:	Compton & Woodhouse Ltd.
U.S.	—
Can.	—
U.K.	£245.00

RW4958
ROSE SELLER
Modeller:	Tim Perks
Height:	8 ½", 21.6 cm
Colour:	Deep red skirt, black bodice, white apron
Issued:	2002-2004
Series:	Street Sellers
U.S.	$285.00
Can.	$350.00
U.K.	£155.00

RW4961
LAVENDER SELLER
Modeller:	Tim Perks
Height:	8 ¼", 21.0 cm
Colour:	Light and dark green dress, purple shawl
Issued:	2002-2004
Series:	Street Sellers
U.S.	$285.00
Can.	$350.00
U.K.	£155.00

RW4962
TENDER LOVE
Modeller:	Richard Moore
Height:	9 ½", 24.0 cm
Colour:	White
Issued:	2002 to the present
Series:	Moments Figures
U.S.	$130.00
Can.	$155.00
U.K.	£ 70.00

RW4965
OLIVIA
Style Three
Modeller:	John Bromley
Height:	8 ¾", 22.2 cm
Colour:	Hunter green
Issued:	2002 in a limited edition of 4,950
Series:	The Jubilee Special Edition
Varieties:	Also known as Serena RW4681
Comm. by:	Compton & Woodhouse Ltd.
U.S.	—
Can.	—
U.K.	£189.00

RW4966
APPLE SELLER
Modeller:	Tim Perks
Height:	8 ½", 21.6 cm
Colour:	Red and tan dress with gold highlights
Issued:	2002-2004
Series:	Street Sellers
U.S.	$285.00
Can.	$350.00
U.K.	£155.00

RW4967
THE MAIDEN OF DANA
Modeller:	Peter Holland
Height:	9", 22.9 cm
Colour:	Royal blue, cream, gold, red and light blue
Issued:	2002 in a limited edition of 7,500
Series:	Celtic Kingdom
Comm. by:	Compton & Woodhouse Ltd.
U.S.	—
Can.	—
U.K.	£198.00

Photograph not available at press time

RW4968
QUEEN ELIZABETH ON CORONATION THRONE
Modeller:	Maureen Halson
Height:	9", 22.9 cm
Colour:	Unknown
Issued:	2001 in a limited edition of 500
Comm. by:	The Guild of Specialist China and Glass Retailer
U.S.	$475.00
Can.	$550.00
U.K.	£250.00

RW4969
CHERRY SELLER
Modeller:	Tim Perks
Height:	8 ½", 21.6 cm
Colour:	Dark blue and cream dress, gold highlights
Issued:	2002-2004
Series:	Street Sellers
U.S.	$285.00
Can.	$350.00
U.K.	£155.00

RW4970
HAPPY ANNIVERSARY / BRIDE AND GROOM
Modeller: Richard Moore
Height: 10 ¼", 26.0 cm
Colour: White
Issued: 1. Happy Anniversary: 2002–2003
2. Bride and Groom: 2003-2003
Series: Moments Figures

U.S. $165.00
Can. $200.00
U.K. £ 90.00

RW4973
LADY OF SHERWOOD
Modeller: Peter Holland
Height: 9", 22.9 cm
Colour: Pale blue, cream, navy, and white with gold highlights
Issued: 2002 in a limited edition of 7,500
Comm. by: Compton & Woodhouse Ltd.

U.S. —
Can. —
U.K. £198.00

RW4974
A SUCCESSFUL DAY AT THE DERBY (ROSE-MARIE)
Modeller: Tim Perks
Height: 6 ½", 16.5 cm
Colour: Red, brown, white, green, pale yellow and blue
Issued: 2002 in a limited edition of 500
Comm. by: Peter Jones (Exclusive)

U.S. —
Can. —
U.K. £250.00

RW4982
CELESTINE
Modeller: Peter Holland
Height: 9 ½", 24.0 cm
Colour: Red, black, red and cream bodice; black stockings, gloves and top hat
Issued: 2002 in a limited edition of 7,500
Comm. by: Compton & Woodhouse Ltd.

U.S. —
Can. —
U.K. £198.00

RW4983
FORTY WINKS
Modeller: Peter Holland
Height: 5 ½", 14.0 cm
Colour: Blue skirt; white jumper; brown desk; tan school bag
Issued: 2002 in a limited edition of 5,000
Series: Great Ormond Street Hospital
Comm. by: Compton & Woodhouse Ltd.

U.S. —
Can. —
U.K. £150.00

RW4986
SUMMER SOLSTICE
Modeller: Pauline Parsons
Height: 9 ¾", 24.7 cm
Colour: 1. White (Wallbody)
2. White, red and yellow with gold highlights
Issued: 2002
Comm. by: Compton & Woodhouse Ltd.

U.S. $375.00
Can. $450.00
U.K. £200.00

RW4988
CATHERINE
Style Two
Modeller: Peter Holland
Height: 9 ½", 24.0 cm
Colour: Silver, white and red
Issued: 2003-2003
Series: Anniversary Figurine of the Year
Comm. by: Compton & Woodhouse Ltd.

U.S. $325.00
Can. $400.00
U.K. £175.00

RW4989
DEVOTION
Modeller: Richard Moore
Height: 11 ½", 29.2 cm
Colour: 1. Pale pink and blue
2. White
Issued: 1. 2003 in a limited edition of 250
2. 2003-2004
Series: 1. Living Sculptures
2. Silhouette

	Coloured	White
U.S.	—	450.00
Can.	—	550.00
U.K.	£300.00	250.00

RW4990
VIVIEN

Modeller:	Neil Welch
Height:	8 ¾", 22.2 cm
Colour:	Green, pink, white and black
Issued:	2002 in a limited edition of 1,000
Series:	Southern Belles
U.S.	—
Can.	—
U.K.	£170.00

RW4992
HARMONY

Modeller:	Richard Moore	
Height:	11 ½", 29.2 cm	
Colour:	1. Metallic blue and light blue	
	2. White	
Issued:	1. 2003 in a limited edition of 250	
	2. 2003-2004	
Series:	1. Living Sculptures	
	2. Silhouette	

	Coloured	White
U.S.	—	450.00
Can.	—	550.00
U.K.	£300.00	250.00

RW4993
REFLECTION
Style Three

Modeller:	Richard Moore	
Height:	11", 27.9 cm	
Colour:	1. Metallic green	
	2. White	
Issued:	1. 2003 in a limited edition of 250	
	2. 2003-2004	
Series:	1, Living Sculptures	
	2. Silhouette	

	Coloured	White
U.S.	—	325.00
Can.	—	400.00
U.K.	£250.00	175.00

RW4996
DESIRE

Modeller:	Richard Moore	
Height:	11 ½", 29.2 cm	
Colour:	1. Metallic blue	
	2. White	
Issued:	1. 2003 in a limited edition of 250	
	2. 2003-2004	
Series:	1. Living Sculptures	
	2. Silhouette	

	Coloured	White
U.S.	—	325.00
Can.	—	400.00
U.K.	£250.00	175.00

RW4997
GEORGIA

Modeller:	Neil Welch
Height:	8 ¾", 22.2 cm
Colour:	Blue with gold highlights
Issued:	2002 in a limited edition of 1,000
Series:	Southern Belles
U.S.	—
Can.	—
U.K.	£170.00

RW4998
FANTASY

Modeller:	Richard Moore	
Height:	9 ½", 24.0 cm	
Colour:	1. Metallic brown	
	2. White	
Issued:	1. 2003 in a limited edition of 250	
	2. 2003-2004	
Series:	1. Living Sculptures	
	2. Silhouette	

	Coloured	White
U.S.	—	350.00
Can.	—	425.00
U.K.	£260.00	185.00

RW4999
ETERNAL LOVE

Modeller:	Richard Moore	
Height:	12", 30.5 cm	
Colour:	1. Metallic brown	
	2. White	
Issued:	1. 2003 in a limited edition of 250	
	2. 2003-2004	
Series:	1. Living Sculptures	
	2. Silhouette	

	Coloured	White
U.S.	—	450.00
Can.	—	550.00
U.K.	£300.00	250.00

RW5001
PASSION

Modeller:	Richard Moore	
Height:	6 ¾", 17.2 cm	
Colour:	1. Metallic pale blue	
	2. White	
Issued:	1. 2003 in a limited edition of 250	
	2. 2003-2004	
Series:	1. Living Sculptures	
	2. Silhouette	

	Coloured	White
U.S.	—	275.00
Can.	—	325.00
U.K.	£225.00	150.00

RW5002
GOLDEN GIRL OF THE MAY
Modeller: Peter Holland
Height: 8 ¾", 22.2 cm
Colour: Green gown with gold design
Issued: 2003 in a limited edition of 7,500
Series: Celtic Kingdom
Comm. by: Compton & Woodhouse Ltd.

U.S. —
Can. —
U.K. £198.00

RW5004
ELATION
Modeller: Richard Moore
Height: 13", 33.0 cm
Colour: 1. Metallic brown
2. White
Issued: 1. 2003 in a limited edition of 250
2. 2003-2004
Series: 1. Living Sculptures
2. Silhouette

	Coloured	White
U.S.	—	350.00
Can.	—	425.00
U.K.	£260.00	185.00

RW5006
SWEET CHILD OF MINE (Bust)
Modeller: Peter Holland
Height: 9 ½", 24.0 cm
Colour: White (Wallbody)
Issued: 2002 in a limited edition of 2,450
Comm. by: Compton & Woodhouse Ltd.

U.S. —
Can. —
U.K. £195.00

RW5007
QUEEN ANNE
Style Two
Modeller: Martin Evans
Height: 9", 22.9 cm
Colour: Red, cream, blue, gold highlights
Issued: 2003 in a limited edition of 4,500
Comm. by: Compton & Woodhouse Ltd.

U.S. —
Can. —
U.K. £245.00

RW5010
ZOE
Modeller: Neil Welch
Height: 9 ½", 24.0 cm
Colour: Red dress with gold design; burgundy shawl
Issued: 2003-2003
Series: Figurine of the Year
Comm. by: Compton & Woodhouse Ltd.

U.S. $375.00
Can. $450.00
U.K. £200.00

RW5011
'CAN I COME TOO ...?'
Modeller: Peter Holland
Height: 7", 17.8 cm
Colour: Grey school uniform, white shirt; brown and white dog
Issued: 2002 Ltd. edition of 5,000
Series: Great Ormond Street Hospital
Comm. by: Compton & Woodhouse Ltd.

U.S. —
Can. —
U.K. £150.00

RW5013
FRUIT SELLER AT STOW FAIR
Modeller: Martin Evans
Height: 9", 22.9 cm
Colour: Mother: Blue skirt, white blouse, green vest and red shawl
Daughter: Green skirt, white blouse and apron and red shawl
Issued: 2003 in a limited edition of 500
Series: Gypsy Fairs
Comm. by: The Guild of Specialist China and Glass Retailers

U.S. —
Can. —
U.K. £395.00

RW5015
CORONATION BALL, 'CHRISTINA'
Modeller:	Carolyn Froud
Height:	9 ½", 24.0 cm
Colour:	White dress, gold highlights; red rose
Issued:	2003 in a limited edition of 7,500
Comm. by:	Compton & Woodhouse Ltd.
U.S.	—
Can.	—
U.K.	£198.00

RW5016
HER REGAL MAJESTY
Modeller:	Martin Evans
Height:	8 ¾", 22.2
Colour:	White gown; blue sash
Issued:	2002 in a limited edition of 4,950
Comm. by:	Compton & Woodhouse Ltd.
U.S.	$375.00
Can.	$450.00
U.K.	£200.00

RW5017
ELEANOR
Style Two
Designer:	Elizabeth Greenshields
Modeller:	Richard Moore
Height:	9", 22.9 cm
Colour:	Blue dress with white detail
Issued:	2003-2003
Series:	Premiere Figurine of the Year
U.S.	$275.00
Can.	$325.00
U.K.	£150.00

RW5018
MUCHA ROSE
Style Two
Modeller:	Martin Evans
Height:	9 ¼", 23.5 cm
Colour:	Pink and green
Issued:	2002 in a limited edition of 500
Comm. by:	Past Times / Retail Variations
U.S.	—
Can.	—
U.K.	£ 70.00

RW5019
GYPSY PRINCESS
Modeller:	Peter Holland
Height:	10 ½", 26.7 cm
Colour:	Red, white and blue; gold highlights
Issued:	2003 in a limited edition of 7,500
Comm. by:	Compton & Woodhouse Ltd.
U.S.	—
Can.	—
U.K.	£225.00

RW5020
LAUREN
Style Two
Designer:	Elizabeth Greenshields
Modeller:	Neil Welch
Height:	8 ¾", 22.2 cm
Colour:	Caramel gown, butterscotch bodice and underskirt
Issued:	2003-2003
Series:	Collectors Club Exclusive
U.S.	$275.00
Can.	$325.00
U.K.	£150.00

RW5021
ROSE OF CAMELOT
Modeller:	Peter Holland
Height:	9 ½", 24.0 cm
Colour:	Hunter green, white, red with gold highlights
Issued:	2003 in a limited edition of 7,500
Comm. by:	Compton & Woodhouse Ltd.
U.S.	—
Can.	—
U.K.	£245.00

RW5022
PRINCESS MARGARET IN HER CORONATION ROBES
Modeller:	John Bromley
Height:	9 ½", 24.0 cm
Colour:	White, purple, and gold highlights
Issued:	2003 in a limited edition of 4,500
Comm. by:	Compton & Woodhouse Ltd.
U.S.	—
Can.	—
U.K.	£245.00

RW5023
ROSES OF LOVE
Modeller:	John Bromley
Height:	9", 22.9 cm
Colour:	White dress; red roses; gold highlights
Issued:	2004 in a limited edition of 7,500
Series:	Roses
Comm. by:	Compton & Woodhouse Ltd.
U.S.	—
Can.	—
U.K.	£195.00

RW5024
ALEXANDRA
Designer:	Elizabeth Greenshields
Modeller:	Richard Moore
Height:	8 ¾", 22.2 cm
Colour:	Red dress; black jacket, ermine furs and hat
Issued:	2004-2004
Series:	Premiere Figurine of the Year
U.S.	—
Can.	—
U.K.	£145.00

RW5025
CATHY (Withering Heights)
Modeller:	Richard Moore
Height:	8", 20.3 cm
Colour:	1. Green dress, pale yellow underskirt, red shawl
	2. As above with gold shoes and highlights
Issued:	1. 2003 to the present
	2. 2003 in a limited edition of 500
Series:	1. Ladies of Literature
	2. Special Gold Edition
Comm. by:	2. Compton & Woodhouse Ltd.

	Regular	Gold Edition
U.S.	—	—
Can.	—	—
U.K.	£165.00	175.00

RW5026
LORNA (Doone)
Modeller:	Richard Moore
Height:	8 ¾", 22.2 cm
Colour:	1. Light brown dress, brown and black cloak; gold highlights
	2. Yellow dress, brown and black cloak; gold shoes and highlights
Issued:	1. 2003 to the present
	2. 2003 in a limited edition of 500
Series:	1. Ladies of Literature
	2. Special Gold Edition
Comm. by:	2. Compton & Woodhouse Ltd.

	Regular	Gold Edition
U.S.	—	—
Can.	—	—
U.K.	£165.00	175.00

RW5027
EMMA
Modeller:	Richard Moore
Height:	6 ¼", 15.9 cm
Colour:	Pale blue dress; royal blue jacket and hat
Issued:	2004 to the present
Series:	Les Petites
U.S.	—
Can.	—
U.K.	£87.50

RW5028
MEGAN
Modeller:	Richard Moore
Height:	6 ¼", 15.9 cm
Colour:	Red dress and hat; white gloves
Issued:	2003 to the present
Series:	Les Petites
U.S.	—
Can.	—
U.K.	£87.50

RW5029
GAY GORDONS
Designer: Elizabeth Greenshields
Modeller: Martin Evans
Height: 8 ½", 21.6 cm
Colour: Blue gown with white underskirt; tartan sash
Issued: 2004-2004
Series: New Years Eve Figurine of the Year
Comm. by: Compton & Woodhouse Ltd.
U.S. $375.00
Can. $450.00
U.K. £200.00

RW5030
LUCY
Style Three
Modeller: John Bromley
Height: 8 ¾", 22.2 cm
Colour: Red dress with black lace bodice
Issued: 2004-2004
Series: Figurine of the Year
Comm. by: Compton & Woodhouse Ltd.
U.S. $375.00
Can. $450.00
U.K. £200.00

RW5031
BE MINE
Modeller: Neil Welch
Height: 8 ½", 21.6 cm
Colour: Dark purple gown
Issued: 2004 in a limited edition of 7,500
Comm. by: Compton & Woodhouse Ltd.
U.S. —
Can. —
U.K. £198.00

RW5032
DAUGHTER OF ERIN
Modeller: Peter Holland
Height: 8 ½", 21.6 cm
Colour: White, gold, blue and yellow
Issued: 2004 in a limited edition of 7,500
Series: Celtic Kingdom
Comm. by: Compton & Woodhouse Ltd.
U.S. —
Can. —
U.K. £198.00

RW5033
JAYNE
Modeller: Peter Holland
Height: 9 ½", 24.0 cm
Colour: Pale green, pale yellow, white, lilac and pink
Issued: 2004-2004
Series: Anniversary Figurine of the Year
Comm. by: Compton & Woodhouse Ltd.
U.S. $325.00
Can. $400.00
U.K. £180.00

RW5034
GYPSY GIRL AT NOTTINGHAM GOOSE FAIR
Modeller: Martin Evans
Height: 8 ¾", 22.2 cm
Colour: Red, white, navy and green
Issued: 2003 in a limited edition of 500
Series: Gypsy Fairs
Comm. by: The Guild of Specialist China and Glass Retailers
U.S. —
Can. —
U.K. £275.00

RW5035
CARMEN / AMBER
Designer: Elizabeth Greenshields
Modeller: Neil Welch
Height: 8 ¾", 22.2 cm
Colour: 1. **Carmen:** Dark red dress, gold design, black fan
2. **Amber:** Chocolate brown dress, gold design and tan fan
Issued: 1. **Carmen:** 2004 to the present
2. **Amber:** 2004 in a limited edition of 450
Series: 1. **Carmen:** Summer Romance
2. **Amber:** Special gold colourway
Comm. by: 2. **Amber:** Compton & Woodhouse Ltd.

Name	Carmen	Amber
U.S.	—	—
Can.	—	—
U.K.	£155.00	155.00

RW5038
JESSICA
Style Two
Modeller:	Jack Glynn
Height:	8 ¾", 22.2 cm
Colour:	Green, gold highlights
Issued:	2003 in a limited edition of 950
Varieties:	Also known as Olivia RW4639
Series:	Special Collectors Edition
Comm. by:	Compton & Woodhouse Ltd.
U.S.	—
Can.	—
U.K.	£115.00

RW5039
SUMMER BALL
Modeller:	Martin Evans
Height:	8 ½", 21.6 cm
Colour:	Pink butterfly dress with white trim; platinum highlights
Issued:	2004 in a limited edition of 2,950
Comm. by:	Compton & Woodhouse Ltd.
U.S.	—
Can.	—
U.K.	£198.00

RW5041
HUSH A BYE BABY
Modeller:	Peter Holland	
Height:	8 ¼", 21.0 cm	
Colour:	1.	White
	2.	Pink and blue
Issued:	1.	2003 in a limited edition of 7,005
	2.	2003 in a limited edition of 495
Comm. by:	Compton & Woodhouse Ltd.	
U.S.	—	
Can.	—	
U.K.	£189.00	

RW5043
SCOTTISH — HEATHER
Modeller:	Neil Welch
Height:	8 ½", 21.6 cm
Colour:	Purple skirt, green and purple bodice, gold highlights
Issued:	2004 to the present
Series:	Ladies of the Isles
U.S.	—
Can.	—
U.K.	£145.00

RW5044
WELSH — SIAN
Modeller:	Richard Moore
Height:	8 ¾", 22.2 cm
Colour:	Black skirt, white blouse and gloves; red shawl; gold highlights
Issued:	2004 to the present
Series:	Ladies of the Isles
U.S.	—
Can.	—
U.K.	£145.00

RW5045
IRISH — CAITLIN
Modeller:	Neil Welch
Height:	8 ¾", 22.2 cm
Colour:	Green dress, white underskirt; platinum highlights
Issued:	2004 to the present
Series:	Ladies of the Isles
U.S.	—
Can.	—
U.K.	£145.00

RW5046
ENGLISH — ROSE
Modeller:	Richard Moore
Height:	9", 22.9 cm
Colour:	Pink dress with platinum highlights
Issued:	2004 to the present
Series:	Ladies of the Isles
U.S.	—
Can.	—
U.K.	£145.00

RW5049
SWEET LADY FAIR
Modeller:	Peter Holland
Height:	9", 22.9 cm
Colour:	Female: Light blue, gold and white Male: Blue, gold, red, white and blue
Issued:	2003 in a limited edition of 950
Series:	Celtic Kingdom
Comm. by:	Compton & Woodhouse Ltd.
U.S.	—
Can.	—
U.K.	£545.00

RW5050
VENETIAN MASQUERADE
Designer:	Kathryn Russel
Modeller:	John Bromley
Height:	9", 22.9 cm
Colour:	Red, pink, white; gold highlights
Issued:	2004 in a limited edition of 7,500
Series:	Venetian Masks
Comm. by:	Compton & Woodhouse Ltd.
U.S.	—
Can.	—
U.K.	£225.00

RW5053
MOONLIGHT AND ROSES
Modeller:	John Bromley
Height:	9", 22.9 cm
Colour:	Dusty blue dress; white roses
Issued:	2004 in a limited edition of 7,500
Series:	Roses
Comm. by:	Compton & Woodhouse Ltd.
U.S.	—
Can.	—
U.K.	£195.00

RW5055
GRAND HOTEL
Modeller:	Martin Evans
Height:	8 ½", 21.6 cm
Colour:	Green dress; gold shawl
Issued:	2004 in a limited edition of 4,950
Comm. by:	Compton & Woodhouse Ltd.
U.S.	—
Can.	—
U.K.	£185.00

RW5056
QUEEN ELIZABETH I IN HER CORONATION ROBES
Modeller:	Peter Holland
Height:	9", 22.9 cm
Colour:	Gold, ermine trim; multicoloured jewels
Issued:	2004 in a limited edition of 4,500
Comm. by:	Compton & Woodhouse Ltd.
U.S.	—
Can.	—
U.K.	£265.00

RW5057
LAURA
Style Two
Modeller:	Carolyn Froud
Height:	9", 22.9 cm
Colour:	Blue dress with gold highlights
Issued:	2005-2005
Series:	Figurine of the Year
Comm. by:	Compton & Woodhouse Ltd.
U.S.	—
Can.	—
U.K.	£195.00

RW5069
SNOW QUEEN
Designer:	Shirley Curzon
Modeller:	Peter Holland
Height:	9 ½", 24.0 cm
Colour:	Metallic light blue, white and platinum highlights
Issued:	2004 in a limited edition of 7,500
Comm. By:	Compton & Woodhouse Ltd.
U.S.	—
Can.	—
U.K.	£295.00

ENCHANTED EVENINGS

RW4547
The Fairest Rose

RW4532
Queen of Hearts

RW4552
Sweetest Valentine

RW4562
Belle of the Ball, Style Two

COMPTON & WOODHOUSE LTD. RELEASES

ANNIVERSARY FIGURINE OF THE YEAR

RW4778
Anniversary 2000
2000

RW4852
A Golden Moment
2001

RW4904
Anniversary Ball
2002

RW4988
Catherine, Style Two
2003

RW5033
Jayne
2004

COMPTON & WOODHOUSE LTD. RELEASES

FIGURINE OF THE YEAR

RW4779
Hannah, Style Two
2000

RW4851
Lauren, Style One
2001

RW4922
Charlotte, Style Two
2002

RW5010
Zoe
2003

RW5030
Lucy, Style Three
2004

RW5057
Laura, Style Two
2005

COMPTON & WOODHOUSE LTD. RELEASES

VICTORIAN AND EDWARDIAN LADIES

RW4947
**The Country Diary
of an Edwardian Lady**

RW4686
Summer's Lease

RW4862
250th Anniversary of Royal Worcester, Tableau

COMPTON & WOODHOUSE LTD. RELEASES

THE GRACEFUL ARTS

RW4600
Embroidery

RW4680
Music, Style Two

RW4579
Painting

RW4708
Poetry

COMPTON & WOODHOUSE LTD. RELEASES

MOTHER AND CHILD

RW4560
Mothering Sunday

RW5041
Hush A Bye Baby

RW4622
First Smile

RW4777
Mother and Child 2000

RW4572
First Touch

COMPTON & WOODHOUSE LTD. RELEASES

CHARITY FIGURINES

RW4727
I Dream

RW4698
I Wish

RW4499
A Posy for Mother

RW4983
Forty Winks

RW4442
Lullaby

RW5011
'Can I come too...?'

COMPTON & WOODHOUSE LTD. RELEASES

THE CELTIC KINGDOM

RW4839
The Princess of Tara

RW4967
The Maiden of Dana

RW4931
The Fair Maiden of Astolat

RW4903
The Chalice of Love

RW5032
The Daughter of Erin

RW5002
The Golden Girl of the May

COMPTON & WOODHOUSE LTD. RELEASES

ANIMAL BROOCHES
AND MENU HOLDERS
EQUINE STUDIES

RW2953
FOX HOUND (Walking)
MENU HOLDER
Modeller: Doris Lindner
Height: 2 ½", 6.4 cm
Colour: White with brown markings
Issued: 1932

U.S. $325.00
Can. $400.00
U.K. £175.00

RW2954
FOX HOUND (Running)
MENU HOLDER
Modeller: Doris Lindner
Height: 2 ¾", 7.0 cm
Colour: White with brown markings
Issued: 1932

U.S. $325.00
Can. $400.00
U.K. £175.00

RW2955
FOX HOUND (Seated)
MENU HOLDER
Modeller: Doris Lindner
Height: 2 ¼", 5.7 cm
Colour: 1. Coloured
        2. White
Issued: 1932

	Coloured	White
U.S.	$325.00	325.00
Can.	$400.00	400.00
U.K.	£175.00	175.00

RW2956
FOX (Walking) MENU HOLDER
Modeller: Doris Lindner
Height: 2 ¼", 5.7 cm
Colour: Reddish-brown fox; beige menu holder
Issued: 1932

U.S. $325.00
Can. $400.00
U.K. £175.00

RW2957
FOX (Stalking) BROOCH / MENU HOLDER
Modeller: Doris Lindner
Height: 2 ½", 6.4 cm
Colour: Reddish-brown
Issued: 1932

	Brooch	Menu Holder
U.S.	$325.00	325.00
Can.	$400.00	400.00
U.K.	£175.00	175.00

RW2958
SEALYHAM TERRIER BROOCH / MENU HOLDER
Modeller: Unknown
Height: 2", 5.0 cm
Colour: Cream with reddish-brown face and ears
Issued: 1932

	Brooch	Menu Holder
U.S.	$325.00	325.00
Can.	$400.00	400.00
U.K.	£175.00	175.00

RW2959
AIREDALE TERRIER BROOCH / MENU HOLDER
Modeller: Unknown
Height: 2", 5.0 cm
Colour: Reddish-brown with black markings
Issued: 1932

	Brooch	Menu Holder
U.S.	$325.00	325.00
Can.	$400.00	400.00
U.K.	£175.00	175.00

RW2960
DANDIE DINMONT BROOCH
Modeller: Unknown
Height: 2', 5.0 cm
Colour: Grey, cream and reddish brown
Issued: 1932

U.S. $325.00
Can. $400.00
U.K. £175.00

RW2961
**COCKER SPANIEL BROOCH /
MENU HOLDER**
Modeller: Unknown
Height: 2", 5.0 cm
Colour: 1. Black
2. Liver and white
Issued: 1932

	Brooch	Menu Holder
U.S.	$325.00	325.00
Can.	$400.00	400.00
U.K.	£175.00	175.00

RW2962
**FIELD SPANIEL BROOCH / MENU
HOLDER**
Modeller: Unknown
Height: 2", 5.0 cm
Colour: Black
Issued: 1932

	Brooch	Menu Holder
U.S.	$325.00	325.00
Can.	$400.00	400.00
U.K.	£175.00	175.00

RW2963
COLLIE BROOCH
Modeller: Unknown
Height: 2", 5.0 cm
Colour: Brown and white
Issued: 1932

U.S.	$325.00
Can.	$400.00
U.K.	£175.00

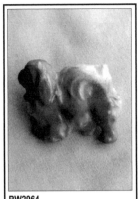

RW2964
**PEKINESE BROOCH / MENU
HOLDER**
Modeller: Unknown
Height: 2", 5.0 cm
Colour: Light reddish-brown
Issued: 1932

	Brooch	Menu Holder
U.S.	$325.00	325.00
Can.	$400.00	400.00
U.K.	£175.00	175.00

RW2965
CAIRN BROOCH
Modeller: Unknown
Height: 2 ½", 6.4 cm
Colour: Brown
Issued: 1932

U.S.	$325.00
Can.	$400.00
U.K.	£175.00

RW2966
**SETTER BROOCH / MENU
HOLDER**
Modeller: Unknown
Height: 2", 5.0 cm
Colour: Chestnut red
Issued: 1932

	Brooch	Menu Holder
U.S.	$325.00	325.00
Can.	$400.00	400.00
U.K.	£175.00	175.00

RW2967
DACHSHUND BROOCH
Modeller: Unknown
Height: 2", 5.0 cm
Colour: Reddish-brown
Issued: 1932

U.S.	$325.00
Can.	$400.00
U.K.	£175.00

Photograph not
available
at press time

RW2969
**WEST HIGHLAND TERRIER
BROOCH**
Modeller: Unknown
Height: 2", 5.0 cm
Colour: Unknown
Issued: 1932

U.S.	$325.00
Can.	$400.00
U.K.	£175.00

RW2970
WIRE-HAIRED TERRIER BROOCH
Modeller: Unknown
Height: 2", 5.0 cm
Colour: White with reddish-brown and black patches
Issued: 1932
U.S. $325.00
Can. $400.00
U.K. £175.00

RW2971
ALSATIAN BROOCH / MENU HOLDER
Modeller: Unknown
Height: 2", 5.0 cm
Colour: Brown with darker brown shading
Issued: 1932

	Brooch	Menu Holder
U.S.	$325.00	325.00
Can.	$400.00	400.00
U.K.	£175.00	175.00

RW2972
SCOTTISH TERRIER BROOCH / MENU HOLDER
Modeller: Unknown
Height: 2", 5.0 cm
Colour: White
Issued: 1932

	Brooch	Menu Holder
U.S.	$325.00	325.00
Can.	$400.00	400.00
U.K.	£175.00	175.00

RW2973
FOXHOUND BROOCH
Modeller: Frederick M. Gertner
Height: 2", 5.0 cm
Colour: Unknown
Issued: 1932
U.S. $325.00
Can. $400.00
U.K. £175.00

RW2974
CHOW BROOCH
Modeller: Unknown
Height: 2", 5.0 cm
Colour: Reddish-brown
Issued: 1932
U.S. $325.00
Can. $400.00
U.K. £175.00

RW2975
GROUSE BROOCH
Modeller: Frederick M. Gertner
Height: 2", 5.0 cm
Colour: Reddish-brown
Issued: 1932
U.S. $325.00
Can. $400.00
U.K. £175.00

RW2976
SNIPE BROOCH
Modeller: Frederick M. Gertner
Height: 2 ½", 6.4 cm
Colour: Brown and cream; green base
Issued: 1932
U.S. $325.00
Can. $400.00
U.K. £175.00

RW2977
BULLFINCH BROOCH
Modeller: Frederick M. Gertner
Height: 2", 5.0 cm
Colour: Red and black
Issued: 1932
U.S. $325.00
Can. $400.00
U.K. £175.00

RW2978
SPARROWHAWK BROOCH
Modeller:	Frederick M. Gertner
Height:	2", 5.0 cm
Colour:	Unknown
Issued:	1932
U.S.	$325.00
Can.	$400.00
U.K.	£175.00

RW2979
PARROQUET BROOCH
Modeller:	Frederick M. Gertner
Height:	2", 5.0 cm
Colour:	Unknown
Issued:	1932
U.S.	$325.00
Can.	$400.00
U.K.	£175.00

RW2980
OWL BROOCH
Modeller:	Frederick M. Gertner
Height:	2", 5.0 cm
Colour:	Unknown
Issued:	1932
U.S.	$325.00
Can.	$400.00
U.K.	£175.00

RW2981
SWALLOW BROOCH
Modeller:	Frederick M. Gertner
Height:	2", 5.0 cm
Colour:	Brown
Issued:	1932
U.S.	$325.00
Can.	$400.00
U.K.	£175.00

RW2982
ROBIN BROOCH
Modeller:	Frederick M. Gertner
Height:	2", 5.0 cm
Colour:	Brown and red
Issued:	1932
U.S.	$325.00
Can.	$400.00
U.K.	£175.00

RW2983
BLACKCOCK BROOCH
Modeller:	Frederick M. Gertner
Height:	2 ½", 6.4 cm
Colour:	Black with dark brown markings
Issued:	1932
U.S.	$325.00
Can.	$400.00
U.K.	£175.00

RW2984
QUAIL BROOCH
Modeller:	Frederick M. Gertner
Height:	1 ¾", 4.4 cm
Colour:	Brown and cream
Issued:	1932
U.S.	$325.00
Can.	$400.00
U.K.	£175.00

RW2985
WILD DUCK BROOCH
Modeller:	Frederick M. Gertner
Height:	2 ½", 6.4 cm
Colour:	Green and browns
Issued:	1932
U.S.	$325.00
Can.	$400.00
U.K.	£175.00

RW2986
WOOD PIGEON BROOCH
Modeller:	Frederick M. Gertner
Height:	2 ½", 6.4 cm
Colour:	Grey and red
Issued:	1932
U.S.	$325.00
Can.	$400.00
U.K.	£175.00

RW2987
KINGFISHER BROOCH
Modeller:	Frederick M. Gertner
Height:	2 ½", 6.4 cm
Colour:	Teal blue and dark red
Issued:	1932
U.S.	$325.00
Can.	$400.00
U.K.	£175.00

RW2988
PHEASANT BROOCH / MENU HOLDER
Modeller:	Frederick M. Gertner
Height:	2 ½", 6.4 cm
Colour:	Browns
Issued:	1932

	Brooch	Menu Holder
U.S.	$325.00	325.00
Can.	$400.00	400.00
U.K.	£175.00	175.00

RW2989
PENGUIN BROOCH
Modeller:	Frederick M. Gertner
Height:	2 ½", 6.4 cm
Colour:	Black and white with orange beak
Issued:	1932
U.S.	$325.00
Can.	$400.00
U.K.	£175.00

RW2990
WOODCOCK BROOCH
Modeller:	Frederick M. Gertner
Height:	2", 5.0 cm
Colour:	Unknown
Issued:	1932
U.S.	$325.00
Can.	$400.00
U.K.	£175.00

RW2991
JAY BROOCH
Modeller:	Frederick M. Gertner
Height:	2", 5.0 cm
Colour:	Blue
Issued:	1932
U.S.	$325.00
Can.	$400.00
U.K.	£175.00

RW2992
SEAGULL BROOCH
Modeller:	Frederick M. Gertner
Height:	2", 5.0 cm
Colour:	White
Issued:	1932
U.S.	$325.00
Can.	$400.00
U.K.	£175.00

RW2995
GOLDEN PHEASANT BROOCH
Modeller:	Possibly Frederick M. Gertner
Height:	2", 50 cm
Colour:	Browns
Issued:	1932
U.S.	$325.00
Can.	$400.00
U.K.	£175.00

RW2996
LADY AMHERST'S PHEASANT BROOCH
Modeller: Possibly Frederic M. Gertner
Height: 2", 5.0 cm
Colour: Unknown
Issued: 1932

U.S. $325.00
Can. $400.00
U.K. £175.00

RW3002
BULL TERRIER BROOCH
Modeller: Unknown
Height: 2", 5.0 cm
Colour: White
Issued: 1932

U.S. $325.00
Can. $400.00
U.K. £175.00

RW3003
BEDLINGTON TERRIER BROOCH
Modeller: Unknown
Height: 2", 5.0 cm
Colour: Unknown
Issued: 1932

U.S. $325.00
Can. $400.00
U.K. £175.00

RW3004
GREYHOUND BROOCH
Modeller: Unknown
Height: 2 ½", 6.4 cm
Colour: Tan
Issued: 1932

U.S. $325.00
Can. $400.00
U.K. £175.00

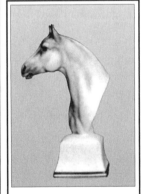

RW3005
DALMATIAN BROOCH
Modeller: Unknown
Height: 2 ½", 6.4 cm
Colour: White with black spots
Issued: 1932

U.S. $325.00
Can. $400.00
U.K. £175.00

RW3007
SPRINGER SPANIEL BROOCH
Modeller: Unknown
Height: 2", 5.0 cm
Colour: White with reddish-brown markings
Issued: 1933

U.S. $325.00
Can. $400.00
U.K. £175.00

AETHON
Modeller: Doris Lindner
Height: 5", 12.7 cm
Colour: 1. White
2. White with tan markings
Issued: 1. 1982
2. 1983
Series: Equine Studies

	White	White/Tan
U.S.	$ 80.00	175.00
Can.	$100.00	200.00
U.K.	£ 45.00	100.00

ASTROPE
Modeller: Doris Lindner
Height: 5", 12.7 cm
Colour: 1. White
2. White with grey markings
Issued: 1. 1982
2. 1983
Series: Equine Studies

	White	White/Grey
U.S.	$ 80.00	175.00
Can.	$100.00	200.00
U.K.	£ 45.00	100.00

BRONTE
Modeller: Doris Lindner
Height: 5", 12.7 cm
Colour: 1. White
2. White with grey markings
Issued: 1. 1982
Series: Equine Studies

	White	White/Grey
U.S.	$ 80.00	175.00
Can.	$100.00	200.00
U.K.	£ 45.00	100.00

CHRONOS
Modeller: Doris Lindner
Height: 5", 12.7 cm
Colour: 1. White
2. White with grey mane
Issued: 1. 1982
2. 1983
Series: Equine Studies

	White	White/Grey
U.S.	$ 80.00	175.00
Can.	$100.00	200.00
U.K.	£ 45.00	100.00

EOUS
Modeller: Doris Lindner
Height: 5", 12.7 cm
Colour: 1. White
2. White with brown face and neck
Issued: 1. 1982
2. 1983
Series: Equine Studies

	White	White/Brown
U.S.	$ 80.00	175.00
Can.	$100.00	200.00
U.K.	£ 45.00	100.00

LAMPON
Modeller: Doris Lindner
Height: 5", 12.7 cm
Colour: 1. White
2. White with grey markings
Issued: 1. 1982
2. 1983
Series: Equine Studies

	White	White/Grey
U.S.	$ 80.00	175.00
Can.	$100.00	200.00
U.K.	£ 45.00	100.00

PHAETHON
Modeller: Doris Lindner
Height: 5", 12.7 cm
Colour: 1. White
2. White with light tan shading
Issued: 1. 1982
2. 1983
Series: Equine Studies

	White	White/Tan
U.S.	$ 80.00	175.00
Can.	$100.00	200.00
U.K.	£ 45.00	100.00

PHLEGON
Modeller: Doris Lindner
Height: 5", 12.7 cm
Colour: 1. White
2. White with brown face and neck, darker brown mane
Issued: 1. 1982
2. 1983
Series: Equine Studies

	White	White/Brown
U.S.	$ 80.00	175.00
Can.	$100.00	200.00
U.K.	£ 45.00	100.00

PYROEIS
Modeller: Doris Lindner
Height: 5", 12.7 cm
Colour: 1. White
2. White with pale brown face and neck
Issued: 1. 1982
2. 1983
Series: Equine Studies

	White	White/Brown
U.S.	$ 80.00	175.00
Can.	$100.00	200.00
U.K.	£ 45.00	100.00

P2
ALPHEUS / CORYDON

Modeller:	Neal French
Height:	5 ½", 14.0 cm
Colour:	1. **Alpheus:** Turquoise jacket; striped breeches; pink hat
	2. **Corydon:** Purple breeches; white top with purple pattern; green hat
	3. Porcelain, glazed
Issued:	1970-1971
Series:	Fontainebleau

	Alpheus	Corydon	Porcelain
U.S.	$225.00	225.00	225.00
Can.	$275.00	275.00	275.00
U.K.	£125.00	125.00	125.00

P3
DELIA / HELENA

Modeller:	Neal French
Height:	5 ½", 14.0 cm
Colour:	1. **Delia:** White skirt with pink dots; pink top
	2. **Helena:** Red skirt; red, black and white striped top
	3. Porcelain, glazed
Issued:	1970-1971
Series:	Fontainebleau

	Delia	Helena	Porcelain
U.S.	$225.00	225.00	225.00
Can.	$275.00	275.00	275.00
U.K.	£125.00	125.00	125.00

P4
DAPHNIS / SYLVANUS

Modeller:	Neal French
Height:	5 ½", 14.0 cm
Colour:	1. **Daphnis:** Turquoise breeches; striped jacket; white stockings; black shoes
	2. **Sylvanus:** Green jacket; white breeches; green and white striped stockings; red shoe
	3. Porcelain, glazed
Issued:	1970-1971
Series:	Fontainebleau

	Daphnis	Sylvanus	Porcelain
U.S.	$225.00	225.00	225.00
Can.	$275.00	275.00	275.00
U.K.	£125.00	125.00	125.00

P5
CHLOE (Style One) / SCYLLA

Modeller:	Neal French
Height:	5 ½", 14.0 cm
Colour:	1. **Chloe:** White skirt with green pattern; yellow bodice
	2. **Scylla:** Yellow skirt; turquoise and white bodice
	3. Porcelain, glazed
Issued:	1970-1971
Series:	Fontainebleau

	Chloe	Scylla	Porcelain
U.S.	$225.00	225.00	225.00
Can.	$275.00	275.00	275.00
U.K.	£125.00	125.00	125.00

P6
PARIS / STREPHON
Modeller:	Neal French
Height:	5 ½", 14.0 cm
Colour:	1. **Paris:** Brown, blue, white, purple and yellow
	2. **Strephon:** White, red, yellow, green and white
	3. Porcelain, glazed
Issued:	1970-1971
Series:	Fontainebleau
U.S.	$225.00
Can.	$275.00
U.S.	£125.00

P7
FLORINDA / PHYLLIS
Modeller:	Neal French
Height:	5 ½", 14.0 cm
Colour:	1. **Florinda:** Pink, blue and yellow
	2. **Phyllis:** White, blue, yellow, pink and turquoise
Issued:	1970-1971
Series:	Fontainebleau
U.S.	$225.00
Can.	$275.00
U.K.	£125.00

P10
SPRING
Style Three
Modeller:	Arnold Machin
Height:	17 ¾", 45.1 cm
Colour:	Porcelain and ormalou
Issued:	1968 in a limited edition of 150
Series:	The Four Seasons, Series Two
Comm. by:	Thomas Goode & Co.
U.S.	$700.00
Can.	$850.00
U.K.	£375.00

P11
SUMMER
Style Two
Modeller:	Arnold Machin
Height:	18", 45.7 cm
Colour:	Porcelain and ormalou
Issued:	1968 in a limited edition of 150
Series:	The Four Seasons, Series Two
Comm. by:	Thomas Goode & Co.
U.S.	$700.00
Can.	$850.00
U.K.	£375.00

P12
AUTUMN
Style Two
Modeller:	Arnold Machin
Height:	17 ¾", 45.1 cm
Colour:	Porcelain and ormalou
Issued:	1968 in a limited edition of 150
Series:	The Four Seasons, Series Two
Comm. by:	Thomas Goode & Co.
U.S.	$700.00
Can.	$850.00
U.K.	£375.00

P-13
WINTER
Style Two
Modeller:	Arnold Machin
Height:	17 ¾", 45.1 cm
Colour:	Porcelain and ormalou
Issued:	1968 in a limited edition of 150
Series:	The Four Seasons, Series Two
Comm. by:	Thomas Goode & Co.
U.S.	$700.00
Can.	$850.00
U.K.	£375.00

P17
NIGHT (BUST)
Modeller:	Arnold Machin
Height:	10 ½", 26.7 cm
Colour:	Porcelain, glazed
Issued:	1970 in a limited edition of 250
Varieties:	RW4780 Charis (Night)
U.S.	$500.00
Can.	$600.00
U.K.	£275.00

Note: Also available on wooden plinth.

P18
DAY (BUST)
Modeller:	Arnold Machin
Height:	10 ½", 26.7 cm
Colour:	Porcelain, glazed
Issued:	1970 in a limited edition of 250
U.S.	$500.00
Can.	$600.00
U.K.	£275.00

Note: Also available on wooden plinth.

Days of the Week - Girls
From left to right: Monday's Girl, Tuesday's Girl, Wednesday's Girl, Thursday's Girl, Friday's Girl, Saturday's Girl, Sunday's Girl

Days of the Week - Boys
From left to right: Monday's Boy, Tuesday's Boy, Wednesday's Boy, Thursday's Boy, Friday's Boy, Saturday's Boy, Sunday's Boy

Freda Doughty's "Days of the Week" figurines were reissued in 2004. The only difference is the size of the figure, which varies between 9.9 cm and 16.0 cm, while the original figures are 12.1 cm to 21.6 cm. They do not carry the original RW numbers. The issue price is £29.95

CANDLE SNUFFERS

RW4729
QUEEN ELIZABETH I
Modeller: Sally Hamer
Height: 4 ½", 11.9 cm
Colour: Red, black, green, gold and white
Issued: 1999-2000
Series: Tudor Royals

U.S. $160.00
Can. $185.00
U.K. £ 90.00

RW4738
KING HENRY VIII
Modeller: Sally Hamer
Height: 4 ¾", 12.1 cm
Colour: Brown, red, blue, gold and black
Issued: 1999–2000
Series: Tudor Royals

U.S. $160.00
Can. $185.00
U.K. £ 90.00

RW4740
JANE SEYMOUR
Modeller: Sally Hamer
Height: 4 ½". 11.9 cm
Colour: Blue, yellow, pink, gold and green
Issued: 1999–2000
Series: Tudor Royals

U.S. $150.00
Can. $175.00
U.K. £ 85.00

RW4743
ANNE BOLEYN
Modeller: Sally Hamer
Height: 4 ¼", 10.8 cm
Colour: Red, blue, green, white and gold
Issued: 1999-2000
Series: Tudor Royals

U.S. $150.00
Can. $175.00
U.K. £ 85.00

RW4744
CATHERINE OF ARAGON
Modeller: Sally Hamer
Height: 4 ¾", 12.1 cm
Colour: Red, green, gold, black and white
Issued: 1999-2000
Series: Tudor Royals

U.S. $150.00
Can. $175.00
U.K. £ 85.00

RW4746
CATHERINE PARR
Modeller: Sally Hamer
Height: 4 ½", 11.9 cm
Colour: Blue, orange, pink, gold and green
Issued: 1999-2000
Series: Tudor Royals

U.S. $150.00
Can. $175.00
U.K. £ 85.00

RW4747
CATHERINE HOWARD
Modeller: Sally Hamer
Height: 4 ½", 11.9 cm
Colour: Yellow, blue, gold and green
Issued: 1999-2000
Series: Tudor Royals

U.S. $150.00
Can. $175.00
U.K. £ 85.00

RW4748
NELSON ELEPHANT
Modeller: Nigel Weaver
Height: 5", 12.7 cm
Colour: Blue, red, pink, gold and white
Issued: 1999 to the present
Series: Animals

U.S. —
Can. —
U.K. £120.00

RW4750
ANNE OF CLEVES
Modeller:	Sally Hamer
Height:	4 ¼", 10.8 cm
Colour:	Pink, dark yellow, black and gold
Issued:	1999-2000
Series:	Tudor Royals
U.S.	$150.00
Can.	$175.00
U.K.	£ 85.00

RW4751
MANDARIN
Designer:	Mr. Sharp
Modeller:	Tim Perks
Height:	3 ¾", 9.5 cm
Colour:	Orange, red, blue, black and green
Issued:	1999 in a limited edition of 500
Varieties:	RW4846
U.S.	$150.00
Can.	$175.00
U.K.	£ 85.00

RW4753
JAPANESE GIRL
Modeller:	Sally Hamer
Height:	3", 7.6 cm
Colour:	White, yellow, black, green and gold
Issued:	1999 to the present
Series:	Orientals
U.S.	—
Can.	—
U.K.	£67.50

RW4755
KINGFISHER
Modeller:	Sally Hamer
Height:	4 ¾", 12.0 cm
Colour:	Blue, mustard yellow, white and gold
Issued:	1999 to the present
Series:	Animals
U.S.	—
Can.	—
U.K.	£87.50

RW4762
BLUE TIT
Modeller:	Nigel Weaver
Height:	4", 10.1 cm
Colour:	Blue, mustard yellow, white, gold and green
Issued:	1999 to the present
Series:	Animals
U.S.	—
Can.	—
U.K.	£82.50

RW4763
IMARI COCKEREL
Modeller:	Sally Hamer
Height:	5 ¼", 13.3 cm
Colour:	Orange, blue, pink, gold and white
Issued:	1999 to the present
Series:	Animals
U.S.	—
Can.	—
U.K.	£100.00

RW4764
TAWNY OWL
Modeller:	Sally Hamer
Height:	3 ¾", 9.5 cm
Colour:	Orange, mustard, white and gold
Issued:	1999 to the present
Series:	Animals
U.S.	—
Can.	—
U.K.	£82.50

RW4766
GILES CAT
Modeller:	Nigel Weaver
Height:	4 ½", 11.9 cm
Colour:	Blue, pink, green, gold and white
Issued:	1999 to the present
Series:	Animals
U.S.	—
Can.	—
U.K.	£72.50

RW4798
CARDINAL WOLSEY
Modeller:	Scott Shore
Height:	4 ½", 11.9 cm
Colour:	Red, black and gold
Issued:	1999 in a limited edition of 500
Comm. by:	Sinclair's
U.S.	—
Can.	—
U.K.	£70.00

RW4799
ROBIN
Modeller:	Sally Hamer
Height:	3 ½", 8.9 cm
Colour:	Red-brown, white, gold and blue
Issued:	2000 to the present
Series:	Animals
U.S.	—
Can.	—
U.K.	£82.50

RW4800
TEDDY BEAR
Modeller:	Tim Perks
Height:	3 ½", 8.9 cm
Colour:	Light brown, blue, red and gold
Issued:	2000 to the present
Series:	Novelty Teddies
U.S.	—
Can.	—
U.K.	£82.50

RW4801
ABBESS
Designer:	William Boynton Kirk
Modeller:	Tim Perks
Height:	3 ¾", 9.5 cm
Colour:	White, grey and black
Issued:	2000 to the present
U.S.	—
Can.	—
U.K.	£72.50

RW4804
MILLENNIUM CHAMPAGNE
Modeller:	Royal Worcester Design Studio
Height:	4 ¼", 10.8 cm
Colour:	Blue, red and gold
Issued:	2000 to the present
U.S.	$55.00
Can.	$65.00
U.K.	£30.00

RW4820
SAMURAI
Modeller:	Scott Shore
Height:	4 ¾", 12.1 cm
Colour:	Purple, pale yellow and gold
Issued:	1999 in a limited edition of 250
Comm. by:	Connaught House
U.S.	$175.00
Can.	$200.00
U.K.	£100.00

RW4826
SNOWY OWL
Modeller:	Scott Shore
Height:	3 ¾", 9.5 cm
Colour:	Blue, white, black and silver
Issued:	2000 to the present
Series:	Animals
U.S.	—
Can.	—
U.K.	£82.50

RW4829
LION
Modeller:	Scott Shore
Height:	3 ½", 8.9 cm
Colour:	Brown, red, green, tan and gold
Issued:	2000 in a limited edition of 500
Comm. by:	Wheeler's of Loughborough
U.S.	—
Can.	—
U.K.	£55.00

RW4832
EMPRESS

Modeller:	Tim Perks
Height:	4 ½", 11.9 cm
Colour:	Blue, green, pink, red and gold
Issued:	2000 in a limited edition of 500
Series:	Orientals
U.S.	$175.00
Can.	$200.00
U.K.	£100.00

RW4833
EMPEROR

Modeller:	Tim Perks
Height:	4", 10.1 cm
Colour:	White, green, black, gold and red
Issued:	2000 in a limited edition of 500
Series:	Orientals
U.S.	$175.00
Can.	$200.00
U.K.	£100.00

RW4845
HUSH

Modeller:	Frederick M. Gertner
Height:	3 ½", 8.9 cm
Colour:	1. Red and green; black hair
	2. Lilac; blonde hair
	3. Orange; black hair
Issued:	1. 1999 in a limited edition of 500
	2. 2000 to the present
	3. 2001–2001
Series:	3. Collectors Society Exclusive
U.S.	$120.00
Can.	$135.00
U.K.	£ 65.00

RW4846
MANDARIN

Modeller:	Tim Perks
Height:	3 ¾", 9.5 cm
Colour:	White, black, gold and green
Issued:	1999 to the present
Varieties:	RW4751
U.S.	—
Can.	—
U.K.	£97.50

RW4848
WILTSHIRE MOONRAKER

Modeller:	Scott Shore
Height:	4 ¾", 12.1 cm
Colour:	Tan, dark brown, black and gold
Issued:	2000 in a limited edition of 500
Comm. by:	Watsons of Salisbury
U.S.	—
Can.	—
U.K.	£79.95

RW4863
PETER RABBIT

Modeller:	Sally Hamer
Height:	5 ¼", 13.3 cm
Colour:	Blue, light brown, red, green and gold
Issued:	2003 in a limited edition of 500
Series:	Beatrix Potter
U.S.	—
Can.	—
U.K.	£100.00

Note: 1-100 are commissioned by Wheelers. They carry a gold backstamp

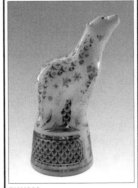

RW4866
POLAR BEAR

Modeller:	Scott Shore
Height:	4 ½", 12.1 cm
Colour:	Blue, gold and white
Issued:	2001-2001
Series:	Connoisseur Collection Annual
U.S.	$175.00
Can.	$200.00
U.K.	£100.00

RW4868
WINSTON CHURCHILL

Modeller:	Amanda Hughes-Lubeck
Height:	Unknown
Colour:	Black, tan and green
Issued:	2000 in a limited edition of 500
Comm. by:	Peter Jones
U.S.	—
Can.	—
U.K.	£75.00

RW4878
TOBY
Modeller:	Sally Hamer
Height:	3 ¼", 8.3 cm
Colour:	Tan, white and gold
Issued:	2001 in a limited edition of 600
Series:	Punch and Judy
U.S.	—
Can.	—
U.K.	£100.00

RW4883
SQUIRREL NUTKIN
Modeller:	Sally Hamer
Height:	4 ¾", 12.1 cm
Colour:	Brown, beige, blue and gold
Issued:	2002 in a limited edition of 500
Series:	Beatrix Potter
U.S.	$175.00
Can.	$200.00
U.K.	£100.00

Note: 1-100 are commissioned by Wheelers. They carry a gold backstamp

RW4884
MOUSE TAILOR
Modeller:	Sally Hamer
Height:	4 ½", 11.9 cm
Colour:	Brown, white, blue and gold
Issued:	2003 in a limited edition of 500
Series:	Beatrix Potter
U.S.	$175.00
Can.	$200.00
U.K.	£100.00

Note: 1-100 are commissioned by Wheelers. They carry a gold backstamp

RW4885
QUEEN VICTORIA
Modeller:	Amanda Hughes-Lubeck
Height:	4 ¼", 10.8 cm
Colour:	Blue, yellow, purple and gold
Issued:	2001 in a limited edition of 600
Series:	Queen Victoria Commemoratives
U.S.	—
Can.	—
U.K.	£100.00

RW4886
PRINCE ALBERT
Modeller:	Amanda Hughes-Lubeck
Height:	4", 10.1 cm
Colour:	Blue, purple, gold and black
Issued:	2001 in a limited edition of 600
Series:	Queen Victoria Commemoratives
U.S.	—
Can.	—
U.K.	£100.00

RW4891
NELSON CAT
Modeller:	Scott Shore
Height:	4", 10.1 cm
Colour:	Blue, orange, gold and white
Issued:	2001 to the present
Series:	Animals
U.S.	—
Can.	—
U.K.	£72.50

RW4893
PRINCE REGENT TEDDY
Modeller:	Tim Perks
Height:	4 ½", 11.9 cm
Colour:	Brown, blue, red and gold
Issued:	2002 to the present
Series:	Novelty Teddies
U.S.	—
Can.	—
U.K.	£82.50

RW4902
BENJAMIN BUNNY
Modeller:	Sally Hamer
Height:	5", 12.7 cm
Colour:	Blue, red, brown, gold and beige
Issued:	2003 in a limited edition of 500
Series:	Beatrix Potter
U.S.	—
Can.	—
U.K.	£100.00

Note: 1-100 are commissioned by Wheelers. They carry a gold backstamp

287

RW4908
MRS. TIGGYWINKLE
Modeller:	Sally Hamer
Height:	4 ¼", 10.8 cm
Colour:	White, red, tan and brown
Issued:	2004 in a limited edition of 500
Series:	Beatrix Potter
U.S.	—
Can.	—
U.K.	£100.00

Note: 1-100 are commissioned by Wheelers. They carry a gold backstamp

RW4909
LITTLE OWL
Modeller:	Scott Shore
Height:	3 ½", 8.9 cm
Colour:	Blue, gold, burgundy and white
Issued:	2002 to the present
Series:	Animals
U.S.	—
Can.	—
U.K.	£82.50

RW4910
GOLDFINCH
Modeller:	Scott Shore
Height:	3 ½", 8.9 cm
Colour:	Red, gold, blue, white and green
Issued:	2001 to the present
Series:	Animals
U.S.	—
Can.	—
U.K.	£72.50

RW4914
HUNCA MUNCA
Modeller:	Sally Hamer
Height:	4 ½", 11.9 cm
Colour:	Brown, lilac, green, tan and white
Issued:	2003 in a limited edition of 500
Series:	Beatrix Potter
U.S.	$175.00
Can.	$200.00
U.K.	£100.00

Note: 1-100 are commissioned by Wheelers. They carry a gold backstamp

RW4915
JEREMY FISHER
Modeller:	Sally Hamer
Height:	4", 10.1 cm
Colour:	Brown, tan, gold, blue, grey and white
Issued:	2003 in a limited edition of 500
Series:	Beatrix Potter
U.S.	$175.00
Can.	$200.00
U.K.	£100.00

Note: 1-100 are commissioned by Wheelers. They carry a gold backstamp

RW4920
CROCODILE
Modeller:	Amanda Hughes-Lubeck
Height:	2 ¾", 7.0 cm
Colour:	Green and gold
Issued:	2001 in a limited edition of 600
Series:	Punch and Judy
U.S.	—
Can.	—
U.K.	£100.00

RW4921
PUNCH
Modeller:	Amanda Hughes-Lubeck
Height:	3 ½", 8.9 cm
Colour:	Pink, green and gold
Issued:	2001 in a limited edition of 600
Series:	Punch and Judy
U.S.	—
Can.	—
U.K.	£100.00

RW4923
BABY
Modeller:	Amanda Hughes-Lubeck
Height:	2 ½", 6.4 cm
Colour:	Blue, white, pink and gold
Issued:	2001 in a limited edition of 600
Series:	Punch and Judy
U.S.	—
Can.	—
U.K.	£100.00

RW4925
POLICEMAN
Modeller:	Amanda Hughes-Lubeck
Height:	3 ¼", 8.3 cm
Colour:	Black, brown and white
Issued:	2001 in a limited edition of 600
Series:	Punch and Judy
U.S.	—
Can.	—
U.K.	£100.00

RW4926
JUDY
Modeller:	Amanda Hughes-Lubeck
Height:	2 ¾", 7.0 cm
Colour:	Blue, white and red
Issued:	2001 in a limited edition of 600
Series:	Punch and Judy
U.S.	—
Can.	—
U.K.	£100.00

RW4934
UNICORN
Modeller:	Scott Shore
Height:	3 ½", 8.9 cm
Colour:	Blue, gold, orange and yellow
Issued:	2002 in a limited edition of 750
Series:	Golden Jubilee Commemoratives
U.S.	$175.00
Can.	$225.00
U.K.	£100.00

RW4935
LION
Modeller:	Scott Shore
Height:	4 ¼", 10.8 cm
Colour:	Blue, gold, red, pink and yellow
Issued:	2002 in a limited edition of 750
Series:	Golden Jubilee Commemoratives
U.S.	$175.00
Can.	$225.00
U.K.	£100.00

RW4938
CLOWN
Modeller:	Scott Shore
Height:	3", 7.6 cm
Colour:	Red, yellow, green, white and black
Issued:	2001 in a limited edition of 250
Comm. by:	Sinclair's
U.S.	—
Can.	—
U.K.	£85.00

RW4940
SMILING BUDDHA
Modeller:	Scott Shore
Height:	3 ½", 8.9 cm
Colour:	Red, pink and gold
Issued:	2002 to the present
Series:	Buddhas
U.S.	—
Can.	—
U.K.	£85.00

RW4941
HOWARD
Designer:	James Hadley
Modeller:	Royal Worcester Design Studio
Height:	3 ¾", 9.5 cm
Colour:	Red, blue, white and gold
Issued:	2002 in a limited edition of 750
Series:	Helen's Babies
U.S.	—
Can.	—
U.K.	£100.00

RW4942
TODDIE
Designer:	James Hadley
Modeller:	Royal Worcester Design Studio
Height:	4 ¼", 10.8 cm
Colour:	Blue, pink and gold
Issued:	2002 in a limited edition of 750
Series:	Helen's Babies
U.S.	—
Can.	—
U.K.	£100.00

RW4943
BUDGE
Designer: James Hadley
Modeller: Royal Worcester
Design Studio
Height: 3 ¾", 9.5 cm
Colour: Blue, tan and gold
Issued: 2002 in a limited edition
of 750
Series: Helen's Babies

U.S. —
Can. —
U.K. £100.00

RW4945
SLEEPING BUDDHA
Modeller: Scott Shore
Height: 3 ¼", 8.5 cm
Colour: Green, blue and gold
Issued: 2002 to the present
Series: Buddhas

U.S. —
Can. —
U.K. £85.00

RW4948
MISS MOPPET
Modeller: Sally Hamer
Height: 4 ¾", 12.1 cm
Colour: Brown, blue, pink, tan,
green and gold
Issued: 2004 in a limited edition
of 500
Series: Beatrix Potter

U.S. —
Can. —
U.K. £100.00

Note: 1-100 are commissioned
by Wheelers. They carry
a gold backstamp

RW4949
WILLIAM SHAKESPEARE
Modeller: Scott Shore
Height: 3", 7.6 cm
Colour: Burgundy, gold, white
and brown
Issued: 2002 to the present
Series: William Shakespeare

U.S. —
Can. —
U.K. £97.50

RW4950
ZODIAC HORSE
Modeller: Scott Shore
Height: 3 ½", 8.9 cm
Colour: Yellow, orange, gold,
red, blue and white
Issued: 2002–2002
Series: Chinese Zodiac Annuals

U.S. $150.00
Can. $175.00
U.K. £ 80.00

RW4951
GIRL WITH MUFF
Designer: James Hadley
Modeller: Royal Worcester
Design Studio
Height: 4", 10.1 cm
Colour: White with gold
highlights
Issued: 2002–2002
Series: Kate Greenaway

U.S. $60.00
Can. $75.00
U.K. £35.00

RW4954
JEMIMA PUDDLE DUCK
Modeller: Sally Hamer
Height: 5 ¼", 13.3 cm
Colour: Blue, red, yellow, white
and brown
Issued: 2004 in a limited edition
of 500
Series: Beatrix Potter

U.S. —
Can. —
U.K. £100.00

Note: 1-100 are commissioned
by Wheelers. They carry
a gold backstamp

RW4959
TOM KITTEN
Modeller: Sally Hamer
Height: 5 ¼", 13.3 cm
Colour: Blue, green, tan, pale
yellow, red and gold
Issued: 2004 in a limited edition
of 500
Series: Beatrix Potter

U.S. —
Can. —
U.K. £100.00

Note: 1-100 are commissioned
by Wheelers. They carry
a gold backstamp

RW4963
DUKE OF EDINBURGH
Modeller: Amanda
            Hughes-Lubeck
Height: 4", 10.1 cm
Colour: Blue, gold, black
            and red
Issued: 2002 in a limited edition
            of 1,000
Series: Golden Jubilee

U.S. $175.00
Can. $200.00
U.K.   £100.00

RW4964
QUEEN ELIZABETH II
Modeller: Amanda
            Hughes-Lubeck
Height: 4", 10.1 cm
Colour: Pink and blue with
            silver highlights
Issued: 2002 in a limited edition
            of 1,000
Series: Golden Jubilee

U.S. $175.00
Can. $200.00
U.K.   £100.00

RW4971
BOTTOM
Modeller: Scott Shore
Height: 4", 10.1 cm
Colour: Brown, purple, green
            and gold
Issued: 2002 to the present
Series: William Shakespeare

U.S.   —
Can.   —
U.K.   £97.50

RW4972
TITANIA
Modeller: Scott Shore
Height: 3 ¼", 8.3 cm
Colour: Fleshtones; purple,
            brown and gold
Issued: 2002 to the present
Series: William Shakespeare

U.S.   —
Can.   —
U.K.   £97.50

RW4976
OTHELLO
Modeller: Scott Shore
Height: 3", 7.6 cm
Colour: Blue, gold and black
Issued: 2002 to the present
Series: William Shakespeare

U.S.   —
Can.   —
U.K.   £97.50

RW4977
DESDEMONA
Modeller: Scott Shore
Height: 3", 7.6 cm
Colour: Fleshtones; green and
            gold
Issued: 2002 to the present
Series: William Shakespeare

U.S.   —
Can.   —
U.K.   £97.50

RW4978
MR. TODD
Modeller: Sally Hamer
Height: 5 ½", 14.0 cm
Colour: Green, red, yellow,
            brown and gold
Issued: 2004 in a limited edition
            of 500
Series: Beatrix Potter

U.S.   —
Can.   —
U.K.   £100.00

Note: 1-100 are commissioned
           by Wheelers. They carry
           a gold backstamp

RW4979
PIGLING BLAND
Modeller: Sally Hamer
Height: 5 ¼", 13.3 cm
Colour: Brown, blue, yellow,
            white, tan and gold
Issued: 2004 in a limited edition
            of 500
Series: Beatrix Potter

U.S.   —
Can.   —
U.K.   £100.00

Note: 1-100 are commissioned
           by Wheelers. They carry
           a gold backstamp

RW4980
ROMEO
Modeller:	Amanda Hughes-Lubeck
Height:	3 ¼", 8.3 cm
Colour:	Green, red and gold
Issued:	2002 to the present
Series:	William Shakespeare
U.S.	—
Can.	—
U.K.	£97.50

RW4981
JULIET
Modeller:	Amanda Hughes-Lubeck
Height:	3 ¼", 8.3 cm
Colour:	Red, tan and gold
Issued:	2002 to the present
Series:	William Shakespeare
U.S.	—
Can.	—
U.K.	£97.50

RW4994
OLD LADY
Designer:	James Hadley
Modeller:	Royal Worcester Design Studio
Height:	3 ½", 8.9 cm
Colour:	Blue, green, white and gold
Issued:	2002 in a limited edition of 600
Series:	Historical
U.S.	—
Can.	—
U.K.	£97.50

RW4995
YOUNG GIRL
Designer:	James Hadley
Modeller:	Royal Worcester Design Studio
Height:	3 ½", 8.9 cm
Colour:	Pink, blue and gold
Issued:	2002 in a limited edition of 600
Series:	Historical
U.S.	—
Can.	—
U.K.	£97.50

RW5003
HERALDIC RAM
Modeller:	Scott Shore
Height:	3 ¼", 8.3 cm
Colour:	Blue, red, gold, green and white
Issued:	2003 in a limited edition of 750
Series:	Heraldic Beasts
U.S.	—
Can.	—
U.K.	£100.00

RW5012
BOY WITH BOATER
Designer:	James Hadley
Modeller:	Royal Worcester Design Studio
Height:	4", 10.1 cm
Colour:	Light grey with gold highlights
Issued:	2003–2003
Series:	Kate Greenaway
U.S.	$60.00
Can.	$75.00
U.K.	£35.00

RW5014
ZODIAC SHEEP
Modeller:	Scott Shore
Height:	3 ¼", 8.3 cm
Colour:	Blue, red, yellow, gold and white
Issued:	2003–2003
Series:	Chinese Zodiac Annuals
U.S.	$150.00
Can.	$175.00
U.K.	£ 80.00

RW5042
ZODIAC MONKEY
Modeller:	Scott Shore
Height:	3 ¼", 8.3 cm
Colour:	Blue, red, white and gold
Issued:	2004–2004
Series:	Chinese Zodiac Annuals
U.S.	—
Can.	—
U.K.	£77.50

INDICES

A

A Celebration at Windsor 223
A Day To Remember 241
A Dazzling Celebration (Lady Cecilia) . . 243
A Farmer's Wife 203
A Gift of Love 239
A Golden Moment. 253
A Kiss So Tender 254
"A Mery New Song" 84
A Posy For Mother 208
A Present For Santa 217
A Royal Presentation 221
A Successful Day At The Derby
 – Rose-Marie 261
Abbess Candle Snuffer 284
Aberdeen Angus Bull
 "Newhouse Jewlian Eric". 146
Aberdeen Toy Terrier. 48
Admiral (The) 1780. 14
Aethon. 275
Affection. 186
Afghan Hound. 179
Afghanistan Hound 107
Airedale Terrier
 Seated 47
 Standing, head to left 53
 Standing, head to right 53
 Brooch 270
 Menu Holder 270
Alexander (The Great). 167
Alexandra 265
Alicia 75
Alice
 Style One. 133
 Style Two. 159
 Style Three. 233
All Mine 120
Alpheus 278
Alphonsine 183
Alsatian
 Style One 89
 Style Two. 111
 Brooch 272
 Menu Holder 272
Amanda
 Style One. 136
 Style Two. 255
Amaryllis 63
Amber 266
American Goldfinch and Thistle
 (Spinus Tristis Tristis)
 Cock 68
 Hen. 68
American Quarter Horse
 "Poco Stampede" 149
American Redstart
 (Setophaga Ruticilla)
 Cock 64
 Hen. 64
American Robin 138
American Robin on Bronze 201
American Saddle Horse 159
American Salmon 153
American Trout 153
Amy
 Style One. 231
 Style Two. 245
An Officer of the Palatine Guard 132
And So To Bed
 Style One. 252
 Style Two. 256

Anemone (Bird) 130
Anita 74
Anna
 Style One 75
 Style Two. 235
Annabel 232
Anne
 Style One. 235
 Style Two. 249
Anne Boleyn 13
 Candle Snuffer 282
Anne Elliot 202
Anne of Cleves Candle Snuffer 283
Annie (1927) 213
Anniversary 224
Anniversary Ball 256
Anniversary 2000 248
Anniversary Waltz (The) 249
Ape 8
Aphrodite (La Tendresse) 202
Appaloosa "Imboden's Driftwood Bob". 158
Applause 63
Apple Blossom Spray and One Bee . . . 98
Apple Blossom Spray and Two Bees . . . 98
Apple of Your Eye 115
Apple Seller 260
Appleby Fair 246
April 105
Aquamarine (Water). 240
Arab Stallion 190
Arab Stallion (and Rider). 214
Arab Stallion "Indian Magic". 148
Arab Stallion's Head 153
Argentina 46
Arkle 155
Art Deco Figurine 258
Ascot Lady. 235
Ashtray (with dog) 72
Astrope 275
At The Meet. 64
At The Seaside. 192
At The Start
 Style One (No. 4) 168
 Style Two (No. 6) 168
Audrey Hepburn. 252
Audubon Warbler and Palo Verdi
 (Dendroica Auduboni)
 Cock 142
 Female 143
August. 109
Autumn
 Style One 96
 Style Two 279
 Style Three 198
 Style Four 210
 Style Five . . . . ??
 Style Six 223
Autumn (Bust) 83
Autumn Song 183

B

Babes In The Wood 90
Baby
 Bon Bon Box / Powder Bowl 67
 Candle Snuffer 287
Baby In Dressing Gown 5
Baby on Cushion: see Treasure
Baigneuse (La Plongee Attendue) 165
Baker's Wife 220
Bal Masqué 64
Bald Eagle (Domed) 199

Balinese Dancer
 Style One. 113
 Style Two. 127
Ballerina 192
Ballet 209
Ballet Dancer
 Style One 77
 Style Two 78
Ballet Master. 187
Baltimore Oriole and Tulip Tree
 (Icterus Galbula)
 Cock 87
 Hen. 88
Banbury Cross 73
Barbara (Polar Bear Bookend) 37
Barn Owl (Domed) 197
Barn Owl (Tyto Alba) 195
Bath Time 206
Bathing Girl 89
Battledore 113
Be Mine 266
Bea (1922). 215
Beadle (The) 4
Bear 64
Bearded Reedling 168
Bears, Mick and Mack
 With base 87
 Without base 92
Beatrice 144
Bed Time
 Style One. 207
 Style Two. 256
Bedlington Terrier Brooch. 275
Bedtime Story 245
Belle of the Ball
 Style One. 182
 Style Two. 217
Belted Kingfisher and Water Lily 195
Bengal Lancer 74
Benjamin Bunny Candle Snuffer 286
Best Buddies 247
Best Dress 251
Betrothal (The). 246
Bette 218
Betty 45
Bewick's Wren And Yellow Jasmine
 (Thryomanes Bewickii)
 Cock 118
 Hen 118
Birthday Girl
 Style One. 193
 Style Two. 252
Birthday Wish 235
Blackcock. 10
 Brooch 273
Blithe Spirit 75
Blue Angel Fish
 Style One. 129
 Style Two. 133
Blue Coat School
 Boy 197
 Girl 197
Blue Jay (American Version). 138
Blue Marlin 152
Blue Tit 78
 Candle Snuffer. 283
Blue Tit Fledgling and Clematis 172
Blue Tit on Bronze
 Style One. 187
 Style Two. 161
 Style Three. 161
Blue Tit on Hogweed 176

Blue Tits (on stump) 101
Bluebeard 38
Bluebell Time 257
Bluebird 139
Bluebird and Apple Blossom
  (Sialia Sialis)
    Cock 68
    Hen 68
Bluebird and Pine Cones 192
Blue-Fin Tuna 152
Blue-Grey Gnatcatcher and Dogwood
  (Polioptila Caerulea)
    Double 117
    Single 117
Blue-Tit and Pussy Willow In Spring
  (Parus Coeruleus)
    Cock 147
Blue-Tit Bathing in an Old Willow
  Stump (Hen) 148
Bobwhite Quail, Style One
  (Colinus Virginianus)
    Cock 93
    Hen 93
Bob-White Quail, Style Two
    Cock 156
    Hen 156
Bogskar 94
Bonzo 29
Bonzo Salt and Pepper Pots 29
Borzoi
    Style One 107
    Style Two 170
Bottom Candle Snuffer 290
Bow (The) 99
Boxer
    Seated 177
    Standing 184
Boy and Dolphin 97
Boy and Rabbit 9
Boy on Boar 34
Boy With Boater Candle Snuffer 291
Boy With Donkey 36
Boy With Hat (Anthony) 154
Boy With Parakeet 60
Brahman Bull "J.D.H. de Ellary Manso" . 155
Brer Rabbit 30
    Flower Holder 6
    Salt and Pepper Pots 30
Bride (The) 187
Bride and Groom 261
    Cake Decoration 230
Bridesmaid
    Style One 79
    Style Two 229
Bridget 157
British Friesian Bull "Terling Trusty" . . . 149
British Red Cross V.A.D. Member 157
Bronte 276
Bubbles 72
Budge Candle Snuffer 289
Bull Terrier
    "Bill" 45
    Brooch 275
Bulldog "Mack" 155
    Dog's Head (Wall Mount) 93
Bulldog Puppies (Two) 67
Bullfinch 82
    Brooch 272
    On Bronze 187
    On Stump 15
Bullfinch and Blackthorne
  (Pyrrhula Europoea) 148

Bullfinch Fledgling on Apple Blossom . . 172
Bumblebee 198
Burmah 56
Bustle (The) 206
Buttercup 45
Butterfly 198
By a Short Head 165

C

Cactus Wren and Prickly Pear
  (Heleodytis Brunneicapillus Couesi)
    Cock 135
    Hen 135
Cairn Brooch 271
Cairn Terrier "Rats" 97
Cairn Terrier "Toto" 94
Calf 36
Calves
    With base 70
    Without base 119
Camille 183
Can I Come Too ...? 263
Canary (On Stump) 15
Candlestick 79
Cantering To The Post 65
Canvasback Duck 156
Canyon Wren and Wild Lupin
  (Catherpes Mexicanus)
    Cock 137
    Hen 137
Captain Raimondo d'Inzeo on Merano . 149
Cardinal 138
Cardinal Wolsey Candle Snuffer 284
Carmen 266
Carolina Wren and Trumpet Creeper . . . 171
Carolina Wren and Wild Rose 192
Caroline
    Style One 144
    Style Two 226
Carp 55
Cat
    Eating 37
    Seated 200
Catherine
    Style One 226
    Style Two 261
Catherine Howard Candle Snuffer 282
Catherine Morland 202
Catherine of Aragon Candle Snuffer . . 282
Catherine Parr Candle Snuffer 282
Cathy (Withering Heights) 265
Cecilia 159
Celebration 233
Celestia 246
Celestine 261
Cerulean Warbler and Red Maple
  (Dendroica cerulea)
    Cock 140
    Hen 141
Chaffinch
    Style One 82
    Style Two 200
Chaffinch (Hen) 113
Chaffinches (On stump) 99
Chalice of Love (The) 256
Chamber Maid 203
Chanticleer (Cockerel) 127
Charis (Night) Bust 248
Charis (Day), Bust 249
Charity 179
Charles I 13
Charles II 16

Charlotte
    Style One 222
    Style Two 257
Charlotte and Jane 153
Charolois Bull "Vaillant" 155
Chasseur and Chaval 179
Cha-U-Kao (Female Clown) 196
Cheetah
    Style One 8
    Style Two 248
Cheltenham 166
Cherry Seller 260
Cheshire Cat 133
Chestnut-Collared Longspur 171
Chic (1933) 188
Chickadee and Daisies 192
Chickadee and Larch
  (Parus Atricapillus)
    Cock 82
    Hen 83
Chiffchaff on Hogweed
  (Phylloscopus Rufus) 148
Child
    Crawling 102
    Seated 102
Child With Butterfly 72
Child With Lamb In Arms 70
Child With Lamb, Flowers In Arms 70
China 57
Chinese Dancer
    Female 78
    Male 78
Chinese Family Group 28
Chinese Figure With Long Tunic 106
Chinese Figure With Short Tunic 106
Chinese Goddess
    Arms crossed 113
    With flower 114
Chinoiserie Boy 98
Chinoiserie Figure
    Female, Kneeling 104
    Female, Standing 104
    Male, Kneeling 103
    Male, Standing 104
Chinoiserie Figure Holding Bird
    Female 109
    Male 109
Chinoiserie Girl
    Head Down 97
    Head Up 99
Chloe
    Style One 278
    Style Two 259
Chow Brooch 272
Christening (The) 214
Christina 242
Christmas 236
Christopher 189
Chronos 276
Circus Horses (Three) 76
City Girl 205
Claire 234
Clara (1925) 210
Clarissa 133
Classical Lady
    With Lyre 14
    With Tambourine 14
Cleopatra 249
Cleopatra 'Queen of Kings' 259
Clown's Head 6
Clown Candle Snuffer 288

Clumber Spaniel
    With base 81
    Without base 9
Clydesdale Stallion 164
Cockatoo Jug 28
Cockatoo Salt and Pepper Pots 28
Cocker Spaniel
    Style One 48
    Style Two 54
    Style Three
        With Base 81
        Without base 91
    Brooch 271
    Menu Holder 271
Cockerel String Box 6
Cole Tits (on stump) 101
Collie Brooch 271
Colonel of the Noble Guard In
    Gala Uniform 132
Colonial Trooper 3
Columbine
    Style One 17
    Style Two 18
    Style Three 50
Coming of Age 180
Congratulations 226
Connemara 178
Constance (1924) 217
Cook 203
Coquelicot (Bird) 130
Coquette
    Style One 35
    Style Two 184
Cora 30
Coronation Ball, 'Christina' 264
Corydon 278
Country Boy 194
Country Diary of an Edwardian Lady . . 259
Country Girl 204
Country Girl
    With gloves 24
    With walking stick 24
Cow 8
Crab Apple Sprays and One Butterfly . . 94
Crab Apple Sprays and Two Butterflies . . 94
Crested Tit 182
Crinoline (The) 205
Crinoline Figure
    With Book 10
    With Cap 10
Crinoline Lady 176
Crocodile Candle Snuffer 287
Crucifix 9
Cupid with Bow 2
Cupid With Sheath 2
Curtsey (The)
    Style One 99
    Style Two 186

D

Dachshund 89
    Brooch 271
Dairy Shorthorn Bull "Royal Event" . . . 152
Daisy
    Style One 127
    Style Two 210
Daisy Chain 194
Dalmatian 89
    Brooch 275
Dance 60
Dance of Time 234

Dancers (The)
    First Version 49
    Second Version 251
Dancing Waves 80
Dandie Dinmont Terrier 47
    Brooch 270
Dandelion 59
Dandy (The) 170
Daphnis 278
Dartford Warbler 168
Daughter of Erin 266
Daughter of the House 205
Day (Bust) 279
Debutante 184
December 110
Delettante 169
Delia 278
"Delicate Cowcumbers To Pickle" 80
Desdemona Candle Snuffer 290
Desire 262
Destiny 246
Devotion 261
Diana
    Style One 184
    Style Two 209
    Style Three 259
Diana, Princess of Wales (Bust) 189
Dickcissel and Sunflower 171
Dinner At Eight 242
Dippers 169
Dodo (The) 134
Dolly 218
Dolphin 150
Don't Let The Cat Out of the Bag 115
Dormouse on Bronze 197
Double Mouse 12
Downy Woodpecker and Pecan
    (Dendrocopus Pubescens)
        Cock 132
        Hen 132
Dreaming 33
Dressing Up 209
Drum: see Drummer 72
Drummer 72
Drummer Boy 23
Dublin Flower Girl 43
Duchess (The) 134
Duchess' Dress
    First Version 63
    Second Version 63
Duck 28
Duck Ring Stand 7
Duke of Edinburgh Candle Snuffer . . . 290
Duke of Marlborough (The) 162
Duke of Wellington (The) 158
Dunfermline 174
Dutch Boy 43
Dutch Girl 43

E

Early Bird 115
Early English Gentleman 5
Early English Lady 5
Earth Song 240
Easter Parade 182
Edward VI 12
Egypt 55
El Condor Pasa
    First Version 250
    Second Version 254

Elaine 159

Elation 263
Eleanor
    Style One 216
    Style Two 264
Elephant
    Style One 61
    Style Two 62
    Jug 28
    Salt, Pepper and Mustard Pots 28
Elf Owl And Saguaro
    (Micropallas Whitneyi Whitneyi) . . . 135
Elizabeth
    Style One 151
    Style Two 242
Elizabeth I
    Style One 12
Elizabeth Bennet 201
Elizabeth Emanuel Black Gown (The) . . 258
Ellen 213
Embassy Ball 239
Embroidery 223
Emily
    Style One 156
    Style Two 182
    Style Three 228
Emma 265
Emma Woodhouse
    Style One 201
    Style Two 241
Emperor Candle Snuffer 285
Empress Candle Snuffer 285
Empress of Austria 253
En Repose (1926) 188
England 58
English – Rose 267
English Bulldog 48
English Costume Figure
    Female 4
    Male 4
English Pointer
    With base 80
    Without base 91
English Redstart on Gorse
    Ruticilla Phoenicurus
        Cock 145
        Hen 145
English Setter 111
English Springer Spaniel
    Standing 48
    With Base 81
Eous 276
Equestrienne 181
Especially For You 236
Eternal Love 262
Eternity 244
Eugéne de Beauharnais 179
Evacuees 97
Evening Engagement 187
Evening Romance 242
Evie (1923) 215
Exmoor Pony 169
Extinct Carolina Paroquets
    (Conuropsis Carolinensis)
        Wall Hanging 137

F

Fair Maiden of Astolat 258
"Fair Cherryes" 90
Fairest Rose 214
Falconer: See Merlin 144
Fan 104

Fan Bearer 244
Fanny Price 202
Fantails. 151
Fantasy 262
Farmer's Boy 108
Father Christmas 258
Fatima 38
Fawn's Head (Vase) 154
Fawns, Young Spotted Deer
    Oval base 92
    Rectangular base 87
    Without base 122
February 110
Felicity
    Style One. 159
    Style Two 257
Female (Name unknown). 3
Female Dancing Figure
    Style One 13
    Style Two 13
Female Nude
    Hand Behind Shoulder 20
    Hand on Breast 20
    Seated, Facing Left 25
    Seated, Facing Right 26
Female Nude With Leaves (Seated). . . . 25
Female Nude With Mirror. 25
Field Spaniel
    Brooch 271
    Menu Holder 271
"Fine Writeing inkes" 89
Fiona 226
First Aid 151
First Cuckoo 59
First Dance
    Style One. 136
    Style Two. 222
First Flight 210
First Kiss 222
First Love 239
First Prize 211
First Quadrille 'Henrietta' 213
First Smile 228
First Steps 206
First Teddy. 238
First Touch. 218
Fish 8
    Ashtray 6
Fisherman 190
Flame Dance (Fire) 239
Flamingo
    Neck Curved. 20
    Neck Stretched Forward 21
Flemish Man 2
Flemish Woman 2
Flirtation
    Style One. 181
    Style Two 227
Florinda 279
Flower Girl
    Style One 33
    Style Two 56
    Style Three 61
Flute Player (The) 38
Flying Fish 148
Foal 77
Foals
    With base 71
    Without base 119
Fortune Teller (The). 43
Forty Winks 261
Four-Eyed Butterfly Fish 128

Four-Eyed Fish and Banded Butterfly . . 129
Fox
    Style One. 103
    Style Two. 191
    Ashtray 32
    Lying, on curved base 49
    Lying, on straight base 50
    Lying, straight, without base 128
    Lying, without base 122
    On bronze 196
    Seated 49
    Stalking
        Brooch 270
        Menu Holder 270
    Tobacco Jar 44
    Walking
        Menu Holder 270
Fox and Hound
    Calendar 50
    Pen Tray 48
Fox Head (Wall Mount) 53
Foxhound
    Brooch 272
    Calendar with fittings 77
    Running
        Menu Holder 270
    Seated
        Menu Holder 270
    Standing
        Style One 102
        Style Two 102
        Style Three 191
    Walking
        Menu Holder 270
Foxhound Puppies (Three) 67
Foxhunter and Lieut.-Col.
    H.M. Llewellyn, C.B.E. 144
Fragrance 178
Francesca
    Style One. 245
    Style Two. 229
French Bulldog "Winston". 188
French Soldier 7
Friday's Child
    Boy 86
    Girl 121
Friendship 223
Frog 193
Frog (The). 69
From All of Us 231
Fruit Seller at Cambridge Fair 259
Fruit Seller at Stow Fair 263
Fulmar 157
Funny Fish 114

G

Galloping Dartmoor Ponies 163
Galloping In Winter 168
Gamecock. 127
Garden Party 233
Gardener 193
Gay Gordons 266
Gentleman in Evening Dress with Cigar . 11
Gentleman of the House 205
Gentleman on Rococo Base 7
Gentleman with Cloak and Opera Hat . . 11
Georgia 262
Germaine 181
Gile's Cat Candle Snuffer 283
Giraffes 36
Girl and Rabbit 46
Girl With Beads 89

Girl With Hat (Sarah Jane) 154
Girl With Kitten Powder Bowl. 51
Girl With Muff Candle Snuffer. 289
Girl With Setter 173
Glyndebourne 222
Goat
    Head raised
        With base 66
Goat (cont.)
        Without base 122
    Licking hind leg
        With base 66
        Without base 122
Goldcrest 95
Goldcrest And Larch
    (Regulus Cristatus)
        Cock 147
        Hen 147
Goldcrest on Bronze
    Style One. 187
    Style Two. 161
    Style Three. 161
Golden Anniversary 224
Golden Crowned Kinglet and Noble Pine
    (Regulus Satrapa)
        Cock 112
        Double 112
Golden Eagle (Aquila Chrysaetos) . . . 199
Golden Girl of the May 263
Golden Jubilee Ball 227
Golden Pheasant Brooch 274
Golden Retriever
    With base 81
    Without base 91
Goldfinch 82
    Candle Snuffer 287
    On Stump 16
Goldfinch Fledgling and Thistle . . . 172
"Good Luck To Your Fishing". 61
Goodnight 252
Goose Girl 217
Goosey Goosey Gander 91
Governess and Child 205
Grace
    Style One. 173
    Style Two 76
    Style Three. 226
    Style Four 244
Grace Kelly 250
Graceful Moment 250
Graduation Night 233
Grand Entrance 241
Grand Hotel 268
Grandmother's Bonnet 207
Grandmother's Dress 58
Grapes 25
Grasshopper. 198
Greece 56
Great Tit. 95
Great Tit Fledgling 171
Greeting 103
Greek Figure Holding Dog (Boy) 5
Greek Figure Holding Flowers (Female) . . 5
Greek Figure Holding Kitten (Girl) 5
Greek Figure With Cape
    Female 4
    Male. 4
Greek Figure With Pointed Hat. 5
Greenfinch
    On Bronze 180
    On Forsythia 180
Green-Winged Teal 156

Grey Wagtail 181
Grey Wagtail And Celandine (Cock)
  (Motacilla Melanope) 145
Greyhound Brooch 275
Greyhounds 36
Grouse Brooch 272
Grundy with Pat Eddery Up 169
Guardsman 3
Gypsy Girl at Nottingham Goose Fair . . 266
Gypsy Princess 264

H

Hacking In The Park 89
Hackney Stallion 163
Hand Maiden With Lyre 253
Handy Man 3
Hannah
  Style One 245
  Style Two 248
Happy Anniversary 261
Happy Boy 51
Happy Days 108
Hare 36
  On bronze 195
Harlequin
  Style One 18
  Style Two 31
Harlequin and Columbine Bookend . . . 30
Harmony 262
Harpist (The) 37
Harvest Mouse on Bronze 195
Heather 125
Hebe 2
Hedge Sparrow 95
Hedgehog on Bronze
  Style One 186
  Style Two 195
Helena 278
Hen Party 116
Henry VIII 12
Her Regal Majesty 264
Heraldic Ram Candle Snuffer 291
Hereford Bull "Vern Inspiration" 142
Hesitation: see Bathing Girl 89
Highland Bull 171
Highwayman 74
"Hit!" 62
Hobby and Swallow 166
Hog Hunting 73
Holland 57
Holly 225
Hometime 189
Hooded Warbler and Cherokee Rose
  (Wilsonia critina)
    Cock 131
    Hen 131
Horse's Head (Vase) 154
Horseman Bookend 32
Hound
  Ashtray 32
  Lying, on curved base 49
  Lying, on straight base 50
  Lying straight, without base
    Style One 122
    Style Two 128
  "Ranter" 98
  Seated 50
  Tobacco Jar 44
Hound Head (Wall Mount) 53
Howard Candle Snuffer 288
H.R.H. Prince Charles on Pans Folly . . 176
H.R.H. Princess Anne and Doublet . . . 162

H.R.H. Princess Elizabeth on "Tommy" . 108
H.R.H. The Duke of Edinburgh on
  His Polo Pony 157
Hunca Munca Candle Snuffer 287
Hunter 185
Huntsman and Hounds 65
Hush Candle Snuffer 285
Hush a Bye Baby 267
Hyperion 151

I

I Dream 244
I Hope 247
I Love Emily 251
I Pray 246
I Wish 240
Imari Cockerel Candle Snuffer 283
Immaculate (The) (Virgin Mary) 10
Imperial Yeoman 2
In the Ring 76
India 57
Indian Brave 40
Indian Chief 40
Indian Squaw
  With Child on Back 40
  With Child on Shoulder 40
Indigo Bunting and Blackberry
  (Passerina Cyanea)
    Cock 100
    Hen 100
Indigo Bunting on Plum Tree
  (Passerina Cyanea) Single 79
Infant Powder Bowl 26
Innocence 170
Invitation
  Style One 146
  Style Two 178
Ireland 76
Irene (Miss 1920) 217
Irina 76
Irish – Caitlin 267
Irish Setter
  With base 80
  Without base 111
Isabella
  Style One 124
  Style Two 255
Isabelle 239
Italy 56

J

Jane 225
Jane Seymour Candle Snuffer 282
January 109
Japan 57
Japanese Girl Candle Snuffer 283
Jay 83
  Brooch 274
Jayne 266
Jeanne 182
Jemima Puddle Duck Candle Snuffer . . 289
Jennifer 240
Jenny 255
Jeremy Fisher Candle Snuffer 287
Jersey Bull "Leebarn Carlisle II" 152
Jersey Cow "Bramley Zenora" 145
Jessica
  Style One 227
  Style Two 267
Jester
  Style One 4
  Style Two 114
Jeux De Plage 166

Jewel Box 249
Jewel In The Crown 238
Jill 255
Joan 42
Joanne 243
Johnnie 108
Joy
  Style One 75
  Style Two 212
Joy Ride 115
Judy 114
Judy Candle Snuffer 288
Juliet 251
Juliet Candle Snuffer 291
Juliette 221
July 109
June
  Style One 39
  Style Two 110
Just For You 232

K

Kate 228
Kate Greenaway Boy
  Style One 23
  Style Two 24
Kate Greenaway Girl
  Style One 23
  Style Two 24
Katie
  Style One 189
  Style Two 237
Keepsake 257
Kek (Kestrel) 169
Kestrel (Domed) 197
Kids at Play
  With base 71
  Without base 119
King George V 60
King George V (Bust) 60
King Henry VIII 208
  Candle Snuffer 282
Kingfisher 82
  Candle Snuffer 283
  Brooch 274
  On Bronze
    Style One 160
    Style Two 161
  On Stump 16
Kingfisher and Autumn Beech
  (Alcedo Ispida) Cock 149
Kiss (The) 55
Kitten
  Lying
    Style One 174
    Style Two 200
  Seated 172
Kittens (Three) 69
Kitty (1928) 213
Knightsbridge 240
Knightsbridge Girl 203
Koala Bears, Billy Bluegums
  With base 88
  Without base 92
Kookaburra 26
  Ashtray
    Circular 27
    Rectangular 27
  Powder Bowl 26

L

L'étude 188
L'Oiseau 131

La Fleur 131
La Leçon. 187
La Midinette 185
La Miroir 131
Labrador (Seated) 177
Labrador Retriever
    With base 81
    Without base 92
Ladies Day. 236
Lady Alexandra 233
Lady Alice 228
Lady Amherst's Pheasant Brooch. . . . 275
Lady Beatrice 230
Lady Bountiful. 61
Lady Camille 237
Lady Charlotte 227
Lady Cicely 237
Lady Dorothy 237
Lady Elizabeth 220
Lady Emily 236
Lady Emma
    Style One. 219
    Style Two. 236
Lady Hannah
    Style One. 221
    Style Two. 237
Lady Helena 238
Lady Henrietta 244
Lady Jane 220
Lady Louisa 236
Lady Louise 233
Lady Margaret 235
Lady of Sherwood 261
Lady of the House 204
Lady on Rococo Base 7
Lady Sarah
    Style One. 221
    Style Two. 243
Lady Sophie
    Style One. 230
    Style Two. 237
Lady Susan 202
Lady Victoria. 229
Lady Violet. 219
Lady With a Rose 59
Lady With Fan. 40
Lady With Mask-Falsehood 13
Lady With Mirror-Truth 13
Lampon 276
Lara 258
Lark Sparrow With Twin Pod
    and Red Gila (Chondestes
    Grammacus Striciatus). 144
Last Dance. 227
Last Waltz 212
Laundry Maid 202
Laura
    Style One. 223
    Style Two. 268
Lauren
    Style One. 253
    Style Two. 264
Lavender 45
Lavender Seller 260
Lazuli Bunting and Choke Cherry
    (Passerina Amoena)
        Cock 139
        Hen 139
Le Cerceau 197
Le Panier. 130
Leçon a La Mer 167

Legal Eagle. 209
Leopards, Nelson and Norah
    With base 86
    Without base 92
Lesser Whitethroat on Wild Rose
    (Sylvia Curruca)
        Cock 146
        Hen 146
Letter (The) 102
Let's Run. 190
Lily 45
Limpetueux 167
Linnet on Wild Rose 179
Linnets (on stump) 100
Lion 62
    Bookend. 32
    Candle Snuffer 284, 288
Lions, Oliver and October
    With base 86
    Without base 92
Lippizanner 172
Liserion (Bird) 130
Lisette 138
Little Boy Blue 91
Little Dancer 34
    Powder Bowl 47
Little Grandmother's Dress 189
Little Jack Horner 91
Little Maid 186
Little Mermaid 193
Little Miss Muffet 90
Little Owl Candle Snuffer 287
Little Owl On Ivy 176
Little Parakeet Boy. 190
Little Princess 247
Liz 218
"London Gazette Here" 88
Long-Haired Cat 135
Long-Tailed Tits on Flowering Larch
    (Acredula Caudata). 149
Lorna (Doone) 265
Lost Slipper 194
Lough Neagh Mary 43
Louisa 145
Love 201
Love Story 247
Loving You. 236
Lucky Spider. 114
Lucy
    Style One. 225
    Style Two. 255
    Style Three. 266
Lullaby. 205
Lute Player (The) 37

M

Mad as a Hatter 116
Mad as a March Hare: see Mad as a. . . 116
    Hatter
Madelaine 152
Magnalia Wabler and Magnolia
    (Dendroica Magnolia)
        Cock 107
        Hen 107
Magnolia Bud 70
Maiden of Dana 260
Maiden With Ball in Right Hand. 16
Maiden With Both Hands Outstretched . 16
Maisie 246
Mallard
    Drake. 154
    Hen. 154

Mallards 191
Man and Woman 163
Mandarin Candle Snuffer 283, 285
March 110
March Winds 187
Mare and Foal. 74
Margaret 249
Margery 246
Marguerite (Cockerel) 130
Marguerite and Don Pedro 184

Maria 250
Marigold. 45
Marion 153
Market Day 215
Marsh Harrier (Domed) 198
Marsh Tit on Daphne 180
Marsh Tit
    Style One. 95
    Style Two. 199
Mary 240
Mary Cassat 197
Mary Mary 185
Mary Queen of Scots
    Style One. 11
    Style Two. 241
Masked Ball 235
Masquerade
    Style One: see Curtsey, Style One . . 99
    Style Two. 188
Masquerade Begins 209
Masquerade Boy: see The Bow. 99
Master Mariner 150
May 110
May Ball 237
Mayfair Girl 204
Mayflower
    First Version 140
    Second Version 151
Maytime
    With base 66
    Without base. 119
Meadow Pipit and Silverweed
    (Anthus Pratensis) Cock 148
Megan 265
Melanie
    Style One. 150
    Style Two. 258
Memories 234
Merlin 144
Merlin Hawk on Bronze 162
Mermaid 73
Mexican Feijoa and Ladybird
    Style One. 107
    Style Two. 107
Michael 40
    Powder Bowl / Bon Bon Box 44
Midnight Encounter 259
Midnight Rendezvous 230
Milkmaid. 206
Mill Reef 164
Millennia 243
Millennium Champagne Candle Snuffer. 284
Millie
    Style One. 211
    Style Two. 249
Minnie (1929) 214
Mischief 41
Miss Moppet Candle Snuffer 289
Mistral (Air) 240
Mistral and Lester Piggot 174
Mock Turtle 134

Mockingbird and Peach Blossom
  (Mimus Polyglottos)
    Cock 94
    Hen. 94
Modesty 183
Molly 212
Monday's Child
    Boy. 120
    Girl. 84
Monkey
    Four feet on ground 154
    Two feet on ground 154
Mongrel Pup (The) 42
Moonlight and Roses 268
Moonlight Cascade 241
Moorhen Chick on Waterlily Pads
  (Gallinula Chloropus). 149
Morning Walk 175
Mother (The) 35
Mother and Child
    Style One 230
    Style Two. 245
Mother and Child 2000 248
Mother and Two Girls 9
Mother Machree: see The Fortune Teller. 43
Mother's Helper 194
Mother's Love 242
Mothering Sunday 216
Mountain Bluebird and Spleenwort Niger
  (Sialia Currucoides)
    Cock 141
    Hen 142
Mourning Doves. 156
Mouse
    Style One 8
    Style Two ??
    Ashtray
      Left 27
      Right 27
Mouse Tailor Candle Snuffer 286
Mr. Todd Candle Snuffer 290
Mrs. Tiggywinkle Candle Snuffer . . . 287
Mucha Rose
    Style One. 254
    Style Two. 264
Music 238
    Male. 6
    Female 6
Musical Moments 194
Musician 253
My Favourite 52
My Little Brother. 256
My Pet. 86
My Prayer 252
Myrtle Warbler And Weeping Cherry
  (Dendroica Coronata)
    Cock 117
    Hen 118

N

Naiad 54
    On plinth. 21
  Powder Bowl
    First Version 25
    Second Version 26
Napoleon Bonaparte 157
Natashia
    Style One 75
    Style Two. 238
Necklace: see Girl with Beads 89
Nefertari 253

Nelson Cat Candle Snuffer 286
Nelson Elephant Candle Snuffer 282
New Arrival
    Style One. 207
    Style Two. 235
New Born 167
New Dawn 250
Nicola 229
Night (Bust) 279
Night at the Opera. 231
Nightingale 95
Nightingale and Honeysuckle
    Style One. 147
Nightingale on Honeysuckle
    Style One ??
    Style Two. 185
Nijinsky 159
Nina La Loge. 195
19th Century Cigar Store Indian. . . . 157
Noel 39
Noelle 213
Norbert 184
November 106
Nude Bather Reclining on Plinth
    Style One 19
    Style Two 21
Nude Boy With Cornucopia 101
Nude Boy With Dolphin 21
Nude Boy With Flowers
    Seated 18
    Standing
      Style One. 19
      Style Two. 22
Nude Boy With Fruit
    Seated, facing left 22
    Seated, facing right 22
    Standing 20
Nude Boy With Roses (Standing) 22
Nude Boy With Seaweed 21
Nude Boy With Vines (Standing) 22
Nude Child (Seated) 19
Nude Female Leaning on a Pedestal . . . 19
Nude Female Putting Slipper on Foot. . . 19
Nude Female Slipper in Right Hand. . . . 20
Nude Girl With Basket of Roses
  (Seated) 23
Nude Girl With Bouquet of Roses
  (Seated) 23
Nude Girl With Cornucopia 101
Nude Girl With Flowers
    Seated 18
    Standing 19
Nude Girl With Garland of Fruit
  and Leaves (Seated) 22
Nude Girl With Garland of Leaves
  (Seated) 22
Nude Girl With Roses and Leaves
  (Standing) 22
Nuthatch 95
    On Bronze 161
Nymph With Convoulvulus 196
Nymph With Daisy 196
Nymph With Hairbell 196
Nymph With Snowdrop 196
Nymph With Viola 196
Nymph With Winter Jasmine 196

O

October 105
Officer of the Blues 136
Officer of the 17th Dragoon
    Guards 1814 17

Officer of the 29th Foot
  (Worcestershire Regiment) 1812 . . 123
Officer of the 3rd Dragoon
    Guards 1806 17
Officer of the Coldstream Guards 1815
    First Version 12
    Second Version 17
    Third Version. 143
Officer of the French Marines 11
Officer of the Life Guards 136
Officer of the Royal Artillery 1815 . . . 14
Officer of the Scots Guards 143
Officer of the Seaforth Highlanders
    1812. 14
Oguri Cap 208
Old English Sheepdog (Seated) 175
Old English Sheepdog Puppy (Playing) . 182
Old Father William 134
Old Friends 193
Old Goat Woman (The) 35
Old Lady Candle Snuffer 291
Olivia
    Style One. 218
    Style Two. 231
    Style Three. 260
Once Upon a Time. 206
Only For You 250
Only Me. 80
Orange Blossom Spray 102
Orange Blossom Spray and Butterfly . . 101
Order of the Garter 258
Othello Candle Snuffer 290
Otter 191
Ovenbird with Crested Iris
  (Seiurus Aurocapillus) Hen. 123
Ovenbird with Lady's Slipper
  (Seiurus Aurocapillus) Cock 122
Over The Sticks 65
Owl Brooch 273

P

Painted Fan, 'Lucinda' 241
Painting 219
Palomino "Yellow Straw" 159
Pansy 45
Papal Gendarme. 132
Parakeet: see Boy with Parakeet 60
Paramour (The) 170
Paris 279
Parlour Maid 203
Parroquet
    Brooch 273
    Female (on stump)
      Style One. 15
      Style Two: see Parrot Male . . . 15
    (on stump)
Parrot, Male (on stump). 15
Party Dress 185
Parula Warbler And Sweet Bay
  (Parula Americana)
    Cock 123
    Hen 124
Passion 262
Paul 113
Pauline. 255
Peace 190
Peacock Menu Holder 7
Pekinese
    Brooch 271
    Dog's Head (Wall Mount) 93
    Menu Holder 271

Pekinese (cont.)
Seated 54
Standing 47
Pekinese Puppies (Four) 65
Pelican
Ashtray 36
Jug 29
Salt and Pepper Pots 29
Penelope
Style One. 138
Style Two. 255
Penguin
Brooch 274
Head Forward 61
Raised Beak 61
Percheron Stallion
"Saltmarsh Silver Crest" 152
Peregrine Falcon
Style One. 199
Style Two. 198
Persian Kitten
On hind legs 179
Seated 175
Peter Pan 52
Peter Rabbit Candle Snuffer. 285
Phaethon 276
Pheasant
Brooch 274
Menu Holder 274
Philanderer 173
Phillip 127
Phillipa 240
Phlegon 276
Phoebe and Flame Vine
(Sayornis Phoebe)
Cock 126
Hen 126
Phyllis 279
Pick a Back 36
Pickaninny 127
Picnic 159
Pied Woodpeckers (on stump) 99
Pierrot 6
Pierette
Style One 18
Style Two 31
Bookend. 30
Pierrot Group 79
Pierrot Puff Bowl 67
Piggyback Ride 248
Pigling Bland Candle Snuffer 290
Pike 55
Pintail
Drake. 156
Hen. 156
Pirouette 75
Planter's Daughter 69
Play Time 207
Playmates 88
Plonguer 165
Poetry 241
Pointer Sleeping 191
Polar Bear 285
Ashtray
Bear bending. 77
Bear seated, looking up 76
Bookend
Bear bending. 55
Bear seated, looking up 55
Candle Snuffer 285
Policeman Candle Snuffer. 288
Polly Kettle. 194

Polly Put The Kettle On 90
Polo Player 73
Pony Stallion 185
Poodle, Champion "Spriggan Bell" . . . 59
Poor Teddy 193
Pope John Paul II (bust on plinth) . . . 188
Poppy (1924) 211
Poupée 150
Powdering Mask 69
Preference. 165
Pretty as a Picture 252
Pretty in Pink 248
Prince Albert Candle Snuffer 286
Prince Regent Pavillion 257
Prince Regent Teddy Candle Snuffer . . 286
Prince's Grace and Foal 158
Princess Margaret In Her
Coronation Robes 264
Princess of Tara 252
Priscilla. 113
Privy Chamberlain of the Sword
and Cape to the Pope in the
Spanish Costume 131
Promenade (1922) 189
Proposal (The). 243
Psyche 2
Puffin 157
Punch 114
Candle Snuffer 287
Purr-Fect Friends 247
Pyroeis. 276

Q
Quail 10
Brooch 273
Queen Anne
Style One. 163
Style Two. 263
Queen Elizabeth I Candle Snuffer . . . 282
Queen Elizabeth I
Style One ??
Style Two. 163
Style Three 202
Style Four 234
Queen Elizabeth I In Her Coronation
Robes 268
Queen Elizabeth II
Style One. 164
Style Two. 248
Style Three 257
Queen Elizabeth II Candle Snuffer. . . 290
Queen Elizabeth on Coronation Throne. 260
Queen Elizabeth the Queen Mother. . . 247
Queen Elizabeth the Queen Mother
In Her Coronation Robes. 258
Queen in the Parlour 78
Queen Mary 60
Bust 61
Queen Mary I
Style One. 163
Style Two. 251
Queen Mary II 164
Queen Mother
Style One. 206
Style Two. 251
Queen of Hearts 212
Queen of the May (The). 212
Queen Victoria
Style One. 164
Style Two. 245
Candle Snuffer 286
Queen's Beasts (The) 117

R
Rabbit. 8
Rachel
Style One. 125
Style Two. 221
Rainbow Lorikeet on Red Flowered
Gum 162
Rainbow Parrot Fish 133
Ram 9
Rameses 253
Rebecca
Style One. 145
Style Two. 183
Style Three 228
Recollections 69
Red Admiral Butterfly on Clematis . . . 149
Red Cardinal on Bronze 192
Red Hind Fish
Style One. 128
Style Two. 133
Red Ribbons
Style One. 146
Style Two: See Morning Walk 175
Red Riding Hood. 118
Red Rum. 167
Red Setter
Lying on base 173
With base 80
Without base 91
Red Shoes. 85
Red Squirrel on Bronze 197
Red-Breasted Nuthatch and Oak 171
Red-Eyed Vireo and Swamp Azalea
(Vireo Olivaceus)
Cock 112
Hen 112
Redstart 181
Reed Warbler 199
Reflection
Style One. 234
Style Two. 247
Style Three 262
Regency 203
Regency Lady 105
Regency Lady With Shawl In Hand . . . 105
Rendezvous 186
Repose 88
Rescue (The) 96
Richard Coeur De Lion 177
Richard Meade and Lauriston 164
Richmond Girl 199
Ring-Necked Pheasant
Cock 155
Hen. 155
"Ripe 'Speragus" 84
Roach 55
Robin 78
Brooch 273
Candle Snuffer 284
On Bronze
Style One 160
Style Two 161
Robin and Narcissus. 192
Robin Fledgling on Branch 172
Robin in Autumn Woods
(Erythacus Rebecula). 147
Robin on Christmas Rose 174
Robin on Holly
Style One. 181
Style Two. 186
Rock Beauty Fish 133

Romantic
   Style One 204
   Style Two ??
Romeo Candle Snuffer 291
Rosalind
   Style One 150
   Style Two 254
Rose
   Style On e 45
   Style Two 125
Rose Maiden: see The Bridesmaid,
   Style One 79
Rose Marie 255
Rose of Camelot 264
Rose Seller 260
Roses 25
Roses of Love 265
Rosie Picking Apples 201
Rough Collie with Pups 170
Royal Anniversary 237
Royal Canadian Mounted Police . . . 153
Royal Debut 217
Royal Enclosure 231
Royal Premiere 224
Royal Tournament 213
Royal Worcester 250th Anniversary
   Figurine 254
Ruby Anniversary
   Style One 224
   Style Two 237
Ruby Crowned Kinglet and Cypress . . . 171
Ruby-Throated Hummingbird and
   Fuchsia (Archilochus Colubris)
     Cock 108
     Hen 108
Rufous Hummingbird 171

S

Sabrina 240
Safe At Last 202
Sail Fish 148
Salmon
   Style One 54
   Style Two 54
   Style Three 191
Saluki (The) 185
Salvage 101
Sam (Polar Bear Bookend) 37
Samurai Candle Snuffer 284
Santa Gertrudis Bull "Prince" 147
Sarah
   Style One 126
   Style Two 228
   Style Three 225
Saturday's Child
   Boy 121
   Girl 86
Sauce 34
Saved 180
Scarf of the Dance 208
Scarlet Tanager and White Oak
   (Piranga Olivacea)
     Cock 121
     Hen 121
Scarlett 257
School Time 207
Scissor-Tailed Flycatchers 136
   (Wall hanging)
Scotland 62
Scottish Heather 267
Scottish Terrier
   Brooch 272

Dog's Head (Wall Mount) 93
   Menu Holder 272
Scottish Terrier (cont.)
   Seated 53
   Standing 48
Scottish Terrier Puppies
   On Cigarette Box 73
Scullery Maid 203
Scylla 278
Sea Breeze 51
Sea Scout 114
Sea Urchin 42
Seagull Brooch 274
Seal 52
Sealyham Terrier 53
   Brooch 270
   Menu Holder 270
   On Cigar Tray 46
   "Thomas" on plinth 45
   Without plinth 46
Sealyham Terrier Puppies Cigarette Box . 65
Seamstress (The)
   First Version 128
   Second Version 128
Seasons of Romance 254
Seaweed 98
Secret Garden 241
See-Saw 210
September 110
Serena 238
Sergeant-Major Fish 129
Setter
   On plinth 31
   Without plinth 49
   Brooch / Menu Holder 271
Sheep 72
Shepherdess
   Style One 4
   Style Two 205
Sheriff 151
Shetland Pony 169
Shire Stallion "Manor Premier King" . . 151
Shorelark 168
Short-Eared Owl 198
Short-Haired Cat 135
Shuttlecock 113
Siamese Dancer
   Style One 113
   Style Two 127
Siamese Kitten (Seated) 179
Silver Anniversary 224
Simón Bolívar 182
Sincerity 180
Sir Walter Raleigh 16
Sister 71
Sister
   Guys Hospital, 1960 232
   Nightingale Training School 141
   St. Thomas' Hospital (London)
   The London Hospital 141
   The University College Hospital, . . . 151
   London
Sisterly Love 256
Skater 188
Skating 194
Slave 249
Sleeping Baby: see Treasure 51
Sleeping Buddha Candle Snuffer 289
Sleeping Doe 32
Sleepy Boy 42
Slide (The) 192

Slow Coach 115
Smiling Buddha Candle Snuffer 288
Snail
   Style One 8
   Style Two 193
Snake 8
Snipe Brooch 272
Snow Bunting 168
Snow Queen 268
Snowball 190
Snowy Owl Candle Snuffer 284
Soiree (1926) 188
Soldier of the Black Watch
   First Version 3
   Second Version 3
Soldier of the First World War
   Seated 12
   Standing 12
Soldier of the Imperial Forces 2
Soldier of the Worcestershire Regiment . . 7
Solitaire 194
Song (The) 38
Song of Spring 243
Sophie 229
Soubrette 74
Southwind 103
Spade Fish 130
Spain 56
Spaniel, Dog's Head (Wall Mount) . . . 93
Spaniels' Calendar 66
Spaniel Puppy "Tony" 99
Spaniel Puppies (Three) 67
Spanish Hog and Sergeant-Major Fish . 129
Spanish Lady: see Argentina 46
Sparrow 82
Sparrowhawk 173
Sparrowhawk and Bullfinch 160
Sparrowhawk Brooch 273
Special Gift 256
Special Mum 234
Special Occasion 226
Spirit of Beauty (The) 259
Spirit of Peace 245
Spirit of The Millennium (The) 250
Spitfire 98
Spring
   Style One 52
   Style Two 96
   Style Three 279
   Style Four 191
   Style Five 208
   Style Six 232
Spring (Bust) 83
Spring Fair 175
Spring Morn 125
Spring Morning 125
Springer Spaniel 170
Springer Spaniel Brooch 275
Springtime 191
Squirrel Fish 133
Squirrel Jug 29
Squirrel Nutkin Candle Snuffer 286
Squirrel Salt and Pepper Pots 29
St. Joseph 11
Stag Beetle 193
Stonechat 182
Story Time 207
Stowaway 100
Strephon 279
Stroller and Marion Coakes 158
Strolling In Satin 232
Suffolk Punch "Beccles Warrender" . . 155

Summer
   Style One 95
Summer (cont.)
   Style Two 279
   Style Three 198
   Style Four 209
   Style Five . . . . ??
   Style Six 224
Summer Ball 267
Summer Day 126
Summer Solstice 261
Summer's Day 126
Summer's Lease 238
Summer's Sweet Kiss 216
Summer Regatta 235
Summertime 180
Summit 70
Sunday Best 216
Sunday Morning 178
Sunday's Child
   Boy 84
   Girl 119
Sunshine 59
Sunshine Days 190
Surprise 139
Susie 84
Swallow Brooch 273
Swallow on Bronze 160
Sweet Anemone 225
Sweet Anne 137
Sweet Astor 228
Sweet Child of Mine (Bust) 263
Sweet Daffodil 232
Sweet Daisy 224
Sweet Dreams
   Style One 203
   Style Two 255
Sweet Forget-Me-Not 223
Sweet Holly 220
Sweet Lady Fair 267
Sweet Nell of Old Drury 51
Sweet Pansy 231
Sweet Peony 226
Sweet Primrose 224
Sweet Rose 218
Sweet Snowdrop 230
Sweet Violet 220
Sweetest Valentine 215
Swordfish 152
Sylvanus 278
Symboli Rudolf 201

T

Tabby Kitten
   Lying 179
   Seated 200
Takai Teio 219
Take Cover 97
Tamara 75
Tangles 42
Tanya / Tea at the Ritz 242
Tarpon 150
Tatiana 75
   Candle Snuffer 290
Tawny Owl Candle Snuffer 283
Tea at the Ritz 242
Tea Party (The) 146
Tea Time
   Style One 190
   Style Two 207
Teddy Bear Candle Snuffer 284
Tender Love 260

Terrier (on Plinth) 31
Terrier Powder Bowl / Bon Bon Box . . . 44
Territorial Soldier 7
Thank You 221
Thief 70
Thoroughbred Foal 186
Thoroughbred Mare 186
Thoughtful 236
Three's Company 189
Thrush
   Style One 82
   Style Two 200
Thursday's Child
   Boy 85
   Girl 120
Tiger 62
   Lying, facing left 24
   Lying, facing right 24
   On plinth 66
Tigers, Maurice and Sonia
   With base 88
   Without base 93
Titania Candle Snuffer 289
Titania, The Queen Of The Fairies
   Style One 256
   Style Two 257
Toad 10
Toby Candle Snuffer 286
Toddie Candle Snuffer 288
Tom Kitten Candle Snuffer 289
Tommy 41
Tortoise 7
Treasure (The) 51
Treasure Trove 150
Trooper of The Swiss Guard of
   His Holiness The Pope 130
Trout
   Style One 54
   Style Two 55
True Love 243
Tryst (The) 239
Tuesday's Child
   Boy 123
   Girl 85
Tutankhamun 244
Two Babies 71
Two Ladies 9
Two's Company 247
Two's Company, Three's None 116

U

Unicorn Candle Snuffer 288

V

Venetian Masquerade 268
Viennese Waltz 229
Vermilion Flycatcher And Pussy Willow
   Pyrocephalus Rubinus Mexicanus
   Cock 140
   Hen 140
Victoria 245
Village Bride (The) 214
Violet 125
Virginia Cardinal and Orange Blossom
   (Richmondena Cardinalis)
   Cock 77
   Hen 77
Vivandière 23
Vivien 262

W

Wales 62
Wall Creeper 169
Wandering Minstrel
   Female 3
   Male 3
Washington (George) 160
Water Baby 71
Waterlily and Butterfly 186
Watteau Figure
   Female, Seated 105
   Female, Standing 104
   Male, Seated 104
   Male, Standing 104
Wax Wing 138
Wedding Day (The)
   Style One 215
   Style Two 222
Wedding Day
   Boy 175
   Girl 175
Wednesday's Child 207
Wednesday's Child
   Boy 120
   Girl 85
Weekend Girl 204
Weighed Out (Jockey) 5
Welsh – Sian 267
Welsh Cob Stallion
   "Ilanarth Flying Comet" 174
Welsh Corgi 83
Welsh Corgi "Taffy" 100
Welsh Mountain Pony
   "Coed Coch Planed" 153
West End Girl 204
West Highland Terrier
   Brooch 271
   "Mack" 98
Western Tanager 139
Westwind 103
White Boy 127
White Doves 162
White Rabbit 134
Wild Duck Brooch 273
Wild Horses 111
Wilfred 28
Will You, Won't You? 148
William Shakespeare Candle Snuffer . . 289
William The Conqueror 181
Willow Princess 254
Wiltshire Moonraker Candle Snuffer . . 285
Wind 9
Windy 194
Wine Pourer (The) 244
Winner (The) 143
Winner with Jockey and Stable Boy (T . 142
Winston Churchill Candle Snuffer . . . 285
Winter
   Style One 96
   Style Two 279
   Style Three 195
   Style Four 211
   Style Five . . . . ??
   Style Six 228
Winter Waltz 177
Winter's Morn 183
Wire-Haired Terrier
   Brooch 272
   Seated 47
   Standing, head to left 53
   Standing, head to right 53

Wise as an Owl 116
Wistful 225
With All My Heart 250
With Love
    Style One. 229
    Style Two. 251
Wolf 118
Wood Pigeon
    Style One. 106
    Style Two. 106
    Brooch 274
Wood Warbler 79
Wood Warbler on Cherry 174
Woodcock Brooch 274
Woodland Dance 58
Woodland Walk 189
Woodpecker 83
Worcestershire County Cricket Club . . 246
Wren 78

Wren and Burnet Rose
  (Troglodytes Parvulus)
    Cock 146
    Hen 149
Wren Fledgling on Leaves 172
Wren on Bronze
    Style One. 160
    Style Two. 161
Wren on Clematis 185

Y

Yellow Bunting on Blackberry 178
Yellow Grunt Fish 129
Yellow Headed Blackbird and Spiderwort
  (Xanthocephalus Xanthocephalus)
    Cock 111
    Hen 111
Yellowhammers (on stump) 101
Yellow-Throat and Water Hyacinth
  (Geothlypis Trichas)
    Cock 124
    Hen 124

Yonder He Goes 74
You're A Star 259
Young England 150
Young Entry 74
Young Farmer: see Johnnie 108
Young Foxes (Three) 67
Young Girl Candle Snuffer 291
Young Horse 33
  Ink Blotter 33
Young Huntsman
  With Top Hat 24
  With Whip 24

Z

Zodiac Candle Snuffers
  Horse 289
  Monkey 291
  Sheep 291
Zoe 263

WORCESTER
PORCELAIN
Museum

We cater for all Shapes and Sizes

OPEN 7 DAYS A WEEK. Mon to Sat: 9am-5.30pm. Sun: 11am-5pm.
Severn Street, Worcester WR1 2NE. Tel: 01905 746000
www.worcesterporcelainmuseum.org.uk